Wild Life
ILLUSTRATED

ODHAMS PRESS LIMITED LONG ACRE LONDON, W.C.2

CONTENTS

WILD BEAUTY

The unbroken mustang of Arizona, as seen here, is probably descended from horses that escaped into the wilds in the early days of the occupation of the New World.

CHAPTER ONE

WILD ANIMALS AND MAN

by E. G. BOULENGER, F.Z.S.

THE wild animal life of the world is an inexhaustible source of interest to man. In past ages it was vital to man's existence to slay dangerous beasts, to track down those that provided food and clothing and to train, for his own purposes, those which could be useful to him alive. To-day, though man has raised himself by the gift of intelligence to an increasing mastery over his surroundings, the link is still close. Fur, hides, ivory still satisfy some of his material needs, but the stage has been reached when it is our task to conserve animals rather than to destroy.

This desire to conserve has taken practical form on a vast scale in centres where Nature is at her richest, like Tanganyika Territory, the Belgian Congo and the Yellowstone Park, which embraces the southernmost extremity of the Rocky Mountains. In Africa the gunman has already wiped out the quagga. The white rhinoceros has been saved just in time. Fur and plume hunters of the past are also to blame for the annihilation of many creatures once abundant, and were it not for the reservations and animal parks the age of mammals would certainly be hurrying to its close.

In Britain the Society for the Preservation of the Fauna of the Empire has been formed. The Society has been instrumental in inducing local governments to dedicate large reservations in all parts of the Empire and ensuring that they shall be adequately patrolled. Thus in India special steps have been taken to protect the great Indian rhinoceros. To-day there are twenty game preserves scattered over British territory in Africa alone, and they cover 200,000 square miles. Possibly the finest game preserve is the Kruger National Park, which embraces a stretch of country some 200 miles by 60 miles. Here the great game animals roam at large, as in no other part of Africa. Not only do giraffes, zebras, elephants, antelopes, lions, etc., propagate their kind in peace, but their presence draws to the country large numbers of enlightened sightseers— people who hunt with the camera and prefer to return home with memories and photographs rather than trophies.

Another notable reserve is that which the late Carl Akeley, the well-known American explorer and naturalist, created with the patronage and enthusiastic assistance of the late King of the Belgians. The Parc National Albert, as this reserve is called, is in the heart of the Belgian Congo; it embraces almost every type of country—swamps, forests, dense jungles, plains and towering heights. As may be imagined, it has an extraordinarily rich and varied fauna. Many of the creatures found within its boundaries are unknown elsewhere. The dense jungles of the lowlands shelter

5

ANIMAL MEETING PLACE
Zebra and wildebeest are seen at an African pool, meeting place of the animal world.

strange dwarf species including the so-called pigmy elephant. In the perpetual twilight of the forest dwells that strange giraffe-like animal, the okapi, discovered by the late Sir Harry Johnston less than fifty years ago. From the Belgian Congo also come such unique forms as the rare bongo antelope and the giant gorilla.

The destruction of the bison in America was prosecuted, less than 100 years ago, on such a scale that the animal was nearly exterminated. Its survival is a striking example of what can be accomplished by preservation. Thanks to the National Bison Society, the animal has so increased of recent years that large numbers are killed annually in order to keep the many herds within bounds. The Yellowstone Park has within the last few decades seen the moose well on its way to reinstatement after having likewise been on the verge of extinction.

Whilst we must be grateful that at last much is being done to encourage the conservation of the larger animals from the purely cultural point of view, it must not be forgotten that the study of animal life in the wild, especially the life-cycles of small invertebrate creatures, has resulted in the solving of many vital problems relating to agriculture and human disease. Of recent years economic biologists in all countries have been working on the animal pests that do so much harm in fields and gardens.

Sometimes such investigations are undertaken on a large scale. Thus the U.S. Department of Agriculture now employs aircraft to investigate the movements of a certain moth whose larvae cause devastation to the cotton crops.

Two chimpanzees, members of a tribe which displays remarkable powers of intelligence.
This has been tested and proved on many occasions. Chimpanzees have been trained to

INTELLIGENCE
count up to ten, dress and undress, thread a needle, ride a bicycle, or skate on roller skates, smoke cigarettes, open a door with a key, and "sing" at the word of command.

LIFE UNDERWATER
This photograph was taken on the seafloor in the Bahamas. At left is an angel fish.

All over the world scientists are seeking to readjust the balance of nature by combating some animal menace with its own enemies. As an example one may quote how the Hawaiian sugar-cane crop, threatened with destruction some years ago by a species of weevil, was saved. After years of search, the entomologist Muir discovered on Amboina a fly that proved an effective check on the beetle whilst it was yet in the larval stage. Similarly the noxious coconut moth of Fiji has been exterminated by the introduction of a parasitic ichneumon fly which lays its eggs in the coconut moth's caterpillars.

These instances show interfering with Nature to some good purpose, and are in striking contrast to some haphazard and unorganized methods that have from time to time been employed. An unfortunate instance was the bringing of slipper limpets with American oysters to British oyster beds. These slipper limpets multiplied so fast that they literally swamped the young oysters, and although many tons of the pest are dredged annually from oyster grounds, they have caused a serious shortage of "natives" and a resulting increase in their price.

A ludicrous case of "unbalancing" is afforded by the introduction many years ago of the goldfish into Madagascar with a view to beautifying the waters of that island. Unfortunately, goldfish, unless supervised, are apt to revert to the drab coloration of their carp ancestors—a dirty olive-grey. But apart from this the imported goldfish multiplied in such numbers that they exterminated the only

edible fresh-water fish in the island. And
insects can be all too easily introduced
where not wanted. Fifty years or so ago a
South American species of ant entered
Madeira as a stowaway inside a con-
signment of sugar-cane. It speedily
invaded the island, and within a few
years destroyed all the orchards and
coffee plantations. As is well known, the
introduction of the rabbit into Australia
was a disaster for that Dominion.
Nearer home, the Canadian squirrel
introduced into Britain as an attractive
addition to its fauna, has proved most
destructive to birds and vegetation.

Practical Value of Animal Study

The importance of the study of the
life-history of animals is revealed in the
field of preventive medicine. Thus the
ravages of that deadly disease of the tropics known as bilharzia, and for which a
fluke is directly responsible, have been
checked as a result of the study of the
life-history of a certain aquatic snail. The
life-cycle of the fluke was worked out by
R. T. Leiper, who found that in its
immature stage it escapes into the water
and may penetrate the skin of man
during washing or drinking. Leiper, in
working out the life-cycle of the fluke,
discovered that a fresh-water snail was a
necessary host of the parasite, which
lives for a certain period within the snail
before escaping and infecting man.

To-day the discovery of the life-
history of the fluke responsible for the
disease and the resulting preventive
measures that are being taken have much
reduced its ravages. Early in the 1914–
1918 war British troops in Egypt
suffered severely from bilharzia. In the
second world war the incidence of the
disease was negligible.

Research is in progress to find what
are the conditions that may in time produce a race immune to diseases which
have hitherto decimated its ranks.

As citizens of the world we should all
be able to appreciate the effects, both
beneficial and otherwise, of animal life
on man. The world, even to-day, is a
place teeming with animal problems or
"mysteries" still to be unravelled.

Before the time of Linnaeus, "the
father of Natural History", the names
given to animals were at best only
vaguely descriptive. It remained for the
famous Swedish naturalist in his "Sys-
tema Naturae" of 1758 to invent a
system by which every animal was given
two names, the one denoting its genus or
"group", the other describing some less
important feature which entitled it to be
regarded as a distinct species. The names
given to animals in Linnaeus's work still
hold good, but since its publication
several million species have been added to
the list and names have had to be found
for nearly 200,000 new genera.

Hunting with a Camera

This book is designed not only to
appeal to all nature lovers but also to
serve as a useful book of reference. The
photographs illustrating it cast a vivid
spotlight on animal life in its native
haunts. Big-game hunting is fortunately
not what it was, it being no longer
possible for the moron with a "trigger
itch" to obtain a licence and count his
trophies by the thousand. The hunter
himself has to a large extent replaced the
rifle by the camera. Most of the photographs here presented have been taken
not in zoos but by adventurous explorers
of jungles, swamps, forests and deserts.
Many are, indeed, unique.

WONDER OF FLIGHT

This beautiful photograph shows the white ibis, a bird inhabiting Nubia, the Sudan and Abyssinia. It was held sacred by the ancient Egyptians to whom its silvery white plumage symbolised the light of the sun. The line of the wings is emphasised by the black tips.

LIONESS COMING TO HER OWN KILL

This flashlight photograph surprised a lioness at her kill at a distance of about nine yards. She was one of a party of about eight who all expected to share the feast.

CHAPTER TWO

CATS OF THE WILD

by A. RADCLYFFE DUGMORE, F.R.G.S.

The Lion; distribution, size and speed. Its relations with man. Stalking the prey. The Tiger; its ferocity and man-eating propensities. The Leopard. The Jaguar and the Mountain Lion or Puma of America. The Lynx, Cheetah, and other Cats.

THE Cat tribe, which includes about half a hundred species, has two strange distinctions. It supplies the Royal Family among animals, and, on the other hand, it has given its name to some undesirable characteristics in human beings. On account of the fine appearance of a full-maned lion, he has been called "King of Beasts", but only the appearance of the animal has been considered in bestowing this title, for certainly the lion is far from kingly in habits. He is not especially brave, and added to this, he indulges in the unpleasant habit of eating meat in an advanced state of decomposition. Then, as we know, the name "cat" is applied to humans who are spiteful and vindictive. Cruelty is also a special attribute of at least some cats. This is only too well known a peculiarity. It is doubtful whether any other animals take real pleasure and satisfaction in torturing their prey.

Cats of various kinds have about the greatest range of habitat of any animals, being found from the frozen North to the super-heated tropics, from high mountains and dense forests to snow-covered or sandy plains. Nearly every part of the world has representatives of the wild family. Exceptions are: Australia and Oceania, Ireland and Madagascar, as well as various other remote or isolated islands scattered about the globe. All cats are carnivorous, and if we except the grizzly bears, which are really omnivorous, they are the largest of the carnivore. All true members of the race have retractile claws—that is to say, they can withdraw their claws into sheaths, so that when walking the spoor shows no sign of the nails. The forefeet have five toes and the hindfeet four.

So much for the cat family as a whole, and, to conform to custom, we will deal first with the Lion, as the best known in the family. Its appearance is so familiar to us that a detailed account would be superfluous, though the specimens usually seen in captivity are somewhat different from those in the wild state. One difference is the line of the back. Captive animals have usually a rather hog or arched back, probably due to the contraction of the abdominal muscles, which in turn is caused by the rationed diet which is provided for them in captivity. Wild specimens have straight or slightly drooping

KING OF BEASTS

Although not the largest, strongest, or even the bravest member of the animal world, the lion possesses physical magnificence that justifies his title of "King of Beasts". A compact

ROARS HIS DEFIANCE

*mass of muscle and grace, such a specimen as that seen above weighs some 500 lb. Lions
are found mainly in Africa, but some exist in parts of Asia, notably in Persia and in India*

LIONESS ON THE PROWL

This lioness, photographed in her native Africa, has a sinister and purposeful air.
Though lions do most of their hunting at night habits vary, and they sometimes roam
abroad during the hours of daylight and in open country.

backs and heavier paunches. Moreover the great mane, either black or tawny, is not by any means usual in wild life. Occasionally a full black mane is found, or a tawny one, but more often the manes are small. They vary, however, from insignificant tufts of hair on the head and neck to large masses completely covering the head and fore parts. The cause of this great variation is not known. It seems to be purely individual and not, as so often asserted, due to living among thorn bush, which is supposed to tear away the hair. Nor can it be said with certainty that the forest lion is less hairy than that which lives on the plains. The fact that in the plains and open country lions are more frequently seen probably accounts for the theory that the forest lion is less often maned. The manes, especially the dark ones, attract attention and are conspicuous in the open country, while in the forest the dark mane tends to render the lion extremely difficult to see, as it blends in with the surrounding foliage.

Size and Weight of the Lion

The weight of a full-grown lion is approximately 500 lb., height nearly $3\frac{1}{2}$ feet and length almost 11 feet from nose to end of tail. A peculiarity of the tail whose purpose is not understood is the hard, claw-like bone concealed in the tuft of black hair at the extremity.

The range of the lion included most parts of Africa south of Algeria and some regions of Asia, such as Mesopotamia and southern Persia, Syria and Arabia and the north-west districts of India. In India to-day it is to be found mainly in Rajputana. But Africa is the chief habitat of lions, and they used to be found as far north as Algeria. The writer can remember when at Bougie, east of Algiers, he was invited to tea by the British Consul. Tea was much delayed, however, because three lions had occupied the road, and had to be driven off before the Consul's carriage could pass. It is probably many years since lions were found in that area, but from there, all the way south, and from east to west coast they exist, and are still abundant in parts of Tanganyika and Kenya, even quite near to Nairobi. In Asia lions are still to be found, but are nowhere abundant. The lion of India, Persia and other parts of Asia is identical with the African species, though seldom is he such a fine specimen. Not very much is known of the lions of Asia, but in Africa their habits have been carefully observed, and

LIONS RACE FOR FOOD

In the Serengeti district of Kenya lions are strangely indifferent to the presence of man or motors. They will even follow the carcass of an animal when it is towed behind a lorry.

they vary greatly in different districts. For example, except in the Serengeti plains they are more or less nocturnal and wild, or perhaps cautious would be the better word, and do not indulge in tree-climbing, except on rare occasions; whereas the tribe frequenting the Serengeti are not only ridiculously tame, but take to trees without the slightest hesitation, even sleeping on the branches. The lions of this region are a quite peculiar lot and it would be wrong to describe them as typical of the species. No one can account for their tameness, indifference to the presence of human beings and generally strange behaviour. It is, therefore, very difficult to lay down any rules for the habits of lions or, in fact, of most wild animals. Conditions vary, and of course to a great extent regulate the creature's habits. On cloudy days, such as those which herald the coming of the rains, lions which are habitually nocturnal, will be found roaming about during daylight, even in quite open country, but it is fairly safe to state that lions do most of their hunting during the night, and spend their days resting and sleeping.

Hunting and Mating

Regarding their method of hunting, there is no rule, any more than there is for the way they roam. Single specimens are no more common than parties, or "prides", from two to a dozen or even at times to as many as sixty or seventy. Strangely enough, when found in large prides there is seldom a well-maned specimen among them. Three is the number most frequently seen, and these may be all of one sex, either male or female. One male and his two mates are a usual group, for the majority of lions have two wives, and apparently live in complete harmony, the cubs being taken care of by both the mother and the foster mother. Whether mating is for life is not certain, but it is quite possible. There is no special time for the cubs to be born, and they vary in number from three to five. More males than females are born, but fewer attain maturity, hence the taking of two mates by the lion. It is nature's method of adjusting the life of the species. So far as it is possible to say definitely there is an interval of two years between breeding.

Young Lion and Parent

Young lions have conspicuous markings along the sides, but these gradually become shadowy with age, so that a mature specimen shows scarcely any sign of what are known as "puppy markings". The young do not accompany their parents on hunting expeditions until they are half grown or even older. They stay in their dens or lairs, and have their food brought to them. Later they gradually go farther and farther afield, but always with at least one of the parents to watch over them. Their home may be in a deep rocky den, or in suitable cover of grass or bush. If in a deep den it appears to be the rule not to take food far inside. At least, the writer judges this to be the case, because in those he has examined all bones were outside the opening, but whether they were carried there after the flesh had been eaten, it was hard to say.

Lions are fairly long lived, at least in captivity, when thirty to forty years is about their limit. In their wild state their power of hunting decreases with advancing age, until they are no longer able to kill large animals, and have to turn to easier prey. Finally they become scavengers. Whether killing of human beings

A LION FAMILY IN THE SERENGETI PLAIN OF EAST AFRICA

An acceptable offering of food frequently induces wild animals to "pose" for the hidden cameraman. In the above photograph a carcass lashed to a tree attracted a small "pride" of lions led by the magnificently maned patriarch who may be seen at the extreme left.

Lions frequently roam in bands, known as "prides", which may comprise as many as sixty of these beasts. Although most of their hunting is done at night, a cloudy day is utilized for

is invariably a direct result of their in-ability to tackle larger and better-pro-tected prey seems doubtful, but certainly man-killing (except in cases of self-de-fence) is by no means common. How-ever, once the taste for human flesh has been acquired, and the ease with which killing can be done realised, lions become

a menace, and a very serious one, too, for they grow increasingly daring with each successful hunt. Cases have been known where even fire failed to prevent an attack, though it is generally sup-posed to be a certain protection. In one instance a number of natives, porters and others were seated round a large blazing

THE SERENGETI PLAINS

a daylight expedition, as is seen above. The photograph shows a "pride" of African lions sharing a meal in harmony. In the larger "prides" few well-maned specimens are found.

fire on a dark evening when suddenly, without the least warning, a pair of lions sprang into their midst, seized two unfortunates and were gone before anyone could make a move.

The well-known book "The Maneaters of Tsavo" gave convincing accounts of the extraordinary audacity of the lions living in that area and how they proved even more cunning and daring than the men engaged on the construction of the Uganda Railway. For a time they paralysed the activities of both the white and the coloured men.

When camping in Kenya it is the usual practice to have large fires kept

VULTURES DISPUTE

The lion in these pictures on the Serengeti Plain, Tanganyika, has made a kill, but vultures have sighted the capture, descending from miles around to share the meal. When the lion

LION'S PREY

returns from a nearby water-hole, to discover his prize being devoured, his fury is likely to prove fatal to the carrion birds. Vultures are regarded as parasites by man and beast.

burning all night near the tents, but the writer considers a mosquito net is just as effective and not nearly so disturbing as the flickering light on the canvas. A lion will not attack what he cannot see, and the mosquito net effectively conceals whoever is inside. The writer has often found evidence of lions having been within a few feet of the tent during the darkness, but they never disturbed him.

If a person is travelling alone and has to spend the night in the bush, he usually builds a fire, goes to sleep and feels quite safe. Should he forget to wake up occasionally and attend to the fire it is just too bad, for he runs very serious risk. Once near Marsabit in northern Kenya, the writer's party came upon evidence of what happens when a man is careless. A native letter-carrier, too tired to bother about the fire once he had lighted it, let it die down. The poor chap paid the price for his neglect. They found his remains, silent evidence of what had happened, also the leather mail-pouch, clawed and bitten, so they sent it on to its destination together with a report, stating "letters and parcels herewith, but one postman missing".

The question of how lions hunt and kill is somewhat difficult to answer, for methods vary with conditions of the country, time of day or night and the species being hunted. One method which has been observed by many travellers makes one wonder how far the lion's intelligence is developed; for example, three of the hunters go out together to secure food; when they discover a herd of antelopes or zebras feeding, one lion will slowly make its way *up-wind* of the unsuspecting herd. He will keep far enough away so that his scent will be very faint, and the carefully hunted animals will simply become aware of the proximity of their enemy, but, not fearing immediate danger, they will quietly go on feeding *down-wind*. But there the other two hunters will be waiting and watching. They are infinitely patient, and so long as the antelopes continue to move in their direction they are content to wait. Then at last they are within range, and suddenly one or more of the wretched creatures is startled by seeing one of the tawny hunters rushing with terrific speed. The next instant death has come. It is too late to attempt to avoid it, for the speed of a charging lion is unbelievably great. If all goes well with the attack there will be two dead antelopes before the rest of the herd has become aware of the tragedy which has taken place. It is said that the speed of a charging lion is greater than that of any other animal, but it is of short duration, and probably lasts for not much more than one or two hundred yards.

How the Lion Kills Its Prey

Much has been written about the lion's method of killing its prey: whether it jumps on an animal's back and bites the neck, or whether it strikes from the ground. Both methods are probably used, largely depending on the size of the victim. A small antelope, for example, is either killed instantly by a sharp blow from the lion's powerful paw, or pulled down and the neck bitten. In the case of an animal as strong as a buffalo, the lion is said to grasp the wretched beast by the nose and, pulling the head down with a sharp jerk, to break the neck. The one thing that is fairly certain is that a lion can kill instantly, also that he will tackle almost any animal, regardless of its size.

One of the most peaceful and harmless of animals is the giraffe, yet, though the lion relishes the meat, he does not attack without careful consideration, as he knows only too well the terrible force of the kick from a giraffe's long leg and sharp hoof. The young giraffe is a particularly tasty morsel, but as it seldom strays far from its watchful parents, it is not often one of the lion's victims.

Unwritten Laws of the Wild

The time selected by lions for hunting is, as a rule, between sunset and midnight, and then, when the kill has been made, either by one lion or more, part of the carcass is eaten at once. Usually the hind quarters are chosen first, and the remainder is very carefully hidden to protect it from hungry vultures. Having satisfied their immediate hunger, the lions usually visit the nearest water, and after indulging in a long drink, retire to some quiet place and enjoy a sleep. The dry bed of a river or a dry papyrus swamp is a favourite place for a temporary rest, but with the coming of morning they go to their regular lair or den, where they spend the remainder of the day in sleep, for they are rather lazy animals. It is unlikely that lions will kill at, or very near, water-holes. Whether this is due to an unwritten law of the wild, no one can say with certainty, but the writer has examined many hundreds of water-holes of all sorts, and has never seen any evidence of a kill having been made except by man.

It is difficult to understand the relationship existing between lions and

AFRICAN LIONESS AT A WATER HOLE

After a lion has satisfied its hunger, it is customary for it to make for the nearest water, there to slake its thirst with a long drink. It is a very interesting fact concerning these beasts that the actual kill is seldom, if ever, made at a water-hole.

AN ADULT LIONESS

But for the sinister figure of the lioness, lapping the water in a manner reminiscent of the domestic members of the cat tribe, the scene shown above might have been mistaken for a

28

DRINKS HER FILL

quiet corner of rural England. Actually it depicts a pool in the heart of Africa, where animals of all sizes, the peaceful with the ferocious, go down to drink their fill at eventide.

This is not, as would seem at first sight, a battle to the death between these two lions, but merely a more or less friendly "sparring match". In common with the other cats, lions are known to enjoy a game of make-believe, although occasionally what begins as harmless play

the various animals that furnish them with their food. For instance, not at all an uncommon sight is that of a herd of antelopes and zebras feeding along quite quietly when one lion or more may walk past them without causing the slightest alarm or even interest. Perhaps one antelope will look up for an instant and then resume feeding, as though there

were not an enemy in the country, even though the lion may be within a hundred yards or so. Somehow they seem to know that the lion is not hunting and therefore they are perfectly safe from attack. No one is able to explain this. It is just one of the things connected with the lives of wild animals that we know from observation yet do not understand.

30

A MOCK COMBAT

turns into something serious when tempers are lost. Among cubs and half-grown members of the family, such mock battles are a preparation for adult life when the tolerant protection of the parents is withdrawn, and the lion stands or falls by his own resources.

There is a popular belief that a lion will protect its young at all cost. We are brought up to accept that. Yet experience shows that it is not an invariable rule. The following instance of one lot of lions which would not risk their own lives to protect their young demonstrates how dangerous it is to generalize on the habits of any wild animal. It was in Kenya, and the writer's party was roused very early one morning by a report brought in by some of the porters who had been collecting firewood. Lions had been seen in a nearby donga or gully. No time was lost, and the party was off in a few minutes, accompanied by a number of the porters who were in a wild state of excitement. The writer

LIONESS ADMONISHES HER CUBS

The cubs receiving a lesson in deportment have the "puppy markings" which will gradually become shadowy with age. They will not go on hunting expeditions until half grown. Meanwhile they stay in or near the rocky den or lair, and wait for food to be brought.

had promised them a present if, through their efforts, he managed to secure photographs of lions. They, of course, were to act as beaters, and judging by the strange assortment of their noise-making utensils the lions were in for a disturbing time. About a mile or so from camp they came to a small ravine. The guides said that they had seen lions, several of them, going into this, so the writer stationed himself in a good position on the edge of the papyrus and sent the porters down below to beat the cover. Very soon there was a grand row, enough to scare any animal. While listening to the weird noises he was suddenly surprised to see a movement in the papyrus only four or five yards away. If it was a lion, it was much too close for comfort or delay, so he fired, and the movement ceased, but almost immediately something else shook the dry reeds, and out rushed a young lion, about half grown. This was exactly what he wanted. He called to the men, and soon they had caught the little fellow. And what a little fiend it was ! The young lion bit and screamed, and the parents might have been expected to come straight for the intruders. The writer had visions of the wonderful photograph he should get of a lion actually charging him. But that was not to be. True, the parents of the angry cub appeared about a hundred and fifty yards away—a fine black-maned lion and his mate—but they only gazed, lashed their tails, and after a few moments —moments of intense excitement—they moved off, leaving the watcher utterly astonished and even disappointed. A little later they appeared again. This time the old lion had his two mates with him, as though to give him courage, but they stayed only a few minutes and then disappeared. It is doubtful whether any other animal would have made so little effort to save or protect its young. Even

a deer or a rabbit would have acted with more solicitude, but it shows how difficult it is to say what animals will do under various conditions.

On the point of impressive beauty a well-developed Tiger must be given first place among the cats; the deep orange colour of the upper part of the head and body contrasting with the white underpart and the clear, blackish, more or less vertical stripes, combine to give a most striking effect. To this must be added the graceful build and movements of this magnificent creature, whose size is about the same as that of the lion.

JUNGLE VICTORY

Many hours of silent waiting enabled the photographer to take this remarkable flashlight photograph of an Indian water-hole. It reveals a tiger beside a crocodile he has killed. The tiger kills its prey by flinging it to the ground, using the full force of its powerful jaws, and not, as is often imagined, by a blow administered with its paw.

B

(W.L.)

The range of the tiger is confined to the continent of Asia, chiefly the central and southern parts, from the Caucasus, including southern Siberia, southward through India, especially in the forests of Bengal, Burma, Assam and to the islands of Sumatra and Java, although it is not found in Ceylon.

Strangely enough, though regarded as dwellers in tropical regions, tigers are found also at high altitudes where cold prevails. This peculiarity applies to many kinds of animals, and shows how adaptable they must be. Most people think of the tiger as one of the most cunning and dangerous of wild creatures. Of its cunning there is not the slightest doubt. Wherever it is found it is regarded with fear, if not with respect, not only because of the terrible destruction it causes among the herds of domestic animals, but also because of the number that not infrequently become killers of human beings. Consequently tiger shooting, especially in parts of India, is regarded as a highly praiseworthy form of sport.

Methods of Tiger-hunting

Big drives are organized in the effort to reduce the numbers of these troublesome killers. A common method employed by sportsmen is to place bait—usually a living animal, such as a goat—beneath a suitable tree, in the branches of which a "machan" is constructed. In this the sportsman waits and hopes. But the utmost care must be taken to hide all traces of man-scent and tracks, for the tiger, although it may live in a man-inhabited region, is about as suspicious as any animal can be, and when approaching the unfortunate living bait, does so with surprising care, often circling round and round to make sure

there is no taint of human scent. So quietly does it move that only the keenest ear can detect the almost inaudible sound of movement in the bush. Shooting in the dark—for most of this work is done at night—is not easy, and it is safe to say that fatal shots are none too common. As often as not the animal is wounded and goes off, perhaps to die, perhaps to recover, but more likely to escape with merely a bad fright and a lesson to be more careful in the future. It is not a nice form of sport, but is justified by the need to destroy the dreaded man- or cattle-killer in any possible way.

Tigers have no particular time for breeding, and produce from two to five cubs at a birth. These are most carefully guarded, and so far as we know the mother will protect them at all costs, even at the sacrifice of her own life.

Leopard, or Panther

Next to the lion and the tiger the most important member of the cat family is the Leopard, sometimes called Panther. It is very widely distributed, both in Africa and in Asia, and its range includes India, Burma, Ceylon and other islands in the Indian Ocean and adjacent seas. It is also found north and west, in Arabia, Palestine and Syria.

The leopard is much smaller than its two big cousins, its length seldom exceeding 8 feet, including the long tail. It is a really dangerous beast, even to man, but though it has made a great many attacks, few have ended fatally. There have been numerous miraculous escapes with no more serious results than severe mauling. The well-known American naturalist and traveller Carl Akely had a hand-to-hand, or hand-to-claw, encounter with a leopard which very

A MAN-EATER SEIZES ITS VICTIM

This remarkable photograph of a tiger attempting a man-kill was taken by a member of the Hoefler expedition. The animal has attacked a beater, and is in the act of pulling the unconscious man into the bushes. The beater was rescued, though fatally injured.

TIGER IN THE INDIAN JUNGLE

This magnificent animal is shown here in its native home. The very distinctive black, orange and white markings are effective as camouflage in the jungle.

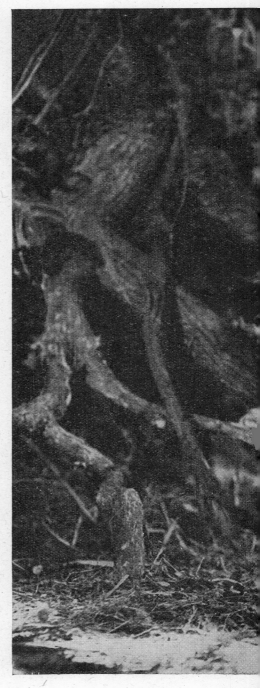

nearly cost him his life. Only by keeping his head and making a supreme effort did Akely, unarmed as he was, finally succeed in choking the creature, and so managed to escape with his life.

Both in colouring and in size, the leopard varies more than any of the other cats. The colour ranges from black to dull pale yellow, with closely arranged dark spots, the form of which resembles cat's footprints. The individuals having the dark yellow ground colour are by far the most beautiful, those of lighter colour the least attractive. Black is only a colour phase, and does not mark a distinct species. It is very rare in Africa, but less so in India. Once the writer had the unusual experience of seeing a pair of these black leopards in Kenya, not very far from Nairobi, and it was only by a matter of seconds that he missed getting a photograph of them as they were approaching a small water-hole.

Few animals are more thoroughly disliked than the leopard, both by settlers and travellers, especially those who have dogs. The latter are such a temptation that a leopard will run almost any risk to try to get hold of one, even coming into an occupied room or verandah and seizing the unfortunate dog before any-one realizes what has happened. The leopard's usual food is anything from guinea-fowl and other birds, tame or wild, to coneys and fair-sized antelopes. The writer remembers once, when in a house which was roofed with corrugated iron, being disturbed by a hungry

DANGER AFLOAT

Although the cat family is popularly supposed to have a hatred of getting its fur wet, streams and rivers present no insurmountable obstacle to the determined tiger, who plunges in without hesitation and swims easily across, as shown in the photograph.

leopard which was trying to find the owner's pet dog. For several hours the creature scrambled about on the roof in search of an opening, all the time making such a noise that none of the inmates could sleep. But he noticed that no one was particularly anxious to go out of the house and drive the animal away. Evidently the leopard was hungry, and equally evident was the fact that the night was extremely dark. Safety first was a slogan that appealed to them very strongly in such circumstances, and this can hardly be thought surprising.

People occasionally try to keep leopards as pets, but, like most of the cats, they are not trustworthy. They will be perfectly docile, and even show signs of affection one minute, and then, without any apparent reason, they will turn on their best friend. As pets they are not to be recommended.

Leopards do most of their hunting by night, and they are about the most silent of all the larger hunters, being able to make their way through the densest vegetation without a sound. Unlike the lion, they seldom if ever eat carrion, but prefer freshly killed food. Domestic animals suffer a great deal from the depredations of these graceful creatures. Their occasional gruff, rumbling growl is one of the strange uncanny sounds of the forest or the open spaces. It has none

SNOW LEOPARD

Among the branches lurks the snow leopard, or ounce, which is considered to be the most beautiful member of the leopard family. It is found in the mountainous districts of Central Asia. It is lighter in colour and sparser in marking than the African leopard.

FEROCITY OF THE LEOPARD

Though smaller than the lion, the leopard is one of the most ferocious of the cats, being dangerous even to man. The sinister beauty of the animal is conveyed by the photograph above, and the cubs, below, already show the savagery of their tribe. In its handsome markings and lithe grace the leopard challenges comparison with the tiger.

of the wonderful majesty of the lion's roar, which is a fascinating sound.

Besides the ordinary species there is the Snow leopard, or Ounce, the most beautiful of the family. It has long hair of a whitish or cream colour with true leopard spots somewhat more sparsely placed. The range of these handsome cats is in the high regions of central Asia in the Altai and other mountains and in Sakhalin Island off the coast of Siberia.

Another species of this family is the Clouded leopard, which has a length of slightly under 6 feet, and is found in the south-east parts of Asia from the Himalayas to Assam, Burma, Malay Peninsula and in some of the East India Islands. Unlike the other leopards, it lives largely in trees. Other members of the family of cats found in Asia and Africa include the Leopard cat, Serval, Marbled, Golden and Fishing cats. Then there is the common wild cat of Europe, now rare, but still found in England and Scotland.

In the New World the two most important of the cats are the Jaguar and the Mountain lion, Cougar or Puma.

The jaguar differs from the Old-World leopard chiefly in its much heavier build and usually darker colour and larger spots, while the animal itself is smaller, a little over 6 feet in length.

Its range is from north of Mexico and Texas to Patagonia. Its habitat is chiefly in the thick forest, where it preys on any animal or bird that comes within its reach. Its larger game include peccary, tapir and deer. Instead of actively hunting its quarry, the jaguar prefers to wait on a branch overlooking a track or path until the unsuspecting animal or bird comes near enough to be easily caught. Its powerful build and massive jaws enable it to kill with little difficulty.

SPEED OF THE CHEETAH

That the cheetah or hunting leopard is the fastest of all animals has been questioned by some observers, but it has in actual trials shown its superiority over the greyhound.

SINUOUS GRACE

Posed for flight like a ballet-dancer, this beautifully-marked little wild cat of the Peruvian jungle reminds us of the domestic kitten in playful mood. In actual fact it is very savage, like the now rare wild cat of the European continent and British Isles.

MEXICAN WILD CAT
Denizen of the thick forests, the Mexican wild cat is known as the Tigrillo—an indication of its fierce and intractable nature. These cats of the American continent have a deserved reputation as stealthy and accomplished hunters.

In North America the mountain lion or puma is both the largest and best known of the cats. It furnishes good material for Wild West stories and for films, both of which endow this stealthy hunter with remarkable powers. Like all cats, it is extremely graceful and very beautiful with its soft tawny colour, free from all markings. The length of a fully grown animal is about 8 feet, including the very long tail.

Formerly the mountain lion was found throughout the greater part of the North American continent up to the more southerly part of Canada, and in earlier times it used to be common in the Eastern states. To-day, however, the puma is found only in the west and south.

Though regarded with a certain amount of fear, it very rarely attacks a human being unless cornered, wounded or in defence of its young (which number from one to four), but it does kill young cattle and deer and even, it is claimed, buffalo. It eats small animals such as jack-rabbits, marmots and gophers, and even devours the humble grasshopper and other insects.

Pumas usually prefer to live in the rough mountain country which offers good cover in case of pursuit, but they are also found in Florida, which is as flat as any country can be. They commonly resort to tree-climbing, especially when chased by dogs, and if necessary in their effort to escape they will jump from the upper branches of a tree, thereby causing consternation among dogs and men.

The most beautifully marked of all the cats is the South American Ocelot. Its skin looks as though it had been painted by a master decorator. Another of the family is the common or bob-tailed cat, which is still found within a few miles of New York and over almost all the continent northward to the upper regions of Canada, being equally at home in a Florida swamp or in the extreme cold of the snow-bound north.

Then there is the Lynx, with its curious tufted ears, and well-covered paws which enable it to walk with ease even on the soft snow which is found all over its northern range, for its home is chiefly in the more northern parts of North America. It lives in remote forest land, and is extremely shy. By trappers it is much sought after on account of its lovely soft fur, which is so much admired by well-dressed women. This fur is invariably black when sold, though the natural colour is either a warm or a cold grey. Lynx fur takes black dye particularly well, gaining a beautiful silky gloss which is lacking in the natural state. It is a case where man really improves on nature. Although so much associated with the New World, the

PUMA AT HOME

With the grace natural to all cats the puma reclines in its rocky lair. A stealthy hunter of the small animals of the wild, it is the subject of many fearsome stories though it rarely attacks a human being unless brought to bay or in defence of its young.

ELUSIVE AND SOUGHT AFTER

The lynx, celebrated in popular legend for its keen sight, is a shy creature of the remote forest tracts of North America. This photograph shows it among the snow-covered trees of its native land. Its soft and beautiful fur causes it to be sought after by trappers.

FELINE EXPRESSION

The fierceness of the cat tribe seems concentrated in this mountain lion, photographed in a rocky fastness, though the animal itself is not so dangerous as the leopard.

lynx is found also in northern Europe, but not in Africa.

Though not belonging strictly speaking to the cats, the Cheetah is so like them in appearance that it seems appropriate to include it in this chapter. Actually cheetahs belong to a separate genus and have only partly retractile claws, whereas the true cats have completely retractile claws. In general appearance these hunting leopards, as they are called, are like very long-legged cats with small heads and very long tails, but there the similarity ends, for in nature they are quite un-catlike. Instead of being untrustworthy, they are kindly in their disposition, easily tamed and have been known to make thoroughly nice pets.

They are found in most parts of Africa and Asia, where they have been used as trained hunters from time immemorial, as evidenced by ancient and accurate drawings. Their great swiftness enables them to overtake any animal, and it is a very wonderful thing to see them at full speed after a fast-running antelope. They appear almost to fly. Whether or not they are the fastest of all animals is questioned by some observers, who assert that the African wild dog is even faster. In size the cheetah is rather smaller than the leopard, being 7 feet in length, and has small dark markings on a pale cream ground.

PUMA IN THE BRAZILIAN FOREST

The puma finds tree-climbing easy, and this photograph of one high up among the branches was taken in Brazil in the forests of the Matto Grosso. Its haunts are various though it favours mountain country offering good cover. A fully-grown puma is about eight feet long.

BEFORE THE SHOWER-BATH

The bull elephant, above, photographed in an African swamp, is about to spray himself with water. His trunk is uplifted for this purpose, not, as might be supposed, in anger.

CHAPTER THREE

ELEPHANT, HIPPO AND RHINO

by A. RADCLYFFE DUGMORE.

Elephant: the African and Asiatic species: distinctive features: stories of the elephant: the elephant as servant of man. Rhino: black, white and Indian: scarcity of the white rhino. Home of the hippopotamus: native methods of hunting: the pigmy or Liberian species.

THERE are, as most people know, two distinct species: the African and Indian or, more properly, Asiatic Elephant. Though these both come from a common ancestor, their development has made them different in many essentials, and they are both unlike the species of antiquity, the chief of which were the mastodon of North Africa, Europe and the American Continent, and the mammoth of Asia and northern Europe.

The African species has the following distinct features: enormous ears, about 4 feet in width and nearly 7 feet in height; the roughly corrugated trunks ending with two finger-like points of equal length; tusks running to a length of over 9 feet, and in exceptional cases to over 11 feet, and weighing up to 300 pounds each; both male and female have tusks, though those of the latter are lighter and smaller; head with graceful convex form sloping to the base of trunk; back highest about the middle (this varies); skin very rough and deeply furrowed; hind foot with three nails; height difficult to estimate, but over 11 feet, and perhaps up to 12, females a foot or so lower. The range of elephants formerly extended over the greater part of Africa, but they have gradually been driven south from their more northern area and north from their southern range, so that today they exist chiefly in the central parts of Africa, more or less south of the Sahara and across from east to west coasts. They are very numerous in the Nile valley.

Now for the Indian species. Its characteristics are: high, domed head, much smaller ears than those of the African species and smooth trunk with only one finger-like extension instead of two; tusks are smaller than those of the African, and are seldom found on females; the front foot has five nails and the hind one four; the skin is fairly smooth; the height rather less than the African, though sometimes it has been known to reach as high as 11 feet. The Indian elephant has been employed by man for countless ages to help in all sorts of work that demands strength, whereas the African species, except in parts of the Belgian Congo, has not within recent

49

Asiatic elephants have long been captured and domesticated for use as transport animals.
Because they do not breed readily in captivity they have to be caught and tamed. The

ELEPHANTS IN INDIA

usual method is to stampede the herd through a funnel-shaped palisade into a small enclosure. The photograph above shows a keddah, or round up, in progress, in Mysore.

THIRSTY TRAVELLER

This lone bull elephant has set out across the dry African plain on a long trek to find water. An elephant can cover up to thirty or forty miles in a day's march.

years been tamed or trained. Elephants may have been used in the past, especially by the Carthaginians, but there is some question as to whether those taken by Hannibal across the Alps were African or Indian. Coins of the Roman Emperor Septimus Severus show designs which seem to represent a combination of the two species.

The Indian species is found in India, Burma, Assam, Cochin-China, Sumatra and Ceylon. Those in the latter country seldom have tusks.

A peculiarity of all elephants is the fact that the young suckle between the front legs, where the mammæ are situated. It is difficult to believe, but we are assured that the elephants' nearest relation is the humble and inconspicuous little hyrax, or, as it is often called, the coney.

So much has been written about the dangerous qualities of the elephant, especially of those in Africa, that we will deal with these first. Whole volumes could be filled with accounts of hunters killed, or nearly killed, by them, but in almost every instance the animal has attacked in self-defence, often after being wounded. Of course where a cow has her calf and feels that it is in danger she may not wait for the threat to develop, but may attack of her own accord.

Once, in Kenya, in the beautiful forest of Marsabit, the writer was waiting in a carefully made "hide" which gave him a good view of a lovely glade through which ran a small stream. By the side of this was a dusting-ground much used by elephants. He had made a screen between himself and the glade, but foolishly had not taken any precaution in the way of concealment from the back, where the forest was fairly thick. One day, after several spent in patient waiting, he heard the sound of something moving in the bushes behind him. In the dim, flickering light and shade he saw several elephants heading towards him, led by a very large cow who was evidently suspicious, for she had her trunk raised and her great ears spread wide. To his disgust, he noticed that she had her calf close by her side. A bad combination! Very slowly that huge beast, with her long, gleaming tusks, approached, a few steps at a time, while the rest of the herd of a dozen or so followed at some distance. The writer's position was, to put it mildly, extremely unpleasant. He could not get away. In fact, he dared not so much as move a finger. All that he could do was to lie flat on the ground and wait for what looked like a very sticky end. That wretched elephant continued to come on until she stood over him, so that he could have touched her feet. For fifteen of the longest minutes of his life he remained petrified with fear. Should the elephant take a step forward he would be squashed flat.

A Hairsbreadth Escape

The fact that her trunk was raised high in the air meant that she did not get his scent. The slight murmuring forest breeze kept the scent close to the ground, and this alone saved his life. That she was suspicious but could not locate the whereabouts of the hidden danger was quite evident. Altogether the situation was tense for both. Probably both were equally frightened. At the end of a quarter of an hour, to the writer's great relief, instead of coming forward, she took a step backward, then turned and joined her companions. He was relieved but also disgusted that he had not been able to secure a film of the episode. But he did have a wonderful opportunity of studying her at very close quarters, and knew exactly what her skin looked like. While she was standing over him he had the feeling of looking up at a mountain.

How Elephants Discern Danger

Elephants have very poor eyesight—as poor as that of any of the larger animals, but their hearing is extremely keen, and with their large ears they can catch the slightest sound. Still, the writer believes they rely for their safety chiefly on their wonderful sense of smell, and when a trunk is raised high and is seen waving slowly from side to side, you may be sure some scent of danger is in the air.

If given the chance, elephants will make good their escape when they suspect danger and, strange as it may seem, these immense beasts, if they believe they have not been seen, can force their way through very dense forest without even the slightest of sounds. They simply melt away like ghosts. If, on the contrary, they feel they have been discovered, they will crash through the undergrowth, knocking down quite fair-sized trees and making the most terrific row.

People who have not seen these great beasts in their wild state do not believe how inconspicuous they can be. So long as they stand absolutely still, as they so often do for a long time, when they have reason to believe there is danger about, they are most difficult to see; even their tusks look like pieces of dead branches,

MUD BATH

This remarkable photograph shows African elephants in their wild state indulging in their favourite pastime of drinking and wallowing in the water. They plaster their sides with mud, rubbing it off when dry. Note the immense size of the ears, so different from those of the Indian species.

while their neutral greyish bodies, toned sometimes to various colours by the local earth with which they dust themselves, seem to blend in with the surrounding vegetation in a remarkable way. They need no protective stripes or colours or pattern to conceal them, yet so many people, naturalists and others, implicitly believe that animals with variously coloured and patterned skins have them for their protection. It does seem strange that a strong pattern and a single tone of grey can be equally difficult to see.

As an example of how invisible an elephant may be the following story will serve. A friend of the writer's in Tanganyika had an interesting and sad experience resulting from his inability to see clearly an elephant for which he was searching, and this led to his making a rather serious mistake. On the slopes of Kilimanjaro, Africa's highest mountain, there dwelt a mighty bull elephant, and he was named the Crown Prince, because of his peculiar profile. He carried such immense tusks that their points dragged on the ground and left distinct tracks when the animal walked. Now, this monster was no fool. He knew the exact boundary of the game reserve, and was most careful not to stray outside of it except at night. The writer's friend coveted those huge tusks, and sent word to all and sundry that if the Crown Prince was seen clear of the reserve he would pay a good reward for the information. One

MAKING A JUNGLE TRAIL

In Siam elephants abound, the rare "White" variety being regarded as sacred. Shown above is a small herd led by a large tusker making their way through the dense Siamese jungle. Asiatic elephants, disliking bright sunlight, keep to the forests as much as possible.

day word came that the elephant was in some native plantation, so off went the man in a very great hurry. Being a careful sort of fellow, he had previously made a thorough examination of the spoor of the Crown Prince, and knew it in all its detail. In due course he came to where his quarry had been seen, and sure enough there were the tracks of the great feet. Filled with wild excitement, he followed them with too great speed and not enough caution when suddenly he spotted an elephant partly concealed by the undergrowth. Of course he thought it *must* be the one he sought. Without making absolutely certain, in his excitement he fired at the one vital spot that was exposed to view, and down came the unfortunate beast. At the same moment there was a terrific crash nearby and the Crown Prince dashed past. The man had killed a cow. This was a trespass against the law, because, by reason of its small tusks, the animal was in the category which is protected and whose destruction is prohibited.

It was doubly unfortunate as his longed-for prize had escaped. And this had all happened because part of the body of the one he had shot had been clearly seen, whereas the one he wanted had escaped his notice altogether, while it had been standing within a few yards of him. One might almost conclude that the wise old creature had understood what was going on, and had acted accordingly.

It is strange that in spite of its thick skin an elephant hates the feeling of dripping water falling on him from the trees. The writer once made a painting of elephants in the Marsabit forest, and it showed a clear, sunlit clearing in the middle foreground, and in that open space he put several elephants, among them a cow and her calf. A very famous naturalist and hunter came to see the picture. He knew Africa as well as any man could, and the habits of the game, and when he noticed the writer's painting he turned to him and remarked that as he had always regarded his work as being true to life, he was surprised at the mistake of showing elephants standing placidly in the sunlight. But in fact the picture was of the Marsabit forest, which is subject to dense fogs or mists, which cover every tree with moisture, and when the sun rises it seems to release a veritable shower of drops, so while this is falling

ELEPHANT LABOUR IN BURMA

Immense strength allied to a high degree of intelligence make the captive elephant a faithful friend of man. In the teak forests of Burma the logs are carted and stacked by elephants who go about their tasks with efficiency. Affection and understanding exists between the elephant and its driver and they are here seen in co-operation.

JUNGLE STAMPEDE

Above is shown a stampede of elephants in India. Heedless of the noise it makes the herd ploughs through and over every obstacle, until checked in its panic-stricken onrush and finally driven into a man-made enclosure waiting to receive them.

will the elephant resort to the open spaces, even though it means being in the sun.

It is strange how much animals vary their habits in different districts, often with no apparent reason: for example, the herds in Kenya and Tanganyika do not as a rule trumpet unless badly frightened, and even then not often, while those in the Nile country will sometimes keep up a constant shrieking which is most disconcerting. The writer once spent some very nerve-racking hours trying to obtain photographs of a famous herd which were known as the suffragettes (because they were mostly females). This was in the country to the west of and not very far from the upper Nile. One morn-ing at dawn, while in camp, information was brought in by a native that the great herd was not very far away—in fact "just over the next hill". There was no time to be lost, so, without waiting for food, the writer started off with the camera-bearers and a few porters. "Not very far" turned out to be some 20 miles. However, eventually he came upon the herd, and they were in very bad country from the photographer's point of view, for it was covered with small thick-leaved trees, which made it impossible to see any distance, but one could hear the petulant shrieks long before seeing the animals themselves, and it made the blood run cold, in spite of the intense heat. The

MOTHER AND CHILD

This captured cow elephant, with her young offspring beside her, appears to wear a doleful expression in captivity. Owing to their reluctance to leave their young, females of a herd are more easily captured than the males, and are valued for their tractability.

whole region looked as though a tornado had swept over it, for, in feeding, the elephants had torn the trees to pieces, leaving a track several hundred yards wide completely devastated.

There seemed to be about 400 in that herd, and among them were two very large bulls with immense tusks. Unfor-

tunately for the writer, while he was trying to secure a good view, a cow with her calf by her side saw him just as he was getting on to a low anthill, and a moment later, without the least hesitation, she charged at full speed. The gunbearer had bolted, and small blame to him, and the writer was unarmed. Just as he

RIVER CROSSING

A troop of Asiatic elephants, with the characteristic high forehead and small ears, is seen in this picture crossing a pool by night in the heart of the jungle. In the forests of Thailand the elephant lives in the wild state just as its ancestors have done from time immemorial.

charge of tanks fitted with special horns.

While elephants may stay in a given locality for quite a long time, they do not object to making a move when necessary, and will travel great distances in search of what they want. They travel with remarkable speed, too. Food, of course, is the usual cause of their migrating, for just as soon as the supply begins to fail, off they go. Their food consists chiefly of tree-branches, and they chew up not only the leaves, but also the wood. It is generally believed that they do not eat grass.

In Search of Food and Drink

However, they do enjoy to the utmost a feed of growing maize or other succulent crop. Water is a matter of very great importance to them, and they will go any distance to obtain it. Where there are no convenient ponds or rivers they will dig holes in the apparently dry bed of a river, and rarely if ever fail to find what they are searching for. Not only do they need water for drinking, but they like to bathe in it and to plaster their skin with mud; then as this dries they rub themselves against tree-trunks until most of it is removed. They also resort to dust-baths, and when the earth is bright, as it is in some parts of Kenya, the effect obtained is truly remarkable. A herd of bright-red elephants is something to cause astonishment, and is about the last thing one expects to see. Taking together the evidence of the accounts by various obser-

thought his last moment had come and could almost feel the elephant's breath on his neck, she, for no apparent reason, suddenly turned and made off with horrible screams, which gave the alarm to the rest of the great herd, and off they went with a terrific sound of crashing trees plus continuous trumpeting that was like a

ELEPHANT VERSUS TIGER

This is one of the most dramatic photographs ever taken of animal life. Out of the jungle a tiger had sprung upon a "convoy" of working elephants. Making use of his weight, and the thickness of his skin to withstand the tearing claws of his striped adversary, the elephant rested his ponderous forelegs upon the tiger. The snarls of the latter grew less terrible and died away—the elephant had won.

vers it seems to be a fact that the African elephant invariably sleeps standing up, and does not lie down, as does the Indian species. Most travellers in Africa will, whenever possible, select an elephant trail to be reasonably sure of easy gradients, for those wise animals appear to be good surveyors, and always choose the best route.

It might be well to touch on the much-discussed subject of the so-called elephant cemeteries or graveyards. These are supposed to contain great stores of tusks, *but*—and this is important—there are never any bones or teeth. Now, from all the data available there seems to be this explanation: hunters, traders, or tribesmen collect tusks for sale, which by a mischance, such as death from disease or battle, may disappear. Perhaps they hid their store of tusks when danger threatened and never came back. For many years the treasure remains hidden, and then possibly some chance traveller comes across it and proclaims that he has discovered one of the elephant's famous graveyards. But, of course, the idea is quite ridiculous, for there is a definite answer to the question "Where do elephants go to die?" Like all wild animals, they know when death is coming, and they go off *alone* to die, in some remote spot in the forest. The various scavengers—birds, animals and insects—soon make away

with all the meat. Then the bones are eaten by mice or other creatures. Vegetation grows quickly on the spot. Shortly all trace of the carcass has vanished. But there is no cemetery, fiction-writers to the contrary.

While we think of the African elephant as a creature of the wilds, free and at large, bowing to no human, we look on the Indian species as a servant of man, a figure gorgeously attired for parades and

spectacles or doing all sorts of heavy work which his master demands of him. Yet it does exist in the wild state, living its own life in the forests, as its ancestors have done from time immemorial, though for many centuries it has been hunted, trapped and taken prisoner, to be trained for menial labour and arduous tasks.

Sportsmen still hunt the Indian elephant for ivory, but they are carefully protected in most of their range, except when a rogue appears in a district, when his destruction is necessary. But the mere fact of the Indian elephants' value as workers means that they are far more valuable alive than dead, and this accounts for their not being exterminated even in the thickly populated districts in which they live. They are respected even by the bloodthirsty sportsmen who consider it great fun to destroy elephants and other grand animals of the wild.

ANIMAL LUMBERJACKS

Elephants employed in timber work in India soon develop a nice sense of balance, enabling them to rest the huge logs of wood upon their tusks, keeping them in position by the pressure of their trunks. This fine photograph shows a group returning home in dignified procession with their loads.

The five distinct known species of Rhinoceros are confined to the continents of Africa and Asia, and, of these, the Black, or prehensile-lipped, the White and the Indian are the best known. As the African species have had the greatest amount of publicity, and are probably the most interesting, we will deal first with them, starting with the black species.

The black rhinoceros is found in many parts of Central Africa, and is perhaps most abundant in Kenya and Tanganyika. These relics of a past age weigh as much as 2 tons and stand nearly 6 feet in height. They have a well-fitted skin, which is fairly smooth, and is about half an inch thick. Strips of this tough skin are made into whips and sticks and, strangely enough, when dry and polished, look almost like clouded amber. A characteristic of both the African species is the fact that they have two horns. Most horned animals have them arranged on either side of their head; not so the rhino. He has one in front of the other, the forward one being right over the nose. These horns vary considerably both in length and shape: some are straight, some are curved, some are thick, others slender and up to 30 inches in length. Usually the front horn is the longer, and the female as a rule has the longest ones. As a matter of fact, though spoken of as horns, they are actually composed of tightly compressed bristles **forming a very hard**

substance. They are not attached to the skull, but grow out of the skin. Unfortunately, these horns have a high commercial value, and are bought by the Chinese for medicinal purposes, and this has led to the animals being hunted remorselessly. As they are very easy to stalk and shoot, the only thing that has saved them from extermination is the protection afforded them by game laws.

The rhino's nose, or, rather upper lip, is extended and pointed and somewhat prehensile, but perhaps its most noticeable feature is its very uncertain disposition. Some individuals are so thoroughly ill-tempered that they have given to the whole species a very bad reputation. It is all very well for certain people to say that the rhino does not charge, but it so

happens that the writer has been charged, and with ill intent, too, on several occasions. That the charge, if there is only one of the big creatures, can be avoided is true enough, provided you have the presence of mind to keep cool and stay put until the animal is within 5 or 6 feet, and then, just before contact is made, jump aside very quickly, for then the head is held low and the position of the eyes prevents him from seeing you.

The speed at which these great and apparently clumsy beasts can travel is amazing, and must be seen to be believed, and they turn with utmost rapidity.

As a rule the rhino is found in fairly open country, where it can be easily seen, but some prefer to live in the dense forest, where they may be encountered without

the slightest warning at close quarters, and also with disastrous results. For then the sudden meeting with their old-time enemy, man, causes them to rush madly at the intruder, who, owing to the thickness of the undergrowth, is unable to get out of their way.

The food of the rhino consists of leaves: not the large, juicy ones that would seem suitable for so large an animal, but absurdly small and insignificant ones, and so far as the writer has been able to discover they do not as a rule eat grass. Like most of the larger animals, they enjoy bathing and wallowing in the mud. The birds which are found on their backs are not sentinels, as generally believed, but are there simply to pick off the many insects which are such a pest.

(W.L.)

C

IN ARID COUNTRY

African explorers took this photograph when their plane landed in a dry lake-bed in Kenya, causing the rhinoceros to dash away in fright. Though weighing up to about two tons the black rhinoceros is capable of a great turn of speed, and it would test the powers of a good horse to escape from its swift and violent charge. Patches of earth impregnated by salt are eagerly sought by all kinds of animals, and the two rhinos in the lower photograph have come across a plentiful supply. Animal photography is made additionally difficult by the fact that most wild life bestirs itself mainly at night. The scene shown was recorded at about seven o'clock in the morning, before the rhino's "bedtime", and the vantage point of the photographer was a tree conveniently situated close by.

Sometimes their love for water leads to disaster, because, strange as it may seem, crocodiles will actually attack them, in spite of their great size, and drag them under water to their death. In proof of this a photograph was made some years ago showing various stages of the tragedy.

Sight and Hearing of the Rhino

The eyesight of the rhino is well known to be poor, and unless an object is moving they do not seem able to make it out at a distance of much more than 40 or 50 yards. Their hearing is fairly acute, but it is on their sense of smell that they chiefly rely for their protection. They will detect the presence of man a quarter of a mile or more away if the wind is favourable. On getting the fearsome scent, they act in a most amusing manner, rushing about this way and that with tail erect, and often making horrible petulant snorts, and then suddenly off they gallop.

The writer always feels deeply grateful to the black rhino for having given him some of his most thrilling experiences (perhaps somewhat dangerous at times) and his most exciting photographs.

Once he had a rather funny experience with rhino. He was camped in northern Kenya when, in the middle of the moonlit night, he heard some animal making quite a noise very near his tent. Nothing but a rhino would cause such a disturbance and, being afraid the clumsy old creature would break up his camp, he rushed out, dressed only in pyjamas, and there sure enough was the stupid animal, meandering about, very much to the alarm of the porters. Not wanting to hurt him, the writer picked up some stones and pelted the big target, and after he had been hit a couple of times off he went at a fast trot, puffing and snorting as he went.

Rhino breed only once in every two or three years, and usually have a single calf. This stays with its mother until it is quite large. How old they are when weaned is uncertain, but the writer has seen them suckling for a few minutes between browsing on the small leaves which form their regular diet. Some of these healthy children must have weighed upwards of three-quarters of a ton.

The second largest of living quadrupeds is the so-called White rhinoceros, sometimes spoken of as the square-nosed species. It is second in size only to the elephant, and stands rather over $6\frac{1}{2}$ feet in height, but what its weight is can only be surmised—probably about $3\frac{1}{2}$ tons.

Rarity of White Rhinoceros

In former times they were fairly common in many parts of Africa, but owing to the ease with which they can be hunted they have become very rare. Among the few remaining districts where they still survive is one region of Zululand, where the very few are being carefully protected in the hope of starting, not a herd, but a collection. There are some in Uganda north of Victoria Nyanza and in parts of the Belgian Congo, also in the Sudan in the White Nile Provinces of Mongalla and the Bahr el Ghazal. In the neighbourhood of the Yei and Meridi rivers the writer has seen signs of several, but only once had he the luck to see one, and then for but a brief moment. Unfortunately the wind was in the wrong direction, and the great beast made off with surprising speed, only giving time to realize how thoroughly ugly it was.

The name "white rhino" is rather misleading, as they are really a dull grey. Their most conspicuous feature is the remarkable length of their two horns,

CHARGING MONSTER

The black rhinoceros, so often likened to a tank, is seen making an actual charge and was photographed at a range of 15 yards with impressive result. Dodging it was no easy task, but fortunately it was accomplished without having to kill the two-ton beast.

"PREHISTORIC" SCENE OF TODAY

The black rhinoceros has got a bad reputation because, owing to its stupidity and poor eyesight, it really does charge people, occasionally with disastrous results. Mother and calf are here seen in Africa. Unlike the Indian species, the Africans, both black and white, have two horns, composed of compressed bristles which are not attached to the skull.

which in the female attain a length of over 60 inches, while those of the male seldom exceed 40 inches.

The protection of these rare animals is not too easy. In fact it is almost impossible to enforce game laws in so large a country where there are so few officials. The result is that the natives who prize the meat and know the value of the horns, indulge in periodic game drives in which hundreds of natives take part.

It is strange how thoroughly the white differ from the black species. They may be said to be practically harmless, for only on the rarest occasions have they been known to make an attack, and never an unprovoked one. They are very easy to stalk, provided the wind is favourable, for while their sense of smell is keen and their hearing fairly so, they, like the black variety, do not rely on their eyesight, which is very poor.

Whether they can be saved from extermination remains to be seen, but it is a well-known fact that once a species becomes very scarce it is almost impossible, except under most favourable conditions, to stem the tide that sweeps it away.

Though it is quite possible that the Indian and African rhinoceros came originally from the same stock, they have changed greatly both in appearance and habits. The two African species—that is,

On an island in an African river, the "river-horses", as they are known, bask in the sun. They spend a large part of the daytime in and about the water, though when

the black and the white ones—have fairly well-fitting skins, while the Indian does not patronise a good tailor, and therefore wears ill-fitting clothes with deep folds or wrinkles and very rough studded surface. Rudyard Kipling, in an amusing fable, which gives a fanciful account of how the rhino acquired the folds in his skin, remarks on the animal's bad temper. He was referring to the Indian rhinoceros, but the comment ap-

plies even more aptly to the African variety. Certain though it is that the Indian rhino is extremely ill-humoured, his temper is not nearly as bad as that of his African cousin.

The single horn is another conspicuous feature, as against the two horns of both the African kinds, and this horn is very much shorter, anything up to 2 feet being quite rare. In general, Indian members of the tribe seem to prefer swampy country.

72

HAS AN "ESCORT"

night comes they wander considerable distances in search of food. As seen above, egrets, perched on their backs, render service by eating ticks and leeches which infest them.

They are very shy, and always try to escape from their enemies without making trouble. In fact, they are not nearly as cantankerous as the black species. Should they, either in self-defence or otherwise, come into personal contact with man, they attack with their teeth rather than the horn. In size they are rather larger than the black species.

The range of the common Indian species is from the foot of the Hima-layas from Nepal to Bhutan and Assam.

The Javan rhino of eastern Bengal, the Malay peninsula, Java and Borneo has a smoother skin, and only the males carry horns, while the Sumatran species has two horns and is very much smaller, being not more than $4\frac{1}{2}$ feet high at the shoulder.

A Dwindling Tribe

Most people conjuring up a picture of an African river feel that it would not be

73

complete unless it contained at least one Hippopotamus. Yet today only too many of the old places will never see a hippo again. They have become very greatly reduced in numbers and are restricted to certain limited areas. Even the White Nile, where they used to be very abundant, has had its herds decimated, and the few that remain have become more and more shy. People who called themselves sportsmen used to shoot them from the steamers going up and down this second largest river of the world, but that form of so-called sport has been stopped.

Formerly the hippo was very widely distributed in Africa and, strangely enough, also in Europe, but that was a long time ago. Thirty years ago in the Tana river (Kenya) it was quite a common thing to see thirty or forty of the great beasts in one herd, leading their peaceful lives swimming about and blowing jets of water from their noses, or sleeping quietly at the surface or on the rocks. Today one would expect to see only a very occasional individual.

Hippopotamus Ivory

Though not objects of beauty, they are very interesting in their own way, and are different from any other animal, both in appearance and habits. Their bodies and heads are enormous, for their weight is estimated at about 4 tons, but with their very short legs they are only 4 feet 8 inches in height, while they are 12 feet long. Their great teeth, which weigh up to 7 lb. each, and have a length of over 30 inches, on the curve, were formerly used for dental ivory, and are still used for ivory ornaments.

The home of the hippo is always in the immediate neighbourhood of rivers or lakes or even swamps, and at night many a traveller has been frightened by their strange roars, which are often mistaken for those of the lion. There is usually one loud roar followed by several grunts—a quite disturbing sound on a dark night. Unfortunately they are very destructive to crops, and though easily kept away by simple scarecrows, the natives, not taking precautions, frequently lose their harvest.

Hunting the Hippo

Natives regard the meat as a luxury, and hunt the hippo in various ways, with harpoons on the Nile and with poison arrows elsewhere. The meat is not at all bad, being like a cross between beef and pork. The skin makes good whips and sticks and resembles that of the rhino in being much like amber when polished.

The hippo is essentially a water-loving animal, and he is really more at home in a river than on land. He swims with surprising ease, and sleeps with only the upper part of the head and back showing. When moving hippos expose nearly half the head, and it is then that they look like a horse. This has resulted in the name of "river horse" being applied to them. They can stay under water for several minutes, and as they rise they send up a fine spray. They feed chiefly at night.

When the mother is expecting her calf she will sometimes go for miles until she finds a suitable and secluded pond. Even a small one will answer. Later she returns to the herd. The probable reason for this is fear of the crocodile, which, while it will not molest a full-grown hippo, readily attacks a young one.

The hippo differs from the rhino in having four instead of three toes.

Besides the common one, there is also the pigmy, or Liberian species, which is $2\frac{1}{2}$ feet in height, and weighs 400 lb.

READY FOR BREAKFAST

Home of the ungainly short-legged hippopotamus is always in the immediate vicinity of water, where they live in herds and formerly were numerous. They are, like most very large animals, vegetarians. This photograph was taken in the Transvaal.

GORILLA IN THE CONGO

Of the two varieties of gorilla, one frequents the forest lowlands, the other lives in mountainous country. The photograph above shows the mountain dweller of the tribe.

CHAPTER FOUR

APES AND MONKEYS

by E. G. BOULENGER, F.Z.S.

Monkeys and man : the man-like apes—gorilla, chimpanzee, orang-outan, and gibbon : intelligence of the apes : communal life of baboons : the amazing mandrill : monkeys of the Old World and the New : the tarsier monkey, primitive forerunner of the human race.

MAN is the final phase in a long series of evolutionary changes which has culminated in the order known as Primates—the highest order of mammals. To this order also belong the man-like apes, the baboons, the ordinary monkeys and the lemurs. Most of its members are very man-like, having normally five fingers and toes with flattened nails. They show, however, much variation, featuring sometimes excessive development of some particular organ. The members of the order primates not only duplicate in varying degrees our own structure, but foreshadow, in a crude fashion, some of our ways of life. In their quadrupedal habits and general internal economy the primates resemble the other mammals, but one feature marks them as unique; this is the grasping quality of their hands and feet.

Apes and monkeys, although often ascending to high altitudes and wearing heavy coats as a protection against the chilling dews, depend with a few exceptions on a constant and luxurious supply of vegetation, and therefore frequent only tropical and sub-tropical countries. Their fossil remains in temperate and even northern latitudes are evidence of the much more genial climatic conditions that prevailed just prior to the human era.

So generally are the broad outlines of the evolutionary process accepted to-day that it is unnecessary to exhaust space in again recounting the furious controversy concerning our origin which raged during the middle part of the last century. Suffice it to say that our kinship with the other primates is established, and it is of more importance here to consider, not the direct origin of the human race, but its many lower branches as represented by the members of the order generally.

Although the human race has only been recognizable as such for about a million years, man-like apes were established in Southern Europe in the Miocene period, about fifteen million years ago. The true Old World monkeys are known to date back to about the same period. The more primitive lemurs, however, originated in the Eocene and Oligocene, many millions of years earlier, both in Europe and North America, disappearing from the latter with the appearance of the apes and monkeys proper. The lemurs are now found in Africa and Madagascar only. They have many features common to the higher monkeys and to a much lower group—that of the tree shrews, which appeared earlier in the Eocene—and these again show affinities with certain small insectivorous mammals: their fore-runners in the closing period of the Age of Reptiles. It is generally agreed, therefore, that the many-branched tree represented by lemurs, monkeys, apes and man has its roots in the tree-dwelling shrews now found only in the Far East, but once having a much wider range. As regards the origin of man, it need only be said that no one country is now regarded as the cradle of the human race.

Monkeys and Man

It is thought more likely that man began as a sporadic adventure, quasi-human creatures cropping up in various parts of the world. These possibly descended from a branch of the small, tailless, erect-walking gibbons—of Oriental countries—and these in their turn may have sprung from some such stock as produced the little tree-dwelling Tarsioids—diminutive lemurs once having a world-wide distribution.

Monkeys are constantly held up as figures of fun, but as a servant of man they have played, and still do play, a not unimportant part. Apart from being exploited as show beasts, they have been put to various economic uses. Thus, in Sumatra the Macaque monkey is still employed for assisting man in the harvesting of coconuts. The procedure of this strange harvest is simple. The coconut farmer sends his monkey, who is induced to throw down the nuts, up a selected tree and directs its movements by means of a cord attached to its waist.

Monkeys were also employed in the past century in assisting in the tea harvest in China. In olden days certain monkeys gave almost as much service as slaves. Robert Fortune, a distinguished botanist of the past century, has described how in Abyssinia these animals were employed to grind millet in a mortar, to draw water from a pitcher and to turn the spit.

In 1902 an authentic account appeared in the newspapers of a baboon living in a signal-box on the Johannes-burg–Pretoria line, which, under the direction of a crippled signalman, actually pulled the levers, and never caused a single accident. This baboon is the subject of a special memoir filed in the archives of the Port Elizabeth Museum.

With so many species of animals being farmed and painlessly killed in order to supply the fur market, it is hard to find an excuse for the trade in monkey skins. The long-furred Guereza and Diana monkeys, represented by several varieties in Africa, suffer most. Fifty years ago over 100,000 of these monkeys were killed in a single year, but in 1930 only about 1000 were found by the fur-hunters.

The Man-like Apes

Man and ape may be said to be almost identical in structure, the brain, with its deep folds or convolutions, and the atrophied non-visual tail being special features which the apes share with man. The term man-like ape is applied to the Gorilla of tropical Africa, the Chimpanzee of Western and Equatorial Africa, the Orang-outan of Borneo and Sumatra, and to the Gibbons of Eastern Asia.

The Gorilla—a name signifying "wild man"—is the largest of the apes, an adult male standing 6 feet high and weighing nearly 700 lb. The female

ROAMING THE FOREST

*Largest of the man-like apes, the gorillas, inhabiting dense forests, are extremely
difficult to study. The above dramatic photograph secured by an explorer is
unique in that it shows a gorilla in its natural haunts in the East African forestland.*

FOREST SPOILER

This chimpanzee in Central Africa has torn up a young tree like a giant in a fairy story. His terrific strength, equal to that of several men, is supported on a diet of young shoots and fruits. Chimpanzees roam about restlessly leaving a wake of destruction behind them.

is a much smaller animal. It may be distinguished from the other apes by, amongst other features, its large splayed nose. Like the chimpanzee, its man-like body is covered with thick dark hair, but it differs from its African relation in its stockier build and smaller ears. There are two varieties of gorilla: one which inhabits the steaming forest districts of the lowlands, and the other which frequents mountainous country. The mountain breed is the larger of the two, and has a much thicker coat. The gorilla, although it occasionally stands upright, normally roams about on all fours with the head close to the ground. Its tremendous physique is kept up on a diet of fruit, roots, shoots and small birds.

Early legends depicted the animal as a ferocious monster—a kind of "King Kong" that attacked man at sight and abducted women. The ape was described for the first time in 1698 by Andrew Bartell, an English prisoner of the Portuguese in Angola. He wrote: "It is a huge and ferocious animal known to the natives as the 'Pongo'. It habitually walks erect and differs little from man. The Pongos cannot speak and have no understanding more than a beast. They go many together and kill many negroes that work in the woods. They often fall upon the elephants that come to feed where they live and beat them with clubbed fists and pieces of wood until they run roaring away from them." Early

MOTHER AND CHILD

There is an expression of almost human intelligence on the face of the orang-outan which is reflected in that of the baby which she hugs beneath her arm. The usual method of carrying a baby is on the mother's hip. Mentally, the orang nearly equals the gorilla and chimpanzee.

WILD MAN OF THE WOODS

Weighing about three hundred pounds, this giant orang-outan was captured in the jungles of British North Borneo by Mr. and Mrs. Martin Johnson. The aptness of its Malayan name, which means "man of the woods", is borne out by the remarkable photograph at right, taken in the jungle.

travellers were much impressed by the gorilla's "demoniacal cry" and the intimidating manner in which it beat its breasts with the open palms of the hand. In reality its voice somewhat resembles the low bark of a dog, whilst its habit of beating its breasts does not necessarily denote anger, being but an expression of excitement, pleasurable or otherwise.

In recent years the gorilla's habits have been studied both in the wild and in captivity, and those entitled to do so give the ape a good character, describing it as normally pacific, sometimes even friendly, as far as its relations with man are concerned. A gorilla which was given the name of John Daniel was kept for some years in a flat in Sloane Street, London. He stood 4 feet in height, loved dressing up and took his meals with his owner and her friends, exhibiting perfect table manners and using the ordinary table service. John, who was exceedingly friendly by nature, lived an almost completely human life. He had a room of his own and always slept in a bed. Following John's death, his owner wrote the following account of her former charge: "John loved to have people come to see him in his home, and whenever visitors called he would show off like a child. It was his custom to take them by the hand and lead them about. His table manners were really very good. He always sat at table, and when dinner was ready would pull his own chair up to his

place. One day I was going out to a party with my sister. I was ready dressed when John wished to sit on my lap. My sister said, 'Don't let him; he will spoil your dress.' As my dress happened to be a light one, I pushed him away and said 'No'. He at once lay on the floor and cried like a child for about a minute. Then he rose, looked round the room, found a newspaper, picked it up, spread it on my lap and climbed up. Even those who saw it said they would not have believed it had they not seen it themselves. Two of my nephews, the wife of one of them and my sister were in the room and can testify to the correctness of the above record."

Patriarchal Life of Gorilla

In his forest home the male gorilla is a patriarch and rules his family with a rod of iron, sending the members to bed every evening up a tree of his own selection, where each individual makes a good pretence at a bed. The "dictator" then establishes himself for the night, sleeping at the foot of a neighbouring tree, against which he is propped in a recumbent position. Dr. Dyce Sharp of the African Medical Service, who has made a special study of gorillas, states that he has repeatedly tried the experiment of lying where the male has lain, and in every case was able to see from his couch the tree-top beds of the several wives and youngsters. The male's bed is a highly elaborate one. It may measure 9 feet by 6, and is constructed of young saplings covered with stout branches, the whole being covered with a layer, a couple of feet thick, of leaves. According to Dr. Dyce Sharp, it is a most comfortable structure, and "is as like a spring mattress as possible considering that it is composed of raw forest material".

Whilst the gorilla may fairly claim priority on academic grounds, the Chimpanzee easily holds first place in public affections. Both its appearance and deportment have made it a universal favourite. No animal could be more attractive in its early years, but, like all the man-like apes, it tends to become morose and untrustworthy when adult. Even when young it is liable to outbursts of hysteria.

The first chimpanzee brought to Europe was one presented in 1641 to the Prince of Orange. Fifty years later a dead specimen reached England, and in 1835 London Zoo received its first living example. It caused a terrific furore, and the keeper despatched to convey it from Bristol docks to London had the greatest difficulty in persuading a stage-coach agency to book him "two-insides".

The chimpanzee ranges over much of Western and Central Equatorial Africa. It is unique amongst man-like apes in its normally flesh-coloured face, hands and ears, and glossy black hair. Dark-brown and black-faced varieties have been recorded. An adult male stands about 5 feet when erect, and has the strength of several men. This terrific musculature, so characteristic of the great apes, is maintained solely on a vegetarian diet of leaves, shoots and fruits.

The Roving Chimpanzee

In its period of gestation and method of carrying the young the chimpanzee resembles the human. It is diurnal, and sleeps at night on a rude platform of twigs, and associates in small family parties under the iron rule of a male "elder". But there are also large bands of "racketeers" that roam through the forest to their own great enjoyment, but at the expense of all else, leaving a trail

THE AMAZING MANDRILL

Extraordinary as is the pattern of this simian face, the colouring makes a nightmare impression. The nose is a bright vermilion and is buttressed by ridges of azure blue. The beard is cream, the ears shell pink. The hindquarters of the animal are also of a vivid colour.

of spoilt fruits, damaged nests and disgruntled animal neighbours in their wake. The chimpanzees live a roving life and seldom frequent the same spot for more than a few days. As soon as they have consumed the fruit and shoots of certain trees they decamp in search of "fresh pastures". These apes not only construct their "nests" or sleeping couches for resting in by night, but sometimes build similar structures for merely enjoying a siesta during the day. These "nests" are erected in trees by the old males, and are seldom built higher than 12 feet from the ground. According to the traveller Kittenberger, who has studied the habits of a black-faced race of chimpanzees living in the eastern Congo forests, these apes, which from a distance are difficult to distinguish from gorillas, when alarmed rarely take to the trees, but run away on their hind limbs, using their hands to part the bushes, and break any branches that may interfere with their progress. Their very human cries, he says, are often accompanied by drumming sounds, the latter being produced, not by the beating of the breast, as in the case of the gorilla, but by the beating of tree-trunks with the palm of the hands. Kittenberger when he first saw the many "nests" of a large troop of chimpanzees in the Congo forest mistook them for an instant for those of large birds of prey. He was puzzled, since he knew that birds of prey never lived in flocks. Later he realized that they were the beds of chimpanzees.

Intellectual of the Animal World

The chimpanzee has made itself world-famous by its sheer force of intellect. In its first few years it learns even quicker than a child of the same age, can be taught to count up to seven, use human clothes and simple utensils, ride a bicycle and to take delight in human society. Up to seven years of age it easily passes all the usual intelligence tests—such as piling boxes one on top of the other to form a ladder by which to reach a prize suspended overhead. At the age of seven, however, its ideas appear to become fixed, its capacity for learning ceases, and as a pet or show animal its value quickly deteriorates. The chimpanzee's voice covers a wide range, from a wheezy giggle of delight to a loud "light tenor" call, or "demoniacal" scream; but attempts to claim for it anything approximating to a language have so far scarcely been justified. Its potential longevity is thought to be about thirty years, but captive specimens seldom survive for more than half this period.

Some Famous Chimpanzees

For over forty years the writer has been associated with famous chimpanzees. The first which comes to mind is "Jimmy", an inhabitant of the London Zoo. Shortly after its arrival, at the age of about four, it was the chief guest of a luncheon party. The little ape conducted himself, until the arrival of the dessert, with the greatest propriety, touching no food with his hands, using table utensils and drinking out of a glass. When, however, at the end of the meal a large bowl of cherries appeared, Jimmy could no longer control himself, and giving up his party manners for those of the wild, screamed with pleasure and plunged both hands into the fruit. The humans present laughed. But the chimpanzee, who up to that moment had participated in the general merriment, did not join them. Instead he covered his face with one hand, painfully embarrassed by a sense of

APE ACROBAT

"Sappho", one of two Concolor gibbons, enjoying the freedom of wild life on an estate in the south of England, poises on the branch of a tree preparatory to hurling itself through space. The leaping powers of the gibbon tribe enable it to cover twenty feet with ease.

SHRILL-VOICED MARMOSET

This small monkey, of South America, has a shrill twittering voice, which occasionally takes on a bird-like note. Though its face is bare, it is otherwise lavishly provided with fur. It is light in weight, small in size, and easily drops from great heights without harm.

having committed a "social error". This behaviour on the part of the ape refutes the assertions of those who believe a sense of shame is limited to humans.

The origin of the late Frank Bostock's long line of "Consuls" was a performing chimpanzee of the writer's acquaintance. His mentality was quite remarkable. During Consul's stay in Paris, where he appeared on the stage, at evening performances only, he was taken one day to a matinée at a rival circus, where he saw and applauded the performance of a clown which was acclaimed by a delighted audience. Whether Consul coupled the comedian's effort with public appreciation, or merely desired to emulate it from sheer mimicry, others must decide, but various of the items in the clown's repertoire were introduced by Consul into his performance when he faced the footlights a few hours later.

There is a fully authenticated story of a Manchester Zoo chimpanzee that fashioned, from a piece of wood left by chance in its cage, a simple "railway" key that unlocked the door.

The Orang-outan is second only to the gorilla in size and strength, but probably slightly below that of the ape or the chimpanzee in intelligence. Its appearance of slow-wittedness may, however, be largely encouraged by its somewhat tardy and deliberate movements. The name "orang-outan" is derived from the Malay meaning "Wild Man of the

BABOON ENRAGED

This photograph was taken in the Belgian Congo. The baboon displays its huge canine teeth in fury and one can understand why even lions and leopards find it a formidable adversary in strength and courage. Ridges over the eyes protect them from the sun.

BABOONS

Baboons of this type were venerated by the ancient Egyptians and frequently make their appearance in Egypt's sculptured monuments. They were even allotted a special burial-

AT HOME

ground from which the remains of their mummies have been dug up. They are to be found in rocky districts of Egypt, Abyssinia and the Sudan and also in Arabia.

NOT ON SPEAKING TERMS

To judge by their attitudes in this picture, these two vervet monkeys seem to have had a tiff. They belong to a species characterized by its long tail and common in South Africa.

Woods". The ape is confined to Borneo and Sumatra. Among its leading characteristics are the great length of the arms, the coat of long, coarse, tangled reddish-brown hair, the very small ears, and in the adult male of certain races the great widening of the sides of the face and immense goitrous sack overhanging the chest. A fully-grown male may weigh over 250 lb. and stand 6 feet high. Like the two foregoing apes, however, the orang never willingly assumes the upright for long, preferring to walk about on all fours. It is essentially a creature of the tree-tops, seldom coming to earth of its own accord. The single infant is carried on the maternal hip.

That the intellectual powers of the orang-outan are of a comparatively high order was demonstrated in the New York Zoo, where one of these animals, as in the case of the Manchester Zoo chimpanzee, fashioned a wooden key with which to unfasten his cage. Another specimen having found an iron spanner, left within his reach by some workmen, used the implement to lever the bars of his cage apart. In this work he enlisted the help of a cage companion.

Smallest of the Man-like Apes

The arboreal Gibbons, smallest of the man-like apes, are all inhabitants of the Far East. The members of the family are the comparatively large Siamang of the Malay Peninsula and Sumatra and the smaller Lar or agile gibbon of Sumatra and Siam, the Concolor of Indo-China, the Hoolock of Assam, and the Silver gibbon of Java. The siamang is distinguished from the other species by the presence of a laryngeal sac—a large, bladder-like organ attached to its throat, and with which is associated the animal's voice production, becoming inflated when the animal gives vent to emotion in song.

In these apes, which vary much in the colour of their fur, the head is neat and rounded—almost globular. Apart from the siamang, their average height is about 3 feet. The body is extremely slender, with a waist-development which resembles that of a greyhound. The fore-limbs, which are very much longer than the hind-limbs, are of such a length that when a gibbon stands erect, the finger-tips all but touch the ground.

Liveliness of the Gibbon

Their bright black faces bespeak a ready intelligence, and their emotions, never far below the surface, at once find expression in their powerful voices: these they can raise to a deafening howl, in response to music, or, in the case of captive specimens, the stimulus of a crowd. But the outstanding feature of the gibbon is its almost incredible leaping and acrobatic powers. It can hurl itself 20 feet or more through space, never missing the desired branch which is its aim: it will drop 40 feet or more through tangled foliage to some well-calculated perch; it can stride arm over arm through the forest roof, faster than a man can run on the ground. It is given to the erect pose more than any other primate, and runs at high speed on the ground or along a branch with a Charlie Chaplin action, the arms held out horizontally. Gibbons live chiefly on fruit, but will also eat insects and the eggs of small birds. They have been observed to capture birds on the wing, but probably only in sport, and not with the object of obtaining a meal. Drinking is always effected by dipping the hand in water. Although emanating from the tropics, gibbons are very hardy.

SACRED MONKEYS

In the sun-splashed courtyard of an Indian temple plays a group of macaques. These monkeys are held sacred in India and take full advantage of their privileged position, congregating in noisy, quarrelsome troupes, and seeming to be aware of the fact that

OF INDIA

no one may interfere with them. They do immense damage to crops and property and show a decided preference for fruits and young leaves. Macaques are found in many parts of Asia and there are some twenty species of the tribe, differing in tail length.

PROBOSCIS MONKEYS

Most fantastic of the monkey tribe are these long-nosed inhabitants of Borneo, the proboscis drooping over the mouth to the chin. They take readily to water and swim strongly.

FAMILY SCENE

Mother performs a necessary part of the toilet of a little red cololus monkey, which undergoes the operation with what seems to be considerable patience. The photograph was taken in Africa on the borders of Kenya and Uganda.

The Baboons are essentially ground-dwellers, and live in open country. They are characterized by massive limbs with short, blunted fingers and toes, a rudimentary tail, bare patches on the hind quarters in the case of the males only—with the exception of one species, in which these patches are present in both sexes—and a long, sensitive, dog-shaped muzzle: an organ upon which the animal relies both for discovering food and for scenting the approach of foes. The eyes are protected from the sun by overhanging ridges. The canine teeth of the males form large, dagger-shaped weapons. Baboons, although they generally live on roots, shoots, birds' eggs, reptiles and insects, are omnivorous. Like many other monkeys, they are provided with cheek-pouches, in which they store food for short periods. The baboons, of which there are a dozen species, are confined to Africa, where they are as a rule found in communities or troops. These communities are composed of many family parties, ruled by an overlord who imposes his will not only upon his several wives, but on a number of younger male camp-followers. There is a marked *esprit de corps* amongst these colonies, and several instances are recorded of baboons covering the retreat of disabled companions. Even the lion and leopard hesitate to attack a baboon colony.

The best-known species of baboon is the big Hamadryad or sacred baboon of

D

(W.L.)

Egypt, Abyssinia, the Sudan and Arabia. In ancient Egypt it was dedicated to the God Thoth, and the city of Hermopolis was given up to the creature. These baboons figured in paintings on the walls of innumerable monuments and tombs. They were also embalmed, many baboon mummies having been disinterred. The species is easily recognized by the greyish colour of its fur, which in the male forms a thick cape over its shoulders, and its bright pink face.

Amazing Colours of the Mandrill

The Mandrill of West Africa is virtually tailless, with limbs worthy of a lion and with heavily ridged cheeks. The male of this species is famous for its amazing colours. The face is azure blue, perfectly set off by a vermilion nose; the hind-quarters display all the colours of a Turner sunset. The animal is further characterized by shell-pink ears, hands and feet and a cream-coloured "imperial" beard. The colour of the body is auburn.

The Drill, also of West Africa, is similar in structure to the mandrill, but the face is uniformly black, the lower lip being in the case of the male coloured "lip-stick" red. Both this animal and the mandrill associate in smaller companies than do other baboons.

The brown Chacma is a native of South Africa, where it does much damage to crops and gardens. Ostrich farms are occasionally invaded by large colonies of these creatures, who rob the birds of their eggs. The depredations of the baboons have led in South Africa to the breeding of speedy and quick-witted baboon dogs, which are specially trained in the strategy of attacking these gangsters. The chacma, although very destructive, is highly intelligent, and numbers have been domesticated. The baboon referred to previously and which worked as a signal-man on the Johannesburg–Pretoria line belonged to this species.

The Gelada also is confined to South Africa. The species is distinguished by both sexes displaying bare red patches on chest and neck, which at certain times of the year become inflamed. In the gelada the nostrils are situated at the sides of the muzzle and not at the extreme end.

The other Old World monkeys are abundant throughout all the warmer and more heavily vegetated quarters of the Old World, save Australia, that continent having become cut off from the mainland prior to the advent of the monkey hordes. The characteristic Old World group is exemplified by the Macaques, which abound throughout Asia, typified in the memories of older readers by the "organ-grinder's monkey" once so familiar. Like all monkeys, macaques associate in troops, and are mixed feeders, with a marked leaning towards fruits and young leaves. The young, born singly, are first carried at the breast, and later ride their mothers jockey fashion. Macaques abound in all the hotter climes, but are very hardy, and in Asia ascend well above the snow line. The common macaque is an Indian species, and is a great nuisance, doing immense damage to crops and property.

Gibraltar's "Barbary Apes"

Another famous macaque is the so-called Rock monkey or "Barbary Ape" of Gibraltar, which once infested the fortress and citadel in some hundreds. The monkeys were at one time under the charge of a celebrated "Sergeant Brown", but despite his well-meant efforts at martial law, clashes with shop-

DEFIANCE

Ensconced among the branches the colobus or guereza monkey looks down on intruders with a seeming mixture of the inquisitiveness of the monkey tribe and anger at being disturbed. The name means "maimed" and refers to the absent or rudimentary thumb.

BUSH-BABY

*This strange little creature, the galago or bush-baby, ranges in size from that of a rat
to a small cat and has a loud wail. It can leap amazing distances.*

keepers, farmers and the garrison became
so frequent that the baboons had to be
disbanded to divers zoos, and now only a
few of the originals remain. Once, when
the brush covering the Rock caught fire,
an unforgettable spectacle was provided
by many scores of monkeys tobogganing
down the steep rain-water catchments
that form a gigantic landmark on the
Rock's seaward aspect.

The Langurs are large monkeys, akin
to the macaques, but with black faces,
silvery coats and very long tails. They
are essentially oriental, and in India,
where they are regarded as sacred, are
dedicated to the god Hanuman and
infest the monkey temple of Hanuman.
Being held sacred, they are treated with
every consideration, with the result that

these monkeys are case-hardened against
any threats of recrimination. Hore's
langur of Bengal is subject to limey
secretions of the intestine. These are
roundish, and are known as monkey-
stones or bezoar stones. They vary in
size from a pea to a hen's egg and are
much valued, especially by the Chinese,
for their alleged medicinal properties.

The Snub-nosed monkeys are giant
langurs with brick-red faces and grotesque snub noses. They frequent the
mountainous districts of China.

In startling contrast to these snub-
nosed monkeys is the Proboscis monkey
of Borneo. In the adult male the nose,
which is of the "Roman" variety, is
enormous, measuring 3 inches in length,
and droops over the mouth as far as the

chin. This grotesque nasal organ appears to offer no obstacle to the monkey, since it is able to travel at high speed through the jungle. The young of this species closely resemble an adult snub-nosed monkey. The proboscis takes readily to water and swims in dog-fashion.

The Guenons and the Mangabeys are two large African clans. They have long tails and often richly coloured coats. The Vervet or guenon monkey, a common arboreal species inhabiting South Africa, is much hunted for its skin, which the Kaffirs convert into aprons. It does much good by mounting on grazing animals and ridding these of insect pests. The guenons make amusing if destructive pets; they justify their French name, which signifies a maker of faces.

In the large Guereza monkeys the thumb is all but absent. The members of this African genus, which is represented by over thirty species, are of large size and have bare callosities on the buttocks. Many are brilliantly coloured and wear elaborate beards, and head adornments. Some guerezas are the possessors of coats, consisting of manes or draperies, which droop far down on each side of the body. The long tail often terminates in a tassel.

Animal Isolationists

The New World monkeys present an interesting example of isolationism. They have developed within narrow limits, being exclusively arboreal, living in dense jungle. Most New World monkeys live largely on an insectivorous diet and are provided with a prehensile tail. Whilst African jungles appear to have been dredged of new species, the still largely unexplored regions of the Amazon are believed to harbour man-like forms as yet unidentified. The nearest approach to

such forms found so far is the little red-faced Uakari monkey which has only a vestige of a tail and long auburn hair. The young have a mottled face, which assumes the vivid red hue only when they attain maturity. Apart from the red-faced species, black-faced and bald uakaris are known. They live in tree-tops. Their chief enemies are harpy eagles.

The Sakis of the Amazon jungle are a group with enormous beards; they are distinguished by non-prehensile tails.

Howler Monkeys' Choir

The bearded Howler monkeys are remarkable in that the bones supporting the tongue form a big cup-like structure which serves the purpose of a resonator or "sound box". As a result these monkeys have exceedingly deep and powerful voices, and when a choir of some fifty strong sing their morning or evening hymn, the sounds carry for a mile or more. The monkeys are said to show an appreciation of their own vocal efforts and to be led by a choir-leader. Buffon has given a fanciful description of the howlers' choral efforts. "As soon as the choir is seated, the choir-leader begins an oration so quick and loud of voice that, at a distance, it might be imagined that a number of monkeys were all making a noise together. During the whole discourse, however, the rest keep a profound silence. When it is ended, he makes a signal to the rest to answer him, and immediately they all set up a cry together, till such time, as by another sign he orders them to be silent."

The best-known of all American monkeys are the little Capuchins which are popular as pets. The name capuchin refers to the peak of hair upon the head, suggestive of the hood worn by the

Capuchin monks. Some twenty species are known, and their range extends from Mexico to Paraguay. Capuchins have prehensile tails and small comical faces. They roam about in troops, consisting of twenty or more individuals, and feed not only on small reptiles and insects, but also on birds. They are unpopular in the land of their origin owing to their raiding poultry runs and creating much havoc in the plantations. Besides giving voice to a characteristic bird-like twitter, a capuchin can grunt, bark and whistle.

" Nursing Fathers "

The Squirrel monkeys, which have a wide distribution, being found from Costa Rica to Brazil and Bolivia, are not specially intelligent, yet they are the possessors of a brain case which is proportionately larger than man's. They have long, non-prehensile tails, which the animal wraps round itself when at rest. They are sociable little monkeys and, like the marmosets, present the phenomenon of the "nursing father", the male taking possession of the baby between meals, nursing it in its early stages on one hip, and later on his back.

The Spider monkeys, ranging from Paraguay to Mexico, are the most specialized of arboreal monkeys, the hands being used as climbing hooks rather than as manipulative organs. In some species the thumb has atrophied as a result of disuse. The underside of the tail—as in the case of the woolly monkeys—is bare, and is so sensitive that it can be used as a probe to explore hollow trees for birds' eggs.

The Woolly monkeys, inhabitants of the forests of Brazil, have, as pointed out by Darwin in "The Descent of Man", the appearance of a "venerable negro". The head is round, the face is black, the body is clothed in a woollen coat of ash-grey. Using its long prehensile tail and its feet to grasp opposite branches, a woolly monkey can lean back against its tail and swing in its own hammock. Despite their exceedingly gentle nature, woolly monkeys have enormous canine teeth, and since fights amongst its own kind are rare, these teeth are used, probably exclusively, for cracking hard-shelled nuts.

The Owl-faced monkeys or Douroucoulis, represented by five species, range from the Amazon and Eastern Peru to Nicaragua. They are small animals with round owlish faces and are strictly nocturnal. They produce cat-like howls.

Those diminutive monkeys the Marmosets have furry bodies with often extravagant ornaments of hair upon the head and tail. The face and ears are always naked, but the latter may carry tufts. The fingers and toes are clawed. Marmosets, of which there are numerous species, inhabit the greater part of South America. They feed upon fruit, eggs and insects and give voice to twittering bird-like notes. They are so light that they can fall from heights of over 40 feet without injuring themselves. The smallest species, which is the possessor of a pair of enormous whiskers, measures under 7 inches in length, excluding tail.

Habits of the Marmoset

As mentioned previously, the marmoset is of interest in the fact that the male nurses the young, taking sole charge of the baby, handing it over to the mother only when it requires food. On such occasions it is entertaining to observe the haste with which the female parent returns her infant to her overworked

AYE-AYE, POTTO AND TARSIER

Above is the Aye-aye monkey, so called from the nature of its cry. It is characterized by very large ears and eyes and also by an extraordinary development of the third finger of each hand, which is especially long and thin and used for extracting fruit juice and for conveying water to the mouth.

Above is the Potto of West Africa, remarkable for the fleshy pads which enable it to achieve a very powerful grip. The Tarsier (left) has some claim to be regarded as the forerunner of the human race. It is found in forest clearings in Malaya and it is a native superstition that it feeds on charcoal. It is hardly larger than a mouse despite its long hind legs.

RING-TAILED LEMUR

One of the most distinguished of monkeys in appearance is the ring-tailed lemur with its soft grey fur and long banded tail.

surface, with a fringed tip which is employed to clean the teeth. The group is chiefly represented in Madagascar, but a few are also to be found in Asia and Africa.

The eight species of true lemur all hail from Madagascar and the Comoro Islands.

The Ring-tailed lemur is a particularly handsome animal, with soft grey fur, white front, and long black - and - white banded tail. It frequents rocky districts and loves sun-bathing. When indulging in a sun-bath it lies on its back with arms outstretched, an attitude which it will keep for hours on end. The single young is first carried curled round the mother's waist, but at a later stage graduates to a jockey seat.

The largest of all living lemurs is the black-and-white Indri of Madagascar. It is a near relative of the extinct giant lemur, and may measure 2 feet from muzzle to buttocks. It is devoid of tail. The indri is rare in museums and has never been exhibited in any zoo.

The Mouse lemurs are little larger than their namesakes. They tide over the very hot dry season when fruit is scarce by going to sleep, a process similar to that known as hibernation, which some animals indulge in in cold climates. Prior to "turning in" for their prolonged sleep they fortify themselves by eating a prodigious amount of food, and as a

consort as soon as she has ministered to its wants. All marmosets are great sleepers, requiring at least thirteen hours rest out of the twenty-four, with a long siesta after the midday meal.

The Lemurs represent the parent stock from which all other forms have been derived, and have certain affinities with the tree shrews. The hands and feet are tactile, the tail, when present, non-prehensile and the dog-like head usually elongated. The majority are nocturnal, as attested by the very large eyes. The teeth are complex; the numerous small and closely set incisors largely serve as a comb in grooming the hair. The tongue is a peculiar organ, having a small additional tongue-like organ on its lower

result accumulate a thick layer of fat, particularly in the tail.

The nocturnal Aye-aye, so called from its cry, is the size of a fox, with immense ears and eyes and a dense coat of dark hair. Its most remarkable feature is the third finger of each hand, which is not only, like its fellows, enormously elongated, but so thin as to suggest a piece of wire, and is used for the purpose of conveying water to its mouth at an astonishing speed—some forty sips a minute. The incisor teeth are rodent-like and very large, and are used for gnawing wood. It shares with nearly all lemurs an aura of the supernatural. The creature is treated with the greatest veneration, being credited by the natives of the old school as harbouring the souls of the departed, and chance specimens found dead are given a state funeral.

The Galagos or bush-babies range in size from that of a rat to a small cat. They have a voice which suggests the efforts of an angry infant, its volume being quite out of proportion to the animal's size. All are nocturnal and have large ears and eyes, the former in the case of the moholi galago folding up when the animal is at rest. The fur is thick and soft and the tail is very long. Galagos are remarkably active, have extraordinary leaping powers and when climbing trees have the peculiar habit of moistening the palms of their hands and the soles of their feet with urine, presumably with the object of obtaining a better grip of the branches.

The Potto's Grip

The woolly-coated West African Pottos are strange creatures with a tail reduced to a mere stump and the first finger and the second toe almost absent. Both hands and feet are provided with fleshy clasping pads, which give phenomenal gripping powers. The natives are afraid of these harmless animals and are loath to handle them, being convinced that should a potto attach itself to one's person it will never let go and has to be carried about throughout the victim's life. A curious feature of some pottos is the exposed points of the neck vertebrae, which are so prominent as to suggest a row of cribbage pegs. Being surrounded by naked skin, they are especially prominent when the animal curls up to sleep.

Monkey Folk-lore

The arboreal Lorises or Asiatic lemurs are nocturnal and have huge eyes, a thick soft coat and padded hands and feet. The Slow loris of Malaya is entirely harmless, but many legends attach to it.

The Slender loris of India and Ceylon is somewhat more lightly built than the previously mentioned species. Being nocturnal, it covers its enormous hypersensitive eyes with its hands when faced with the glare of the sun, which very natural action, say the natives, is clear proof that it is seeing ghosts. In short, the lorises are associated with every form of human activity—good as well as bad, being held responsible for such diverse phenomena as earthquakes, plagues, quintuplets, murders and bumper harvests.

The spectral Tarsier is little larger than a mouse and is, as has been mentioned previously, the survivor of a numerous race which it is believed was the root from which sprang all other primates, including man. To-day it lingers on only in Malaya and the Island of Celebes, where it is found in forest clearings. This small creature is characterized by the enormous length of its hind limbs and the adhesive pads on toes and finger-tips.

GIRAFFES ON THE ALERT

In the open scrub country which they favour, a group of giraffes is on the watch. The long neck enables them to survey the surrounding terrain to a considerable distance.

CHAPTER FIVE

GIRAFFE AND OKAPI

by E. G. BOULENGER, F.Z.S.

Ancestors of the Giraffe : Its mode of self-defence: Unique features :
The Okapi of the Belgian Congo : Its "cloak of invisibility".

ALTHOUGH the Giraffe was known to the ancient Egyptians and was featured in the Roman spectacles in the Coliseum, its proper place in the natural system has only comparatively recently been understood. This has been made possible not only by the strides made in the study of prehistoric remains, but within the past half-century by the discovery of that strange animal the okapi in the Belgian Congo.

The earliest known member of the family was a much smaller animal than the modern giraffe; it had a shorter neck and stood not more than 6 feet at the shoulder. It lived some fifteen million years ago and, like all other members of the group, was confined to the Old World. The primitive giraffe stock gave rise to a number of forms, all of which are now extinct, save the African giraffes as we know them to-day and the okapi. Some of the vanished ancestors of the living members of the family were most impressive creatures. In India lived some enormous bull-necked monsters, fully 7 feet at the shoulder, and built as massively as oxen. Their outstanding feature was their horns—gigantic structures, pointing in various directions. In some cases these horns were united to form one immense battering-ram.

The ancestors of the true giraffes were at one time forest animals. They, however, left their ancestral forests to browse on high trees in open country, and their distinctive feature—the remarkable elongation of their necks—is the result of change of habit and habitat. Most naturalists recognize but a single species of giraffe. They have, however, described a number of local sub-species, founded mainly on the pattern and disposition of the spotted livery. The spotted pattern, so striking and conspicuous in a menagerie, serves as a perfect camouflage in the wild, rendering the animals almost invisible, even at close range. Infant giraffes are miniature representatives of their parents, but the spots are at first disposed so closely together as to make the animals appear almost black. In its native country the giraffe feeds exclusively on leaves, principally the foliage of the mimosa-tree, which it plucks with its long and slightly prehensile tongue. Giraffes congregate in herds of up to 100 strong, progressing at a walk or slow, grotesque, rocking canter. Their chief foe is the lion, against which they will on occasions defend themselves. The great length and strength of their legs make possible a death-dealing kick. According to the well-known naturalist and big

Startled by a 'plane a herd of giraffes makes off through the open, sparsely wooded country. Their gait is awkward and rolling, and they have a curious rocking motion, the

game-hunter, Kittenberger, lions frequently attack giraffes and kill them. He is, however, of the opinion that a single lion is incapable of killing a giraffe unaided, since a well-aimed kick would stop him for good. Giraffes, he says, except in quite uninhabited regions, are very wary and wide-awake. Their powers of scent are poor, but their eyesight is wonderful, and, on account of

DISTURBED

long neck moving from side to side and the hind-legs overtaking the fore-legs in leap-frog fashion. In spite of this apparent awkwardness the giraffe covers the ground swiftly.

their height, they can see a very long way.

An adult bull giraffe stands 18 feet high, about 7 feet being accounted for by the neck. Such an animal weighs about 2500 lb. Its enormous size and grotesque proportions render it necessary for the animal to straddle the forelegs widely when in the act of drinking. The male carries a pair of skin-covered horns; a large bony boss often surmounts its head.

GIRAFFES OF NORTHERN KENYA
This, tallest of living creatures, whose height is almost 19 feet, is the most truly African animal, for it has no close relation in other continents. This photograph shows the giraffe drinking in its peculiar fashion, something rarely seen.

The period of gestation in giraffes is eighteen months. There is only a single young at birth. As in most young hoofed animals, the baby giraffe's legs are much nearer adult size than the rest of its body, making its movements grotesque.

A unique feature of the entire family is the complete absence of vocal chords, with the result that under no stimulus whatsoever can the giraffe emit any sound above a snort, grunt or sharp intake of breath. This is remarkable, since other animals with long necks, like the ostrich and camel, are vocal to a degree.

The Okapi, though giraffe-like in general contour, has a much shorter neck and limbs, standing no more than 5 feet at the shoulder. The tongue is long and prehensile, and the head bears short, skin-covered horns. The face is white, the neck and body a glowing fiery chestnut, and the limbs are striped much like a zebra's, but no two okapis are identical.

In contrast to the plain-living giraffe, the okapi inhabits only the heart of the Ituri forest in the Belgian Congo, where it flourishes in a perpetual steamy twilight, in localities so fever-ridden and abounding with noxious insects that only the native pigmies can endure them for any length of time. Here the beast's bizarre colour pattern is, like that of the giraffe, a cloak of invisibility. The reddish-brown body is lost in the general gloom, while the striped limbs blend with the pencils of sunlight shimmering on the undergrowth. In these surroundings the animal lives on leaves and fruit, and, like the giraffe, produces a single young. Its sharp cloven hooves are its only weapon.

Its discovery was very romantic. As early as the year 1883 Sir Harry Johnston, a diplomat and explorer, suspected the existence of some hitherto unknown donkey-like beast through reading Livingstone's "Darkest Africa". Six years later a diplomatic mission took him to the Ituri, where he obtained from a Belgian officer some strips of skin, used as bandoliers by the natives. Certain hoofprints found later by Sir Harry Johnston deepened the mystery. In 1901 another Belgian officer produced an entire skin and a skull. These were sent to the Natural History Museum in England where its director, Sir Ray Lankester, established the animal's true identity.

The okapi is rigorously protected by the Belgian Government, but there is no doubt that this interesting survival from the past largely owes its continued existence to its inaccessibility.

CREATURE OF THE TWILIGHT

This was the first photograph to be taken of the okapi. Its existence was not suspected until 1883. It was first seen by white men in 1901, its fever-ridden haunts in the heart of the Ituri forest of the Belgian Congo making it extremely difficult of access.

ORIGINAL TYPE OF MODERN RACEHORSE

One of the famous Arab breed of horses is here seen in the North African desert. Its round body and short though extremely powerful limbs are typical. Giants of the Turf are descended from them, though when control is relaxed the highly-bred racehorse tends to lose its special development and to revert to the Arab type.

CHAPTER SIX

HORSE AND ZEBRA

by E. G. BOULENGER, F.Z.S.

Ancient pedigree of the horse: revolutionary changes in its appearance: derivation of the domestic type: the Arab horse: Mustang: Mongolian wild horse: Kiang, Onager, Wild Ass and Quagga: Zebra, the "horse in tiger's skin": the reasons for its striping.

PROBABLY no animal has played a greater part in human history or left a more complete record of its pedigree than the Horse. Its origin is a matter of more than common interest, and therefore it is fortunate that each step in its progress has been set forth in the records of the rocks.

The earliest known equine animal was no larger than a wolf, with four toes on each foot and a long, heavy tail. It had points in common with the earliest forerunners of the rhinoceroses and tapirs, and therefore must have radiated from the same primitive stock. The horse's small ancestors lived some millions of years ago, when the land enjoyed a more equable climate. From the Eocene period onwards, however, a slow but steady change overcame these animals. Judging by their primitive teeth and splayed feet, their ancestors were at one time undoubtedly swamp- and forest-dwellers. In time a notable increase in size took place and the teeth became extremely deep-rooted, with many folded, hard, enamelled crowns, pointing to an adaptation for grinding the maximum nutriment out of a sparse and not very nutritious diet. At the same time the feet underwent a remarkable transformation, and this can be traced through an unbroken series of fossil remains. The weight of the animal was gradually placed upon the central toe, with the result that the other toes, through disuse, began to hang clear of the ground and finally disappeared, only the so-called "canon" bones remaining hidden under the skin. A number of other hoofed animals—the oxen, sheep, deer, antelopes, etc.—developed on much the same lines, but not to the same extreme lengths as the horse. These revolutionary changes in teeth and feet were in direct response to equally remarkable changes of environment. Each step in the evolution of the horse is found to march side by side with the uprising and consequent drainage of the great land masses and a corresponding cooling of the climate. Over vast areas lush tropical forest was giving way to open plains covered with coarse, hard grasses. The horse's fleetness of foot was doubtless developed as much to search out, at short notice, fresh feeding-grounds and drinking-places as to escape from its many foes—wolves,

113

HORSES IN THE GREAT OPEN SPACES

In the beautiful photograph below is seen the concluding stage of a wild-horse drive. A herd of untamed broncos, numbering ninety-two head, in Oregon had been driven from the mountains, and ended by swimming the Molalla river, after a trek which had lasted for forty-two days. The so-called "wild horses" of this kind, so often a feature of romances of the Wild West, are, of course, not wild in the strict sense, but are the progeny of domestic horses which have been allowed to roam at large, often leading nomadic lives in the prairies of parts of the Western United States. The spirit of freedom, however, makes them mettlesome animals, which are broken to the saddle with difficulty. The horses shown were due to play a part in an annual "Buckeroo". At left, horses are galloping over the Turkoman steppes.

hunting dogs and enormous sabre-toothed cats. A feature common to horses is the hardened callosity on the side of each foreleg above the knee. This structure yields a fluid, and functions as a scent-gland.

To-day the horse family, which comprises the Mongolian wild horse, the wild asses of Asia and the wild asses and zebras of Africa, are confined, so far as the wild animals are concerned, to the Old World. Yet in the remote past ancestral horses flourished in America, in which country, however, the horse as we know it was unknown to man until introduced by the Spaniards when they first established themselves as conquerors.

Domesticated horses appear to have been derived from an Asiatic type—from a form similar to the present-day wild Mongolian horse, a short, stocky animal with a shaggy coat. The domestic

RUNNING WILD IN BRITAIN

One of the celebrated New Forest ponies is here seen together with its foal cropping the grass in a clearing. They are, of course, a variety of the domestic horse, though allowed to roam freely and subjected only to a yearly round-up when they are caught and sold.

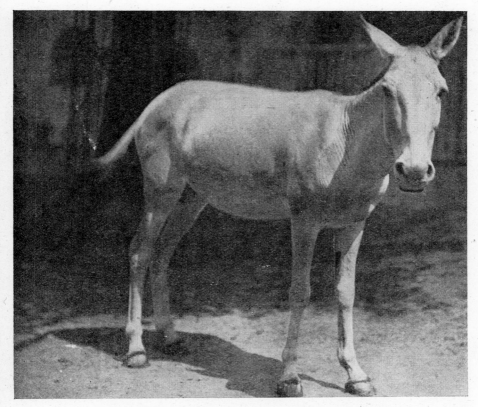

KIANG OR WILD ASS OF CENTRAL ASIA

This animal is a native of Central Asia, where it is found in large herds. It is wild and courageous and although many attempts have been made to tame it most have been unsuccessful. It is very swift on rocky and hilly ground.

horse was used for its milk supply and its skin for raiment long before it was broken to harness. Many breeds of domestic horses have been involved, these ranging from the Shetland pony, an Icelandic breed, little larger than a wolf-hound, to the Shire, standing sixteen hands— that is over 5 feet—at the shoulder, and weighing a ton. The famous Arab horse was derived from a Libyan race, and exported to neighbouring countries by the ancient Egyptians. From the Arab has been derived the modern racehorse, which, once the rigid control usually exercised over its breeding is relaxed, quickly reverts to the original Arab form. Compared with other breeds, the Arab has a rounder and longer body; the limbs are not very long, but their great power is indicated by well-marked sinews and muscles. The Arab, although not a large animal, is exceptionally hardy, and is capable of spending forty-eight hours in tropical weather without food or drink. The first Arabian stallion to be imported into this country was

The group here shown was photographed in the course of a hunting expedition in the northern desert territory of Arabia. The asses watched the intruders from a ridge, but

Markham Arabian, acquired by James I in 1616. It was, however, to three horses—Byerly Turk, Darley Arabian and Godolphin Arabian—imported to England from Arabia some years later, that the evolution of the modern race-horse is due. All the giants of the Turf, without exception, trace their ancestry to one of these three horses. From

Byerly Turk, Herod was descended; Darley Arabian gave rise to Eclipse and Persimmon; and Godolphin Arabian to Matchem. The best Arabian stallions are in the possession of the chiefs and other natives of rank. They are never sold, changing hands only as a result of a gift or legacy, and not of ordinary trade.

The so-called "mustangs", immor-

THE DESERT

before the hunters could get close, they turned about and made off. There are several species of wild ass, but those of Egypt and Africa are the source of the domestic ass.

talized in Wild West romances, are simply the progeny of domestic horses allowed to run wild: they once formed large herds that led nomadic lives on the prairies of Mexico and parts of the Western United States.

Though the Mongolian wild horse has no doubt lived in its present barren and desolate domain for many centuries,

no living example reached this country before 1902. In some respects it recalls certain ancient types of horses, notably in the very long face and absence of the characteristic hollow beneath the eye. There are faint markings, often on the legs; sometimes in the form of a shoulder stripe. This last point prompts the question as to how the ancestral horses were coloured. The standardized restorations of the first horse show them spotted—a pattern producing a not unusual camouflage effect in forest surroundings; it is believed that the spots later combined to form stripes, the accepted cloak of invisibility for an animal living surrounded by tall grass. As open country was invaded, the stripes disappeared and the horse's coat assumed the appearance we know.

A near living relation of the Mongolian wild horse is the Kiang, the so-called wild ass of Central Asia. It is as tall as an average horse, and is found in herds of several hundred strong. It is a wild and courageous beast, standing up to such enemies as the wolf. The stallions fight furiously with teeth and forefeet among themselves. Although living in a country where the horse is almost deified, most attempts to tame the kiang have failed. The kiang approaches the true horse in the great width of its hooves, relatively small ears and general colour. Its voice is a peculiar shrieking bray.

The Onager, of Western Asia and the North-west Indian deserts, is a much smaller animal, with smaller ears and more donkey-like hoofs. There are many local varieties, and the species is figured, like the Mongolian horse, in primitive carvings on the walls of caves.

The common wild ass lives in North-east Africa from Upper Nubia to Somaliland and it is from this animal that the much-abused drudge, now found throughout the world, has been derived. The wild form rarely stands more than

ZEBRA AT WATER-HOLE

Like other African animals, zebra congregate in large numbers at the rivers and pools where water is to be found and this photograph gives an interesting close-up of part of a herd which galloped up to the spot and fell to drinking with the greatest eagerness.

DAZZLE PATTERN

*The zebra's stripes form what is termed a ruptive pattern—in other words, they
tend to break up the general contour. This photograph shows a handsome group.*

twelve hands at the shoulder, has large
ears, and small, narrow hooves. There is
usually present on the back a dark
shoulder stripe and central stripe, together forming a cross.

Most animal colouring tends to
invisibility in the right setting, and the
Zebra's striking striped livery is, under
certain conditions, a perfect camouflage.
The zebra's stripes are what is termed
"ruptive" pattern—*i.e.*, they tend to
break up the general contour, being
almost invisible in the cover of high
grass or scrub.

Grevy's zebra is the largest of "horses
in tiger's skin", as the zebras have been
described. It is horse-like in its wide,
blunt ears, heavily plumed tail and mane
extending to the withers. The striping is
more closely packed and narrower than
in the other species. It differs from all
other zebras in its striding trot—others

canter—and its loud grunt, as opposed to a roaring bark. It comes from Abyssinia and British East Africa, and was probably the first zebra to reach civilization, being the "hippo-tigris" which figured in the Roman circus.

It is the least intractable zebra, teams having been driven in Hyde Park and elsewhere by the late Lord Rothschild, Madame Réjane, the French actress, and other celebrities. Grevy's zebra stands about sixteen hands. Burchell's zebra is a short and stocky animal. It has a wide range, inhabiting Abyssinia and East Africa. The now rare mountain zebra lives in South-west Africa.

Zebras normally live on terms of tolerance with large herds of giraffes, antelopes, ostriches, etc., and are sometimes found associating with domestic cattle. Owing to the great damage that these animals do to crops and fencing,

HERD OF ZEBRAS

This photograph of galloping zebras gives the impression of great speed though in fact they are not such swift animals as they appear, and fall easy prey to the lion. They are found in large herds and are the most numerous of any of the African quadrupeds.

they are no longer protected as formerly. It is, however, accepted as a fact that the true sportsman does not regard zebras as fair game and is reluctant to hunt them. Some cases are known where he has been induced to do so only for the sake of the natives, who are very fond of zebra meat. Many attempts have been made to protect zebras from indiscriminate slaughter, although animal lovers must concede that farmers have

reason to clamour for their destruction. In Kenya they do widespread damage.

The now extinct chestnut-coloured Quagga was a large, heavily-built animal with only the forequarters striped. Early in the past century the quagga abounded throughout South Africa, where its flesh was extremely popular with the natives. By 1870 it was extinct, its extermination being so rapid that even skins and photographs of the animal are now rare.

IN FLIGHT

Like the other members of the horse family, they can be trained for both driving and riding, but only with difficulty. In this photograph the curious shadow markings are clearly seen, although no two animals are quite identical in the pattern of their skin.

BLACK BEAR AND CUBS

This photograph shows a black bear family group in the Canadian forest. Owing to their attacks on farm stock these animals have been barred from inhabited districts.

CHAPTER SEVEN

THE BEAR TRIBE

by RAY PALMER, F.R.E.S., F.Z.S.

Physical peculiarities of the Bear: its pacific but courageous character: the hibernating period: Grizzly and Brown Bears: Black Bears of Africa and Asia: Sloth Bear: Polar Bear, man-hunter of the Arctic: Panda of the Himalayas: the Raccoons.

THE Bear tribe contains comparatively few species, but they have a wide range, being the most extensively distributed of the larger carnivores, and found in Europe, Asia, Africa and America. Bears are very different in form from other members of this order. They are of particularly massive build, with thick legs and extremely short tails.

Anyone comparing a bear with another animal, say a lion or a tiger, will at once notice a difference in the way it walks. This is most evident in the back legs, which appear to bend in the opposite direction to those of other animals. This is because the bear is a plantigrade, walking with the whole of the foot laid on the ground, whereas most animals walk on the toes only. Thus the hock joint half-way up the hind-leg of a dog or a cow, and commonly regarded as equivalent to the human knee, is really the ankle, while in the bears the joint apparently in the middle is really the knee, and so bends forward instead of backward. Owing to this flat-footedness, bears appear to have short legs for their size; but it enables them to stand erect easily without support, the broad surface of the feet and the much greater freedom of the knees enabling a perfect balance to be obtained.

Bears are nothing like so carnivorous as other members of this order, and in general may rather be termed omnivorous. The chief exception to this is the Polar bear, which of necessity subsists mainly on a diet of fish and seals, but even the polar bear seeks vegetable food when it gets the chance.

The Brown bear is the most common and most widely distributed of the species. At one time common in Europe, it now survives only in some of the wilder mountainous regions. It still lingers in the Pyrenees and Norway, and in parts of Germany, Hungary and the Balkans. It is found in greater numbers in Russia. Its range extends right across Asia to the Kamchatka peninsula, and southwards to the Himalayas and Northern India. It also ranges over Alaska, Canada and the United States.

Bears are not really so dangerous as is commonly supposed, and will always avoid a human if at all possible. Unless they are deliberately attacked, it is only when surprised that they are likely to show fight. If, however, the intruder cautiously retires, the bear will be more inclined to do likewise than to follow.

The well-known Canadian naturalist, William J. Long, tells an amusing story of how he met a bear on a narrow ledge beside a river, with a sheer drop to the water on one side and a steep cliff on the other. He was returning to camp after a day's salmon-fishing, and on turning a corner in the path was startled by a deep "Hoo-wuff". Not ten yards ahead was a great bear standing squarely in the track.

Face to Face with a Bear

The shock was mutual. Man and beast stood and stared into each other's eyes for several minutes. The bear showed no inclination to attack and so gain his right of way, as he so easily could have done against an unarmed man; nor would he retreat the way he had come, but he soon began to show signs of worry and nervousness, whining and looking down into the foaming river and then up at the cliff beside him. At last he made a decision; the roots of a tree projected from the cliff face a few feet up, and the bear by standing erect could just reach them. After a struggle he managed to heave himself up and climb to the top of the ridge above, from where he stood looking down to watch the man below resume his interrupted journey. Such is the gist of this great naturalist's delightful story of "Mooween" the bear. It shows that the brown bear at any rate is a good-natured creature, not anxious to fight if any other way can be found.

Bears are nevertheless courageous animals, and a female with cubs, or a bear that has been hunted and perhaps wounded, can be extremely dangerous. Many hunters have been killed by the bears they were hunting. These have either been wounded and charged recklessly, or, having discovered they were being followed, have turned the tables by hunting their hunters. On such occasions a bear can show great cunning, and will often double back on his trail and lie in ambush, charging furiously and with devastating effect as an incautious hunter passes his hiding-place.

Bears possess a very keen sense of smell, but have only poor sight and dull hearing. They are very intelligent, and good climbers and swimmers. They feed very largely on roots and berries, and even insects and such small creatures as frogs, small rodents and fish. They will sometimes kill deer and other large animals, including sheep and young cattle; but they seem to prefer smaller things when obtainable, and will spend hours digging out such small creatures as marmots, or seeking beetle grubs in rotten stumps, or scraping out nests of wild bees to devour the brood and honey.

The Winter Sleep

In the colder parts of their range bears hibernate from about October to April, though they may wake up and prowl around during mild intervals. Before hibernation they feed up and get very fat, but emerge from their retreats in the spring lean and hungry.

It is towards the end of the hibernating period that the female gives birth to her cubs, usually two in number. They are born in a much less developed condition than the young of the dog and cat tribes, for the bear cubs are at first quite naked, as well as blind; they are also extremely small, weighing only about a pound at birth. In few other animals, other than marsupials, are the young

BRUIN ENJOYS LIFE

The national parks of America are happy hunting-grounds for the bear. Above are grizzly and brown bears feeding in Yellowstone Park. The cubs, right foreground, wait until their elders have finished. Below, a peaceful group is indulging in a siesta.

CLIMBING BEARS

All bears have good heads for heights. For climbing trees they favour those with rough bark on which their claws can find a good hold, and find no difficulty in walking to and fro on the branches, or in standing up without losing their balance.

so tiny compared with the adult.

Along the western side of the American continent from Alaska to Mexico there exists a much larger and more formidable variety of bear known as the Grizzly, which has been given the scientific name of *Ursus horribilis*. Opinions differ as to whether this animal is really a distinct species or merely a larger and greyer variety of the brown bear. The two bears are certainly very closely related; but the grizzly has a reputation for much greater ferocity. The fur is coarse and worthless, and the flesh is said to be tough and uneatable. Hunters distinguish the grizzly by the name of "Silver-tip". It is more carnivorous than the typical brown bear, and has caused such devastation among stock—principally sheep and calves—that ranchers have waged war upon it with gun, trap and poison to such an extent that it is now becoming rare in the few districts where it is still to be found.

Many stories have been told of the ferocity of the grizzly, and though these may have been exaggerated, it is undoubtedly a formidable opponent if at bay or wounded, and was greatly feared by settlers before the advent of modern repeating rifles.

Reports of the size of grizzly bears killed by hunters are very unreliable. The measurements were often taken from pegged-out skins and the weights mere estimates. Thus we read of lengths

CUBS GO ALOFT

The climbing propensities of the bear are strikingly illustrated in this photograph of a mother bear and her two cubs nearing the top of a tall tree in Yellowstone Park. The method they generally use is to work themselves up with forepaws encircling the trunk.

up to 10 feet, and weights of 1400 or even 1800 lb. It appears that the actual lengths may be up to 9 feet for a male grizzly, with a weight of from 800 to 1500 lb. The brown bear is said to attain the largest dimensions in Kamschatka, where the maximum length is about 8 feet. The grizzly, owing no doubt to its greater size and weight, is not so agile as the brown bear and does not climb trees.

It is now considered that the reputed "hug" of the grizzly bear is a fiction. When attacking, the bear will rear on its hind feet and strike round with the front paws, armed with formidable claws, which may be up to 6 inches long. A bear may also seize a small animal like a dog and crush it between its front paws, but there is no evidence of hugging to the chest, after the popular conception.

The smaller Black bears are found in the Canadian forests and are very generally distributed throughout the United States. Their habits are similar to those of the brown bear, but they have been exterminated or to a great extent driven away from the inhabited districts, owing to their raids on farm stock, when sheep, calves, pigs and poultry are attacked. On the other hand, they have become firmly established in some of the great national

RECONNOITRING

A black bear prowls at Gibson's Camp, in the Kootenay National Park, British Columbia. Despite its purposeful look, it has become friendly with man, through the immunity it enjoys in such great national reservations and the supplies of food which are brought by tourists.

parks, where, owing to the protection afforded and frequent contact with visitors, they have become extremely tame, sometimes embarrassingly so. Owing to constant feeding by visitors, the bears have got into the habit of frequenting the roadways, and should a car stop, a bear will most likely go up to it and stand erect with front paws on the door until given food. Sometimes a whole line of cars will get held up in this way.

The black bears of Asia are very different from the American species just described. There are several distinct kinds, inhabiting India, Malaya, China and Japan. The best known is the Himalayan bear, which is a forest dweller, ranging from Eastern Persia and Afghanistan, through the wooded regions of the Himalayas, to Assam, Burma and Southern China. It is a smaller animal than the American species, averaging round about 5 feet in length, and is distinguished by a white chevron or V-shaped mark on the chest. The black fur is not thick and woolly like that of most bears, but smooth and short without any underfur, and in summer becomes very thin and scanty. This bear is a solitary animal and mainly a vegetable feeder, but will at times take to killing domestic animals. It seems to like the neighbourhood of

ON THE PROWL

This photograph, taken in Thailand, shows the Asiatic black bear on a solitary expedition in search of food. It is mainly vegetarian but has been known on occasion to raid the farm-yard. Though smaller than its American relatives it is of a fierce and aggressive temper.

AT HOME IN THE WATER

*To polar bears the icy waters of the Arctic offer no discomfort and there they are able
to find abundant food in the form of fish and seals.   But this happy picture showing
two bears in a moment of relaxation indicates that they have their playtime too.*

MONARCH OF A LONELY REALM

*This impressive photograph of a polar
bear on an ice-floe was taken off the coast
of Greenland. In the winter bears wander
southwards in search of food to the edge of
the ice and are often carried as far as Iceland
or Northern Norway, drifting on ice-floes.*

human habitations more than most
bears, and frequently raids the natives'
crops and stock. It is also of a fierce
nature, and more liable than others of its
race to attack without provocation.

A curious animal, one of the most
common in India, being found all over
the forest country or hilly regions, is the
Sloth bear. Like the Himalayan bear, it
has a white chevron on the chest, but in
all other respects it differs so widely from
other bears that scientists place it in a
separate genus.

The sloth bear is an ugly-looking
beast, with something of the form and
habits of the sloth from which it takes its
name. It is nocturnal in habits, spending
the day asleep in some retreat and
emerging at night to obtain food. It has
long, curved claws, which enable it to
climb trees with ease and cling to
branches in a sloth-like manner whilst in
search of fruit or bees' nests. With these
claws, also, the bear can dig for termites,
and pick beetles from dead wood. Its
favourite food is undoubtedly termites
and their larvae, which it is enabled to
suck out of the nests with ease.

Most famous of all is the Polar bear.
This great beast shares with the grizzly of
Alaska the position of largest of living
carnivores. It differs notably from others
in form, being proportionately longer in
the body; the head and neck are longer
and the head smaller proportionately than
in most bears, and the soles of the feet

POLAR BEAR AND CUBS

This picture of a female bear swimming with her three cubs was taken on an Arctic expedition and was the first scene of a tragedy of the wild. The mother was shot and swept away in the current. One of the male cubs immediately took the lead in the escape.

A FINE POLAR BEAR

This magnificent specimen was photographed by the Papanin scientific expedition. The polar bear is one of the largest living carnivores, and the tremendous power of its limbs can here be seen to advantage. It can kill a walrus with one blow.

are hairy to enable the bear to get a good grip on slippery ice.

The range of the polar bear extends right round the Arctic regions, and along the northern coasts of European and Asiatic Russia, Alaska, Canada and Greenland. In Spitzbergen and Nova Zembla it frequents the northern areas where there is permanent ice, and is rare on the south-western coasts where the ice disappears in summer. Northwards towards the Pole over the frozen Arctic Ocean, polar bears are more numerous in summer than they are near the land. Being almost as much at home in the water as on land or ice, they find abundant food in the form of fish and seals. This great white bear is also said to be one of the few carnivores that will deliberately hunt man for food, and it is known that primitive Eskimos without firearms have frequently fallen victims to it in this way. In any case, the Eskimo, in his seal-skin clothing and his body greased with seal blubber, must be very like a seal from the bear's point of view!

In former times polar bears existed in Newfoundland, but they have long since been exterminated, and though they may be met with in winter in Northern Labrador, they have quite disappeared from the southern regions.

With the approach of the long night of the polar winter the bears wander southwards to the edge of the ice, where they can still find food in and near the open water. With the break-up of the ice in the spring polar bears often get carried far to the south on icefloes. They frequently reach Iceland in this way, and sometimes Northern Norway and Finland, while occasionally they have been found on icebergs far south in the Atlantic. The polar bear is of necessity much more carnivorous than other species, but still shows a liking for vegetable food, and in summer, when some of the Arctic land becomes clear of snow, it will eat berries, lichens and grass, also seaweed, which is more readily available.

Polar bears do not hibernate, but during the winter the female lies up in a snug den under the snow to produce her cubs. During this time she takes no food, but has stored up a thick layer of fat under her skin in the days of plenty, and this is sufficient to provide for her own subsistence and milk for her tiny cubs as well; until at last the returning sun enables her to dig out and lead forth her two or three cubs into the wide white world, where the sun, rising higher and higher each day, ceases to set, as the long day of the polar summer begins.

The Raccoon Family

Closely related to the true bears is the Raccoon family, which seems to connect the bears with the weasels. The most bear-like of this group are the Pandas and the Red panda of the Himalayas is also called the "cat-bear". It is a small animal not more than 2 feet in length, excluding the tail, which is about 17 inches. The general colour of the fur is rusty red, with dark rings on the tail. The term "panda" is said to be a corruption of the native Nepalese name, which means "bamboo eater", and the animal is mainly vegetarian in its diet. They are not very active creatures, and are clumsy in their movements, but they have the bears' habit of rearing up in defence, and are powerful for their size.

Giant Panda

A much more interesting animal is the Giant panda. It is only recently that this strange beast has become so familiar in appearance to everyone through the Zoo specimens, and even now its habits in the wild state are hardly known at all. The fact that the giant panda inhabits the most inaccessible regions of Eastern Tibet and North-west China is sufficient to account for it remaining so long undiscovered.

An adult giant panda is the size of a small bear, being some 6 feet in length. The long, close fur has a thick, woolly under-coat, and the general colour is white with small black ears, black rings around the eyes, a broad black stripe over the shoulders and black legs.

The Raccoon is a carnivorous and nocturnal animal, about 2 feet long when mature. Other varieties are the Crab-eating raccoon of South America, the Coati of Central America and Mexico, with long, pointed snout, and the Kinkajou, with its prehensile tail, which inhabits Mexico and Central America.

Once common in North America, raccoons are now reduced in numbers.

RACCOON IN NATIVE HAUNT

The raccoon is a tree-dweller by inclination, though it hunts along the banks of lakes and streams. Once one of the most common animals on the North American continent, it is now greatly reduced in numbers, more than a million being killed each year for their fur.

LOADING THE SHIP OF THE DESERT

The camel in disagreeable mood protests loudly as the baggage is hoisted on to its back in the morning. The photograph was taken in the course of an expedition in South Arabia.

CHAPTER EIGHT

THE CAMEL AND ITS RELATIVES

by RAY PALMER, F.R.E.S., F.Z.S.

The nature and habits of the Camel. The Arabian Camel: its utility to the Arab tribes. The Dromedary. The Bactrian Camel: its adaptation to cold climates. America's native beast of burden, the Llama. The wool-bearing Alpaca. Guanaco and Vicuña.

THE thought of camels has inevitably the suggestion of romance—of the vast Sahara, of the mysterious Arabian deserts, of ancient caravan routes and remote oases. The camel itself, however, is anything but romantic. It is, in fact, a stupid, bad-tempered, ugly and often vicious beast. It never becomes tame and friendly like other domesticated animals, cares nothing for its master, and is always ready to attack him or any other person whenever it gets the chance. It usually utters indignant protests when being loaded or made to kneel down for the purpose, and then will frequently do its best to get rid of the load.

Combined with such an unpleasant disposition is extreme obstinacy and stupidity, so that it is often difficult to lead or drive a camel in a direction in which it does not wish to go. On the other hand, once started, a camel seems indifferent to its destination, and will continue to walk straight ahead indefinitely; unless sight of some possible food tempts it aside, after which it will continue aimlessly in a new direction unless driven back to the track.

Camels are essentially animals of the arid deserts, and have a great aversion to water, only with difficulty being persuaded to cross even the smallest stream. The Arabian Camel with one hump is best known and most widely used as a beast of burden. There are no wild Arabian camels in existence at the present day. There is historical evidence that wild camels existed in Arabia at the beginning of the Christian era, but whether Arabia is the original home of this animal appears doubtful, and some authorities consider that it originated farther east, probably in India.

Notwithstanding its disagreeableness and stupidity, the camel is an exceedingly useful animal. From time immemorial it has, indeed, been the "ship of the desert", and the nomadic Arab tribes have depended on it for their very existence. Indeed, they describe the camel as the greatest of Allah's gifts to mankind. In addition to being used for riding and baggage-carrying, the camel pulls the Arab's plough, works his mills, raises water from the wells, and performs

"ALLAH'S GIFT TO MANKIND"

A white Bishareen camel is here seen with her month-old baby. Camels of this type are the most valuable of the tribe, being very fast and capable of outrunning a horse. They make excellent mounts.

various other work which would be considered too degrading for an Arab horse. It provides rich milk, and the long hair which is shorn off in the spring is woven into cloth and ropes. The meat is highly valued as food, the skin is tanned into excellent leather and the bones are used as a substitute for ivory. Even the dung is dried and used as fuel.

Camels are ruminants, yet very different from all other ruminants. They differ in having incisor teeth in the upper jaw, and in having canine teeth or "tushes". The feet and the stomach also are unlike those of all other animals. The feet are not in the form of hoofs, as with other ungulates, but form a large soft pad undivided beneath, but on the upper surface the division of the two toes is apparent, and they terminate in broad nails. The stomach contains a honeycomb structure with cells that can be closed by muscular action and in which water can be stored. The hump is also an accumulation of fat which acts as a reserve supply of food. Thus is it that camels can go without food and water longer than other animals, though their endurance in this direction is often exaggerated and overtaxed.

There are various breeds of camels recognized by the Arabs, though a European might not appreciate their differences and might regard them as all very much alike. There are, however, two well-marked types—one is a tall, lightly built and finely proportioned

CAMEL HERD

The original home of the camel is a matter of some dispute, though it is traditionally associated with Arabia. It is, however, entirely at home in desert country, the drier

animal—the fast riding camel, the *hygin* or *dalul* of the Arabs, called a "dromedary" by Englishmen. Such an animal can keep up a speed of 8 to 10 miles an hour and cover over 100 miles a day; moreover, it can continue at this rate for four or five days without water and no

more food than a few handfuls of dates, or even meal ground from date kernels.

The baggage camel is a heavier-built and more cumbersome beast; its average pace is a swinging walk of 2½ to 3 miles an hour, and its distance when fully laden with a load of some 700 lb. is about 25

IN AUSTRALIA

the better from the camel's point of view, as it has a great dislike of water. The Arabian camel has been successfully introduced into the desert regions of Australia.

miles a day. The Arabian camel has been introduced into various other countries, but has thrived only in deserts.

The Bactrian camel, distinguished by its two humps, is a more massive animal, though not so tall. The home of this animal is in Central Asia, where it still

exists in a wild state, principally in the Gobi Desert. It has, however, been introduced into all the Asiatic desert regions, including Afghanistan, Mongolia, Southern Siberia and parts of China and India. The country it naturally frequents is more hilly and rocky than the Arabian

ARAB FARMER'S STANDBY

*Among many other useful tasks, the camel
pulls the Arab's plough. Although its
obstinacy is great and it may refuse to set
off in a particular direction, it will walk
straight ahead once it gets off the mark.*

and North African deserts, and the
Bactrian camel is better adapted to such
conditions. Its feet are harder and less
elastic, and it grows a thick coat of woolly
hair for winter protection, which is shed
on approach of the heat of summer.
Whereas the Arabian camel can stand
any amount of heat and greatly dislikes
cold and wet, the Bactrian camel is
adapted to severe winter conditions. In
the hard weather it wanders about the
snow-covered steppes and habitually eats
snow to quench its thirst. The nomadic
tribes of Central Asia use the two-
humped camel just as much as the Arabs
use its one-humped relative, and are
equally dependent upon it.

The only existing relatives of the
camels are the Llamas of South America.
These are much smaller animals without
humps, but in other respects resemble
the camels in structure. The head of a
llama and its general expression are very
camel-like; the neck and legs are proportionately the same length and the feet
of similar type, with two toes with small
nails. The hair is long and woolly and
usually white, but the tail is a mere stump.

The true llama is now known only in
a domesticated state, and there is some
uncertainty as to its origin. Before the
Spanish conquest horses were unknown
in South America, and the llama was the
universal beast of burden. The ancient
Peruvians used it as their sole means of
transport, both as a pack-animal and for
riding; while its various products, in the

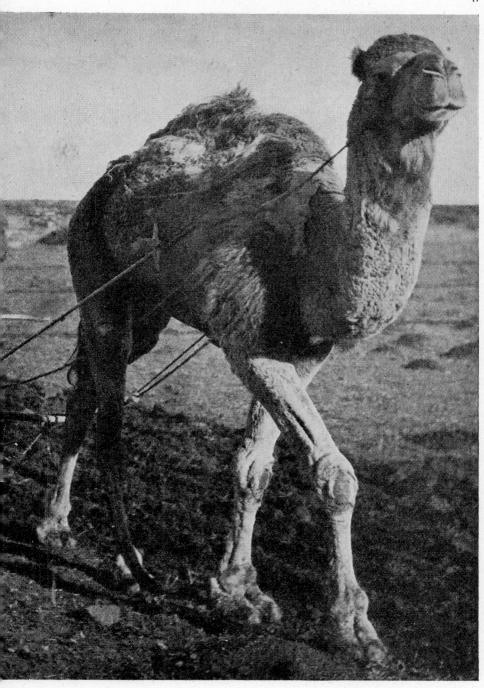

CAMELS IN KAZAKSTAN

These Bactrian camels are distinguished by two humps and are well adapted to severe winter conditions, growing a thick coat of woolly hair for protection against the cold.

form of milk, meat, wool and skin, were used to full advantage by them.

The Alpaca also exists only as a domesticated animal, and is bred merely for the sake of its wool, which is of great length and fineness. It is a smaller animal than the llama and generally black or dark brown in colour. Alpacas are kept in large herds in the highlands of Peru and Bolivia, and driven down annually for shearing like sheep. Attempts to introduce the alpaca into Europe and Australia have not been successful.

The Guanaco is considered by some authorities to be the wild ancestor of both the llama and the alpaca. It is not so large an animal as the llama, and its woolly hair is a light reddish colour. It is found on the western side of South America, from the mountainous regions of Ecuador

and Peru to the plains of Patagonia. These animals roam about in large herds, which may contain several hundred individuals. They are very shy and wild and difficult to approach. It is worthy of note that they take readily to the water and swim well, in this respect being markedly different from the camels.

The smallest of the camel family is the Vicuña, an inhabitant of the mountainous regions of Peru, Southern Ecuador and Central Bolivia. It is of a lighter and more graceful build than the other species. The hair is light brown, with a pale-coloured patch of long hair on the chest and shoulders. Vicuñas are still hunted extensively by the native tribes for their meat and skins, but have never been domesticated, owing to their wild and active nature.

NATIVE SOUTH AMERICAN BEAST OF BURDEN

Llamas are thoroughly domesticated and stand in the street as patiently and quietly as a group of horses. The madrina or herdsman, to be seen on the left of the above photograph, is followed by the leading llama, which in turn is followed by the others.

HERD OF LLAMAS GRAZING

Like large sheep, llamas graze in the Peruvian highlands, with the snow-clad peak of El Misti in the background. They do not readily suggest the camel in appearance, though they are its only existing relative, but the resemblance can be seen in the head and long

IN THE MOUNTAINS OF PERU

neck, while the feet are of similar type. Wool is one of the products for which they are useful and their meat, milk and skin are also used. Llamas were the only means of transport among the ancient Peruvians before the Spaniards conquered the country.

WART-HOG ON THE ALERT

Sinister in appearance is this inhabitant of Africa, with wart-like protuberances on each side of the face. It has four tusks, the upper pair of which curve out and upwards.

CHAPTER NINE

THE PIG TRIBE

by RAY PALMER, F.R.E.S., F.Z.S.

*Difference between the wild and the domesticated pig. The Wild
Boar. Boar-hunting in Europe and India. The African Red River
Hog. The Barbirusa or 'pig-deer'. The Wart-Hog, ugliest of
animals. The Peccaries of the American continent, their ferocity.*

OUR farm pigs have been so altered by long ages of domestication— involving selective breeding, over-feeding and lack of exercise—that little evidence of their wild ancestry seems to remain. Yet, if allowed to return to the wild state, domestic pigs regain much of their original nature; while a few generations of life under natural conditions and having to work hard for their living and defend themselves against enemies produce great changes even in their physical form. An example of this is seen in Australia, where there are in the bush herds of wild pigs descended from individuals that were originally domesticated. These are slimmer and far more active than any tame pigs, and have become very fierce. They are, in fact, hunted for sport, like wild boars. Even in England the pigs of the New Forest are noted for their wildness and uncertain temper. These large black or dark brown pigs are much scarcer now than formerly; but they have lived in the forest in a semi-wild condition for centuries, and are reputed to have in them a large strain of the wild boar, which is not difficult for those who have met with them to believe.

The Wild Boar is undoubtedly one of the ancestors of our tame pigs, having been crossed with various Oriental species, principally the Chinese pig, and is still abundant in many parts of Europe and Asia. It is, indeed, remarkable how such a destructive and dangerous animal, that is constantly hunted for sport or killed for food, has managed to survive in such numbers to the present day. In England wild boars were once abundant in all the forest country, but gradually got killed off as the land became more populated. It is difficult now to ascertain the date at which they were finally exterminated. During the Norman period wild boars were evidently abundant, as the forest laws include "the bore" among the beasts of the chase, and periods were fixed for its hunting. Wild boars are known to have still been plentiful in Oxfordshire in 1339, and their existence in Chartley Forest, Staffordshire, is recorded as late as 1593. It is probable that in the wilder parts of the country, the Scottish Highlands, north of England and in Wales, wild boars survived much later than elsewhere, and there are reports of boar-hunting as late as 1683.

WILD PIGS

These wild pigs, foraging in the dusty slopes of Indian hill country, present an amazing spectacle and remind one of the Gadarene swine of the Bible. Slender, active and fierce, they are very different from the familiar farm pig. Boars will fight tigers and elephants,

OF RAJPUTANA

*and habitually engage in terrible battles among themselves. Their pugnacity makes the
Indian sport of "pig-sticking", which is carried out by mounted men armed with lances,
an exciting and dangerous adventure, for when overtaken the animal charges fearlessly.*

In Europe wild boars are still abundant in many of the wilder regions, particularly the Black Forest. Boar-hunting is an exciting and dangerous sport, as a fierce old boar when he decides to charge is absolutely fearless and can inflict terrible injuries with his tusks on men, horses and dogs. In Europe boars are usually hunted with dogs or shot during forest drives. In India, however, "pig-sticking" is a favourite sport, and far more dangerous than the hunting methods of Northern Europe. Mounted men armed with lances pursue the boars, usually over very rough ground. Although the boars of India can run at a great pace for a certain distance, they cannot keep it up, so that a man on a good horse can eventually overtake them. When overtaken, or if wounded, they are liable to turn and charge, and can easily overthrow and rip open a horse and then attack its rider before he has a chance to recover from the fall. Among themselves wild boars fight terrific battles, and are able to survive most fearful injuries which would be regarded as fatal in any other animal. Boars have even been known to charge an elephant without the slightest hesitation, and to get the best of it in combats with tigers.

Tamed Wild Boar

No one would think that the fat, sleepy sows of our farms had descended from such a wild and pugnacious ancestor; yet in Ireland there still exists in some remote parts a black and bristly domesticated pig, long legged and razor backed, with a long snout and prominent tusks in the males; the old Irish hog is, indeed, little but a tamed wild boar.

It is interesting to note that the young of wild boars and other wild swine are marked with longitudinal stripes of alternate light and dark colour, or else, in some species, blotched with dark patches. The young of some breeds of domestic pigs show dark blotches which may be a reversion towards their original colouring.

Types of Wild Pig

There is a large number of wild pigs in various parts of the world, but only a few representatives can be mentioned. The most strikingly coloured pig is the Red River Hog of West Africa. For a pig it is indeed a remarkably handsome animal. The prevailing colour is a dark yellowish red; with black legs, forehead and ears. The margins of the ears and their hair tufts, the eyebrows and edges of the cheeks, and a crest of bristles along the back are white, while the under parts are pale grey. The river hog frequents the reed beds adjoining river banks, as well as damp forest country. It exists in large herds or "sounders", and can do much damage to the native crops. It has therefore been largely exterminated or driven away from settlements.

The Barbirusa, found in Celebes and other islands of the Malay Archipelago, is one of the most remarkable of all wild pigs. The name means "pig-deer", and the natives have called it this because of the extraordinary development of the tusks, which suggest the horns of a deer. This animal has two pairs of tusks, the lower pair growing upwards from the bottom jaw in the normal manner. The other and larger tusks arise from the upper surface of the snout, curving backwards towards the forehead. In old boars these tusks may almost or quite touch the head above the eyes, and then the ends curve round so that the points are directed forwards. The use of these

WILD BOAR AND YOUNG

The young of the wild boar, like the little fellow seen in the above photograph, are marked with stripes running lengthwise along the body and of alternate dark and light tone.

over-developed tusks is uncertain, but since they are found in the males only, they must be of use in fighting. The lower tusks are certainly formidable weapons of offence, and no doubt the upper tusks act as a fencing mask and serve to protect the face and eyes. The barbirusa is a long-legged pig of somewhat slim build, and much less hairy than others; its dark grey skin is, in fact, almost naked, except for a few bristles along the centre of the back. It is of nocturnal habits and frequents the neighbourhood of water, being a good swimmer and feeding largely on water plants. It has been to some extent domesticated by the natives, and tame barbirusas may be seen wandering about the villages or foraging in garbage.

If the red river hog is the most handsome of its race, the Wart-hog is certainly the ugliest—perhaps the most repulsive in appearance of any living animal. The enormous head has a very broad and flattened snout, with extraordinary wartlike protuberances along each side, the

EVENING DRINK

At nightfall the South American tapir comes to the stream to drink. In general form this strange animal is pig-like and is included here for purposes of comparison with the true members of the pig-tribe, although it is related both to the horse and the rhinoceros.

largest pair of "warts" being just below the eyes, with two further pairs lower down. Like the barbirusa, the wart-hog has four tusks, but the upper pair grow out of the sides of the mouth in the normal manner and curve out and upwards. In spite of its formidable appearance, it is not such a dangerous beast as the Indian or European wild boar. The great tusks are found in both sexes, and seem to be mainly used in digging up roots for food. If hunted, the old boars will turn and face the enemy to cover the retreat of the sows and their young; but when it comes to the point they are more likely to turn and run at the last moment than they are to charge. Wart-hogs are commonly found in Abyssinia and farther south all along the eastern side of Africa. There are two species, Pallas's wart-hog being confined to South-east Africa, while Aelian's wart-hog is of wider range.

In America the pig family is represented by the Peccaries, which differ in various ways from the true pig of the Old World. In peccaries the tusks of the upper jaw are directed downwards, and the lower ones upwards, but both pairs are comparatively small. Other peculiarities are the presence of three toes on the back feet, and a complicated stomach very like that of the ruminants. The peccaries are comparatively small animals, only some 15 inches high, but they are remarkably fierce and aggressive for their size. Indeed, one species, the White-lipped peccary of South America, is quite a dangerous animal, as it goes about in large herds which are ready to attack any man or beast they encounter. These peccaries can inflict serious wounds with their tusks, and hunters are often forced to climb trees to avoid them. The puma and the jaguar prey extensively on the peccaries, yet even these powerful cats can be overcome should a whole herd of peccaries fall on one of them. They have the instinct of combined attack to a remarkable degree. The Collared peccary, which is a somewhat smaller species and comparatively harmless, ranges from Patagonia as far north as Texas. An objectionable feature of these pigs is the presence of a peculiar gland on the back, which secretes an oily substance with a most disgusting smell. If a peccary is killed for food this gland must be removed immediately.

" PIG-DEER "

Pig-deer is the name given by Malayan natives to the Barbirusa, shown in this photograph, partly because of its long legs and also because it develops tusks growing through the flesh of the snout and curving up to the forehead. It lives in Malayan swamps.

TERROR OF THE HEN-ROOST

A fox prowls in the snowy fields, looking for some weak spot through which it can make its foray into the farmyard. It often has a fixed nightly round of visits in search of prey.

CHAPTER TEN

THE DOG TRIBE

by RAY PALMER, F.R.E.S., F.Z.S.

The Dog in its wild state. Likeness between domesticated and wild dogs. The Dingo of Australia. The Wolf in Europe and America. The Coyote. Foxes. The Cape Hunting Dog. Jackals and Hyenas.

DOGS are perhaps the most familiar of all animals, and from their long association with man are the most friendly and faithful, and are the most beloved in return. Many people are fond of cats; but the cat is of a solitary nature, purely self-centred, and though cats undoubtedly appreciate caressing and comfort and warmth, they can give little in return, and are incapable of sharing in a person's activities in the same way as a dog. The dog in its wild state is a gregarious animal, accustomed to constant companionship and to obeying a dominant pack leader; and it is easy to understand how such natural instincts have been taken advantage of by man and developed under domestication. Thus the tame dog finds in its master and his household leadership and comradeship.

All domesticated dogs interbreed freely, and so, in spite of their great variety of form and size, they are regarded by zoologists as forming a single species. Dogs were undoubtedly the first animals to be tamed by man, this dating back to Neolithic times. The primitive hunter would take home living puppies of some dog-like animal whose lair he had discovered. These might be wolves, or jackals, or wild dogs, all of which would interbreed under domesticated conditions and produce a nondescript type of animal. Even to-day the native dogs of the less civilized peoples greatly resemble their wild local equivalents. Thus the true Eskimo dogs are extremely like the northern races of the wolf, and are, indeed, often crossed with wolves to keep up their size and stamina. The Indians of temperate parts of North America have smaller dogs, which are obviously descended from the coyote or "prairie wolf". Of European dogs the Alsatian is obviously the most wolf-like; but collies, wolf hounds, boar hounds and many more specialized types appear to have originated from the European wolf, crossed with other breeds. The Samoyed seems to come from the Siberian wild dog.

The pariah dogs which swarm in the native villages of India have usually a great resemblance to the Indian wolf. In Africa, South Asia, and parts of Southeastern Europe the native dogs are very like the different kinds of jackals that inhabit these regions. Even the Chinese Chow, when its tail is uncurled and held out straight, is remarkably wolf-like. It is also noteworthy that many races of

F

domesticated dogs have developed the
habit of curling the tail over the back,
and also the characteristic drooping
ears. They have also learnt to bark,
which is not the normal voice of any wild
members of their race.

The Dingo, or Warrigal as it is also
called—the wild dog of Australia—is an
animal of somewhat jackal-like appearance, light fawn in colour and with a very
alert manner and active habits. Dingos
are rarely seen during the day-time, but
hunt at night, usually in small family
groups of five or six, although sometimes
in large packs like wolves. They are very
destructive, and kill great numbers of
sheep and poultry, so that the Australian
farmers shoot and poison them whenever
they get the chance.

The black natives of the interior,
however, treat these wild dogs very

YOUNG FOXES AND CUBS

(At left) With stealthy gait young foxes set out on the hunt. (Below) Cubs play at the entrance to the earth. The vixen rarely visits the cubs, leaving food at a little distance, which they pick up for themselves.

differently: they find the pups when young, carry them home to their primitive huts and rear them with care and affection. These domesticated dingos are very useful to their masters for hunting, as they have keen scent and track down game that would otherwise be missed. The aborigines are, indeed, said to bestow more care and affection on them than on their own children. White people also sometimes keep tame dingos, which learn to bark after a time, but they are said to be unreliable, never losing their wild nature. There has been much speculation as to the origin of the dingo. If it were not for the unusual nature of

WOLF AND VICTIMS

A European wolf stands beside the carcases of two goats which it has devoured. The photograph was taken in Spain, where packs of wolves in winter have been known to harry herds on the outskirts of Madrid.

the Australian fauna, it might be regarded as indigenous. It must be remembered, however, that, with the exception of a few small rodents, all the mammals of Australia are either Marsupials—pouched animals like the kangaroo —or Monotremes—still more primitive egg-laying mammals like the Duck-billed Platypus or the Echidna. This fact makes it extremely improbable that the dingo is a true native of the country; it is more likely the descendant of some animal of the jackal type introduced from South-east Asia by the earliest primitive men to reach Australia.

The Wolf is the largest wild member of the dog tribe, though exceeded in size by some domesticated breeds. Authorities differ as to whether the several types of wolf found in Europe, Asia and America are to be regarded as distinct species, or merely as varieties or local races. It is only some 200 years since the last wolf was killed in Scotland. In England they were exterminated much earlier, but in the fifteenth century wolf-hunting was "a royal and noble sport". In the reign of Henry VII rewards were offered for the slaughter of wolves, and this led to their all being killed off early in the sixteenth century. Wolves survived in Scotland to a much later date, and, though killed off in the south, still lingered in remote parts of the Highlands. Tradition has it that the last wolf in Great Britain was killed in Sutherlandshire in 1743. At

CANADIAN TIMBER WOLF

This is a near relative of the European wolf, although it is not so dangerous. It travels alone or in small groups which usually number from five to seven and represent parents and cubs, unlike the enormous packs which in Siberia, for instance, inspire terror.

COYOTE PUP

From the alert look of this small coyote could be guessed the cleverness and cunning of the tribe which are as strongly pronounced as in the fox. It is unusual in its white fur.

this date wolves still existed in parts of Ireland, and their extermination there is said to have taken place some twenty-five years later. There is no room for such a destructive and dangerous beast in a small, thickly populated island, and so the wolf as a British animal is only a legend of the distant past.

On the European continent, however, conditions are very different, and in severe winters wolves may leave their normal hunting-grounds and travel southwards and westwards across Central Europe. Congregated into packs and driven by hunger, they become a serious danger to the inhabitants of isolated villages. The peasant plodding home over the frozen snow in the gathering dusk may suddenly find wolves on his trail, and if he is unarmed and still has far to go, he may easily be pulled down and devoured by the ravenous beasts, and by morning little will remain to tell the tale. The trampled snow, a few rags of clothing, a few gnawed bones—such will reveal the grim story of the tragedy that has been enacted.

In Russia wolves are sometimes a great menace to man and animals, and the vast spaces of Siberia and parts of Western Asia provide breeding-grounds where extermination is impossible. There are many stories of the exciting and often tragic experiences of travellers in Russia whose sleighs have been pursued across the frozen wastes by wolves.

The Canadian timber wolf is a near relative of the European animal; some say merely a local race of the same species. Its habits, however, are very different, and it is far less dangerous. It is mainly solitary, usually being found either singly or in pairs or family parties. If it forms packs in winter these are much smaller than those of the Russian wolves. Wolf cubs number from six to ten in a litter, and the lair selected by the female may be either a cave, a hole in the ground beneath tree-roots, or sometimes inside the hollow of a tree.

The Coyote, although called the "Prairie Wolf", is more like a jackal in form and habits than a true wolf. It was found originally from Southern Canada down to Central America, but has now been practically exterminated in many parts. It is not dangerous to man, and is much smaller, less powerful and less destructive than the common wolf, preying largely on rabbits, small rodents and young birds. Coyotes are very noisy animals, and are in the habit of howling mournfully in chorus at night.

Of the Jackals there are several distinct species, which are all comparatively small animals. The common jackal extends from South-east Europe to India, and all over North Africa, including Egypt and Abyssinia. It is mainly nocturnal and almost omnivorous in its diet, killing small animals, eating carrion, and also vegetable substances such as fruit, sugar cane or maize. Poultry, lambs and young goats are often

DESERT OUTLAW

In spite of its description as "Prairie Wolf", the Coyote is much smaller than the true wolf and more closely resembles the jackal. A native of the North American continent, it is a familiar item in cowboy song. Nowadays, coyotes are rapidly dwindling in numbers.

CAPE HUNTING DOG

An inhabitant of South and East Africa is this long-legged wild dog. It hunts by day and night in packs which run down the speediest antelopes and work havoc on farm stock.

JACKAL—NATURE'S SCAVENGER

This slender animal is the jackal whose name is such a byword as a term of contempt.
Like the hyena, it feeds on carrion and is a scavenger of native villages in India.

killed by jackals, and they go scavenging around the native villages at night.

In South and Central Africa the black-backed jackal and the side-striped jackal feed on small animals such as rodents, hares, small antelopes, etc.; they also follow the lion and other large carnivores and share with the hyenas the remains of the royal kill.

The Indian Wild Dog, or *Dhoule*, is very like a jackal in form, though somewhat larger. It is found throughout the wooded regions of the Himalayas and in the larger forests of India. It hunts in small packs, chiefly by day, but avoids inhabited districts, and therefore is rarely known to attack domestic animals.

The Foxes differ in several structural features from the rest of the group. The most obvious distinction is in the pupil of the eye, which is oval in shape when contracted, while in the true dogs (including wolves and jackals) the pupil is always round. Foxes also have very powerful scent glands beneath the tail, and whenever the animal is startled these glands come into play and give out a most unpleasant musky odour. This in itself appears to have been sufficient to prevent attempts to domesticate foxes.

The common English red fox is well known, but would undoubtedly have long ago followed the wolf to extinction in the agricultural districts of England had it not been for the protection afforded by "the hunt". In Scotland the position is very different, and the hill foxes are regarded merely as vermin by the shepherds and keepers, and shot and poisoned whenever possible. The hill fox of the North is, indeed, a distinct variety; longer legged, larger and greyer than the small fox of the hunting shires. It does much destruction among the lambs, fawns and gamebirds, and thus the hand of every man is against it.

Varieties of Fox

The common fox is found in all parts of the northern hemisphere, though there are various local colour varieties. The well-known "silver fox" is one of these varieties, the normal colour being black with a white tail-tip and some grey-marked hairs which give a silvery lustre to parts of the fur.

The Arctic fox is a small animal, found in all the arctic lands of Europe, Asia and America. It has thick woolly fur, which is brown in summer with a bluish undercoat; in winter the fur becomes completely white, except the tip of the tail, which remains black.

Other kinds include the Desert foxes and the Long-eared foxes. As representatives of the last group may be mentioned the Fennec, which is a pretty little animal found in North Africa and throughout the Sahara Desert. Its colour matches the desert sand, and it is mainly of nocturnal habits. It is notable for its very large ears, which are remarkably wide in proportion to their length. This little creature is the smallest member of the tribe, being only 16 inches long.

Finally we must mention an animal that is so distinct from the rest of the dog family that it is placed by zoologists in a separate genus. This is the Cape Hunting Dog, which, in spite of its name, inhabits not only South Africa, but the whole of East Africa right up to Somaliland. It is a curious-looking animal, the size of a large dog, and with only a scanty coat of hair, but extraordinarily spotted colouring. The ground colour is yellowish-grey, with irregular black spots which vary considerably in different individuals and even on each side of the same animal. It is a long-legged dog with a sharp-pointed nose, large upstanding ears and a long bushy tail. These wild dogs hunt in large packs both by day and night. In their hunting they work together and co-operate in a remarkable way, and can thus succeed in running down the fastest antelopes. The early Boer settlers suffered greatly from the havoc they caused.

The Hyena

Though of somewhat dog-like appearance, the Hyenas do not really belong to the dog tribe. They are, in fact, intermediate between the dogs and cats, though actually included in the cat tribe. Hyenas are mainly carrion-feeders, and have very powerful jaws and enormous teeth, which enable them to crunch up bones which even the lion cannot tackle. In common with jackals, they follow the larger carnivores, and devour the remains of their kills. The spotted hyena is found over the greater part of Africa south of the Sahara, while the smaller striped hyena lives in the desert regions of Africa, Arabia, Syria, Persia and India.

In conclusion it may be noted that the dog family is a very ancient one, and dates back to extinct animals which walked on the flat of the foot, instead of on the toes like modern dogs which have thus gained speed and agility.

FURTIVE WATCHER

Caught by flashlight, this African hyena waits for its share of the lion's kill. This carrion-feeder is an intermediate species between the dogs and cats.

DEER BROWSING

A four-year-old buck makes a meal of leaves near Cass Lake, Minnesota. Fed also by tourists in this region of the United States, the deer have become very tame.

CHAPTER ELEVEN

THE DEER FAMILY

by A. RADCLYFFE DUGMORE

Size and distribution of Deer. Reindeer and Caribou. The mating season. The Moose. Wapiti of America and its European relatives. The Virginia and the Mule Deer. The Fallow Deer and Red Deer of Europe: other members of the tribe found in Europe and Asia.

O F all wild animals, few equal in grace and beauty some members of the large and widely distributed family of the Deer. In all, the family numbers about 100 species, sub-species or geographical variations, and is found in most parts of the world, north of Oceania, from the frozen lands of Siberia and upper Canada right down to the tropical forests of India and South America. Strangely enough, Africa, which has more kinds of wild animals than any other continent, knows the deer only in the regions north of the Atlas Mountains.

People sometimes become confused between deer and antelope. The most noticeable difference between them is that the horns or antlers of the deer are solid and rise from bony pedicles and are shed annually (with one exception), while the antelope have hollow horns which are not shed, but increase their size by annual growth.

Of all the deer, the largest is the Moose (or Elk, as it is called in Europe), and the most abundant is the Reindeer, together with its western and very close cousin the Caribou. (The name caribou does not

come from the French "quatre boeuf", as some writers would have us believe, but from the Indian names "maccarib", "maccaribo" or "caribo".) These, even to-day, exist in their thousands.

Formerly they were found in most parts of Europe, as we know by the wonderful cave-man drawings made in Southern Europe so many centuries ago. To-day we have the reindeer of Northern Europe and Asia, and these are probably, though not certainly, the original species. They still exist in their wild state, but man, to fill his needs, has made very many of them captive and uses them as domestic animals which give him milk, meat, clothing and means of transport, while the various New World species, though numerous, have never been kept in captivity; they simply die, to the great discouragement of the zoo-keepers, within a year or so after being caught. This is one of the most marked differences between the two forms, the reindeer and the caribou. Otherwise they are very much alike, though without doubt the reindeer is the less beautiful. It seems to lack the fine dignified bearing so conspicuous in the western breed,

RED DEER OF THE HIGHLANDS
The herd was caught by the camera, after a patient stalk, as it browsed quietly in the Mai Lodge deer forest. The red deer are the largest of British quadrupeds, although still larger types are found on the European continent and in Asia.

while the Newfoundland and Osborn caribou are the finest. The size of the Newfoundland stag is about 50 inches at the shoulder; it is nearly 7 feet long and weighs up to 500 lbs.

Peculiarities shared by both reindeer and caribou are that the horns, or antlers, are placed above and well back of the eyes, and a very large proportion of the does carry some sort of antlers, often very small single stalks, but occasionally quite large ones. The does of no other deer carry antlers. All deer in the more northerly countries (except perhaps the Indian sambar) shed their horns every year, the stags during early winter and the does somewhat later.

The colouring of the caribou is various shades of mouse-grey in summer, and as autumn approaches the neck gradually becomes more and more white, until in most cases the whole animal is white during the winter. The neck of the stag is covered with a thick white hair which hangs in a deep fringe below and adds much to the beauty of the animal. The fawns do not usually have spots, but in rare instances it has been reported that faint spots were visible.

The caribou are divided into two groups called the "barrenland" and the "woodland", though why, no one can say, as neither name is descriptive. The scientists have had a lot of fun dividing these into no less than eleven species, or, more correctly, geographical variations, of which the two most distinct species

CHALLENGE AND DUEL

The mating season brings with it a time of angry defiance and fierce battling among stags. Above, the challenge. At right, two caribou stags meet with a terrific clash, their long, spreading antlers coming together with astonishing force. This unusual and perhaps unique photograph was obtained after many special journeys in Newfoundland. The click of the shutter gave the alarm and brought the battle to an end.

are the Newfoundland and the Osborn. The latter is the largest, and is found chiefly in the Cassier Mountains of British Columbia and from there northwards. They carry magnificent antlers, larger even than those of the Newfoundland stags, which have very fine compact heads with large brow antlers, or snow shovels as they have sometimes been called. Extra fine heads have as many as fifty points, or even more.

Prior to 1917 the Newfoundland caribou used to make an annual migration from the northern peninsula after the first fall of snow, when thousands of the beautiful creatures would travel in small or large herds across the wild country, through lakes and rivers (for they swim with perfect ease) southwards in search of a winter supply of food, consisting chiefly of ground moss (*cladonia rangiferina*) and some of the tree mosses, when the ground is too deeply covered with snow. The picture of these herds making their way over the barrens, as the moors are called, is for the writer one of the most beautiful memories in his life. The ground, with its fresh covering of snow glistening as though strewn with tens of thousands of diamonds, and the graceful deer moving along so silently, led nearly always by a doe, had a beauty which defies description. But unfortunately those sights are a thing of the past, for something happened, probably an epidemic (the writer does not believe man had anything to do with it), and the great herds simply vanished, and in their place only an odd animal travels on the roads, or leads, made by the countless thousands of their ancestors. It is a calamity that so beautiful an animal should vanish. The number of survivors, however, is reported to be increasing.

One of the most thrilling sights in Newfoundland during the days that have gone was when the large stags engaged in fighting, as they did in the mating season. Caribou are polygamous, and a stag in his full prime collects as many does as he can for his harem. Young or very old stags are driven away if they dare to approach the does. Sometimes it happens that a master stag—for they alone have the right to perpetuate the

IN A SWEDISH FOREST

Reminiscent of Walt Disney's famous film creation "Bambi" is this stag which looks with curiosity at the camera from among the snow-laden trees. Its antlers are still covered with the soft tissue of velvet the purpose of which is to give protection to the developing horns.

species—is challenged by one of about equal size; then the trouble starts. Once the writer had the satisfaction of watching such a fight. For many hours he had followed a herd containing a large stag. It was difficult going, for the chase led through forests and streams, ponds and swamps and bogs, but in the end he was rewarded by seeing a rival stag approach. Almost at once the fight started, and the way those two powerful creatures went for each other, crashing their long spreading antlers together with astonishing force, was a sight the writer will never forget, especially as he was able to secure photographs of the unusual scene (the only ones, the writer believes, ever made of the Newfoundland stags fighting). For eight years he had worked to get this picture, so it meant a lot to him. The click of the shutter gave the alarm to the hundred or more does that were standing all around, suspicious of the strange creature that had been crawling after them. Needless to say they lost no time in proclaiming the fact that their age-old enemy, man, was present, and so the fight ended abruptly.

Unlike most deer, which have noticeably small feet, the caribou have very wide-spreading hoofs and greatly developed cloots or dew-claws. These feet have been grown to suit the animals' habitat as they enable them to walk even

FALLOW DEER DOE AND YOUNG

Best known of the deer of the Old World is the fallow deer, a familiar animal of the large parklands in Britain. It is found in many parts of Europe, and also in Palestine and North Africa. The spotted and the brown fallow deer form two distinct types.

ROE DEER

This graceful little beast, drinking at a rivulet, has nearly full-grown antlers (present only in the male sex). These are enclosed in a soft skin called "velvet" which will eventually rub off. Roe deer are widely distributed in Europe and are found in Britain.

on soft bog or marsh or on snow with the greatest ease, and they also help in swimming. When walking the feet make a strange clicking sound, like that of small castanets.

There are three species of European reindeer in Northern Europe, in Spitzbergen and Siberia, and at least nine geographical races or species of caribou in North America, whose range is from Greenland to Alaska and the far north.

Largest of Living Deer

By far the largest and heaviest of the living deer is the moose, as it is known in America, or elk as it is known in Europe and Asia. It is by no means a graceful animal, for it seems over short in the length of its body and neck and over long in the legs, and it has no tail, or at least none worth mentioning. Yet a fine bull (or stag), which will weigh about 1400 lb., with well-developed, symmetrical, broadly palmated horns presents a wonderful picture, and one only to be seen in the wilds, as they do not grow to ripe old age and great spread of horns in captivity. (Keeping of moose in zoos has been a problem which has baffled the most careful attempts.)

The American moose is finer than the elk of the Old World whose home is in Northern Europe, Siberia and China. The American species or forms (practically the same species, though carrying far finer horns) inhabit the suitable forest lands of North America, from Maine northwards and from Nova Scotia to Alaska. Those of the far west, and known as the Alaskan moose, are found in the Kenai Peninsula, and these carry by far the largest antlers, sometimes spreading to a width of 70 inches.

It is difficult to believe that such massive horns can be grown each year. They start their growth in the very early spring and while covered with the protecting "velvet"—soft, spongy tissue— the horns are very sensitive, and the animal exercises the greatest care not to injure them while going among trees. The moose begins to lose this covering towards the end of summer. When this has been scraped off and polished against the tree trunks and branches it sometimes assumes a bright orange colour, especially when tamarack, or larch, is used.

The cows (they are not called does) are hornless and not at all beautiful. Their very long noses seem almost grotesque, and they have a strangely mule-like appearance. The height of an eastern moose is about 6 feet at the shoulder, while that of Alaska is 6 or 8 inches higher.

Moose as Swimmers

Moose swim with remarkable ease and speed, often going far out into a lake in search of food such as the stems and leaves of the water-lilies, particularly the yellow variety or spatterdock. At such times they will go under water and remain submerged for many minutes, thereby often causing surprise to any one coming near the lake, as at one moment the water appears to be devoid of life, and then suddenly appears the great head of a moose, apparently from nowhere.

During the summer the bulls are usually solitary and live chiefly near swamps or lakes where food is abundant. The water also offers some sort of refuge from the pest of flies of various biting kinds. With the coming of autumn, when the trees take on the wonderful colours of scarlet and gold, the bull moose, his horns fully grown and cleaned of velvet, seeks a mate. He is then in a highly nervous condition, and spends his time between searching for a mate and testing his strength in battle with any possible rival. During this period they leave the swamp land and take to the dry ridges, where they roam about in a restless way. It is then that they can be heard calling out their challenge to a rival, or requesting the pleasure of the cow's company.

Then, as winter comes and the land is covered with deep snow, the moose, for mutual protection, form what are called "yards". These are places in the forest where food is abundant and the snow is trampled into numerous paths over an area of several acres. In this the animals collect in small herds, or families, moving as the supply of young trees becomes exhausted. They "ride" these trees down in order to get at the upper branches, and it is common to find bitten-off twigs at a height far above their reach.

The cows have one or very often two calves in the spring. These calves are distinctly reddish in colour, while the adults are very dark grey, the under-parts and back of the legs being whitish.

Preservation of Moose

A hundred years or so ago moose were so scarce in North America that to see one was an event of local interest and would be mentioned in the papers. Logging camps had nearly wiped them out by employing men to shoot them during the winter, when the wretched creatures, floundering in the deep snow, often crusted over, would fall easy victims to the meat-hunters. The meat is of such good quality that it was always in demand. In 1857 an English sportsman during a trip in New Brunswick declared that if immediate action were not taken to preserve the moose they would soon become extinct. Laws were passed, and to-day it would not be an unusual thing to see twenty to forty in a single day's canoeing. They are probably most abundant in New Brunswick and Ontario, and are also numerous in Michigan and the Rockies.

The Superb Wapiti

As already stated, the moose is the largest of the deer family, and the reindeer and caribou the most numerous, but the finest of all is the wapiti, or elk of Western North America. No deer has such splendid antlers, antlers which measure round the curve over 70 inches and have twenty or more points. A great many of these heads are beautifully proportioned and graceful, while the stag which carries them is a superb beast, standing about 5 feet 8 inches at the shoulder, well built and weighing perhaps 1000 lb. The colour is hard to describe; it is a sort of yellowish dove colour on the body, running abruptly into dark chocolate or chestnut on the neck and head, and fairly dark under-parts, while on the flank is a large patch of cream colour. The hairs on the outer edge are long, and can be slightly raised, forming a sort of rosette when the animal is excited.

Only the bulls (they are seldom called stags) have horns, and these, as with other deer, are shed annually and start their growth in early spring. The polishing of the horns in the autumn precedes the mating, or rutting, season, during which the bull is in a very truculent state of mind and body, and appears to be only too anxious to fight for any does he may collect. How many he

DEER IN THE OLD WORLD AND THE NEW

At top of the page is a photograph of the sambar, a large and sturdily built deer which is found in the wooded hills of India and in Malaya and is noted for its fine curving antlers. The picture below, which was taken in Mexico, shows a spotted fawn and stag feeding.

IN A FOREST GLADE

The elk, as the European equivalent of the moose is termed, steps cautiously across the track. It is found in Northern Europe and Siberia, this photograph being taken in East Prussia. The elk's antlers are not as fine as those of the moose of the New World.

MOOSE TWINS

It is not unusual for the cow moose to have two calves in the spring like the twins shown above. These are reddish in colour, unlike their parents which are a very dark grey.

has depends on conditions, but usually the number is not large. However many he has he guards them most carefully, and will resent intruders coming near.

It is during the mating season that the bugling of the bulls is heard, and it is one of the strangest of the sounds of the wilds. Sometimes it is much like the braying of an ass, and at others it is quite musical.

Formerly wapiti were found in great numbers in the western parts of North America, chiefly on the easterly side of the High Sierras and the Rockies, but they were ruthlessly slaughtered, not only for meat, but also for their teeth, which were (and, the writer believes, still are) worn as a badge by members of a certain society.

In recent years these handsome ani-mals have been re-imported into the Canadian Rockies, and there they have flourished. In fact it is said that they have improved on the original stock brought from either Wyoming or Colorado. In the game reserves that have been estab-lished near Banff, Alberta, they are all strictly protected, with the result that they have become so tame that some people regard them as a nuisance, especially when they take possession of the famous golf links near the town.

It is hard to believe that even the giant Irish elk could have been a more magni-ficent creature. Like most of the Ameri-can animals, wapiti have their near relations in other parts of the world, for there is the Asiatic form of wapiti in the

SUMMER RESORT OF THE MOOSE
The bull moose in summer lives alone on the shores of a swamp or lake where food is plenti-
ful and the water affords a refuge from flies and heat. The scene is Hoodoo Lake, Idaho.

Altai Mountains of Mongolia and in Manchuria; this species, though bearing a close resemblance to the American form, is smaller and has not such large antlers. It is a pity that there should be so much confusion about the name. In America they certainly should be called wapiti, but they are only too often called elk, and as this is the name given to the Old World moose, the result is a good deal of confusion in the public mind.

Before leaving the American continent to deal with the deer of the Old World—most of these are related to the American varieties—it would be well to look at the most truly distinctive of the American deer which have no relationship with other species. These are the Virginia, or white-tail, and the Mule and black-tail. We will take the

Virginia first. It is the common deer of all the more easterly part of North America, and may even be found quite close to New York. It is a very beautiful, rather lightly built and graceful animal, standing about 3 feet high and weighing perhaps 200 lb., though its weight varies greatly in different parts of its range, which extends from a few hundred miles north of the St. Lawrence to Florida and the Southern States and many parts of South America.

The colour of these deer in summer, in the more northern part of their range, is a distinctly reddish tone—a colour which presents a striking contrast to the prevailing green of the foliage. With the coming of autumn the strong contrasting red changes to a more neutral grey, an inconspicuous colour. The fawns, of which there are frequently two, have distinct white spots until well into the autumn. The long white tail, which has given them their name, is usually raised when the animal runs, so that though the deer is otherwise hard to see, this white banner, as it is called, can be distinguished even in the dull light of evening in the forests. Only the stags carry horns, and they are well formed and graceful, about 28 inches long, with several points.

Throughout the eastern half of America and the Canadian Provinces these deer are fairly abundant, and game laws have been passed for their protection.

The mule deer is the western form most closely allied to the Virginia species, and is found west of the Missouri. The two species sometimes overlap in their range. As their name implies, they have very large, mule-like ears. In build they are rather heavier, for though only 2 or 3 inches taller, they weigh fully 50 lb. more. The antlers, too, are somewhat larger, and usually very beautifully formed, and are considered good trophies by those who take pleasure in shooting.

The colour, which does not change much with the seasons, is a soft grey with a patch of white under the throat.

Throughout the Canadian Rockies these handsome deer have, in recent years, become very common, and, thanks to being protected by good laws, are now extremely tame. They will come into a camp and beg for salt in a most amusing manner—in fact they are so tame that it is hard to drive them away, and in the

SWIMMING MOOSE

The moose is an expert and speedy swimmer and often goes far out into a lake in search of such dainties as the leaves of water-lilies. The animal sometimes swims under water for several minutes, reappearing suddenly to the surprise of any canoeist in the vicinity.

ONE DAY OLD

New-born baby moose totters to a precarious standing position beside its mother on the shore of the Flathead River in Glacier National Park, Montana.

town of Banff they parade through the streets as though they owned the place. It is easy to understand that they are not popular with owners of gardens, for they seem to select for their meals the most prized flowers and vegetables.

While the mule and the black-tail deer are considered to be separate species, it is not easy to find the differences between them, as they merge one into the other; the more distinct forms are those found in the mountain ranges on the Pacific coast, and are not found east of the Sierra Nevada.

Leaving the American deer, we will now turn to those of Europe, Asia and Africa. The best known is the common fallow deer, which in fact is so familiar to most of us that but little description is necessary. Because it is so common and found in most of the larger parks, it is generally assumed that it must be indigenous to the British Isles, whereas it is really a foreigner, having been imported from the mainland of Eastern Europe, probably by the Romans.

The range of the fallow deer is quite

wide—that is, the fallow and its geographical sub-species. It belongs to most of Southern Europe and to some of the Greek Islands, to Sardinia, parts of Asia Minor and Northern Palestine. It is also native to North Africa (the only part of Africa where deer are found), from which country it may have been introduced into Europe.

The height of a full-grown stag is about 3 feet, and the colour is very variable, from rich yellow-brown in summer with white spots, to grey in winter; but there are two distinct types—the spotted and the brown, as well as the white, which is so often found in any herd. Both have the palmated antlers, which are shed annually. Formerly there was a very large form of fallow deer, called the Irish elk, which had immense palmated antlers that attained a span of about 11 feet and weighed over 70 lb. Specimens of these giant deer are still found buried in the Irish bogs.

The well-known red deer of the British Isles is especially associated with

FALLOW DEER BUCK

One of the best-known types of European deer is represented by this graceful animal, a familiar and ornamental inhabitant of the larger parks of the British Isles. Its range is wide and it is common in Southern Europe and the countries round the Mediterranean.

WAPITI IN

The herd seen in this impressive picture is leaving the highest of the mountain ranges, during a spell of severe winter weather Wapiti are also known as elk, though they

THE ROCKIES

are not to be confused with the elk of the Old World. Once ruthlessly slaughtered for their meat, they have been reintroduced into the Rockies under strict protection.

REINDEER HERD

This photograph was taken in Lapland and shows the herd trekking across the snowy waste in search of food. Their wide-spreading hooves enable them to move over marshy

the Highlands of Scotland, with Exmoor and parts of Ireland.

It is smaller than its American cousin the wapiti, being but 4 feet in height. The stags carry fine antlers with up to fourteen points. These antlers are shed in February or March, and new ones commence to grow very soon after.

As with most of the deer, the stags engage in violent fights during the mating season, when each stag gathers as many does as he may be able to collect.

In the deer forests of Scotland and Ireland it is a very beautiful sight to come on a herd of these fine animals, the largest of British quadrupeds, especially if by good fortune you can get within close range. That is no easy task, as they have learned that man is their enemy and must not be trusted. A clever stalker, unarmed, can sometimes creep up on a

herd and enjoy the sight they present in their glorious natural setting of the Highland—so called—deer forests, which are so often treeless moors carpeted with purple heather and golden grass.

The largest form of the red deer are found in Germany, where they are said to be nearly a third heavier than the British deer. They are also found in Southern Sweden, in Russia, Austria, Hungary, Turkey and Greece, and in Algeria. A smaller variety exists in Corsica and Sardinia. In Tunisia the form found is named the Barbary stag. Then there is the Caspian red deer, or maral, which stands 6 inches higher than the British form. Other closely allied species are found in North Persia, the Crimea, in Northern Asia and in the Himalayas. The Kashmir stag is about 4 feet 4 inches in height, and carries very

ON TREK

or snowy surfaces with ease. In Scandinavia, Lapland and Sweden reindeer have been domesticated, though wild herds still exist in several parts of the Northern Hemisphere.

fine antlers. Its home is in the forest country at elevations of from 3000 to 12,000 feet.

The Père David deer is a very rare species allied to the red deer. Beyond the fact that its home is supposed to be Northern China, little is known of it.

A large, sturdily built deer is the sambar, which stands 5 feet 4 inches in height and has antlers reaching a length, on the outer curve, of 4 feet. It is found in the wooded hills in many parts of India and Ceylon. Its chief peculiarity is that, unlike other deer, it sheds its antlers only once in every three or four years. There are various forms of this deer in Malaya, Formosa, Luzon, Java, Molucca Islands and Basilian Island.

The Chital or Indian spotted deer is conspicuous for being closely spotted with white on a rich fawn colour. The

antlers, carried only by the stags, are not palmated, but more like those of the red deer, only smaller. This species is common in many parts of India, usually living in wooded country.

Roebuck or roe-deer are fairly numerous, and are widely distributed both in Europe and Asia. They stand only 26 inches in height and weigh about 60 lb. Their antlers, measured on the outer curve, are seldom over 1 foot long. As a rule their young are born in May, and twins are very common. These small deer, which are the object of the chase only too often, are found in England (but not in Ireland), in many parts of Europe, in Palestine and Persia.

Mention should be made, also, of the musk deer—a small deer which has no antlers, and is peculiar for having long canine tusks and glands secreting musk.

(W.L.)

G

YOUNG BUSHBUCK

A handsome antelope is the bushbuck which ranges from Abyssinia to West Africa. The characteristic distinct white stripes on the body are plainly seen in this photograph.

CHAPTER TWELVE

ANTELOPES AND GAZELLES

by A. RADCLYFFE DUGMORE

Distinguishing marks of the Antelope. Eland, Kudu, Bongo, Sitatunga, Bushbuck, Nyala, Oryx, Roan and Sable Antelopes. Various species of Waterbuck, Reedbuck, Gerenuk and Impala. The Gazelles. Hartebeest, Gnu or Wildebeest. Other types.

Pᴇᴏᴘʟᴇ frequently ask what is the difference between a deer and an antelope. The difference is easy to explain: deer have solid horns, or antlers, grown and shed each year (with one exception), and these are branched more or less according to the species, and with most deer the sexes are characterized by the does being hornless. The antelopes, on the contrary, have hollow horns, which, as they grow (in nearly all cases), make rings as evidence of their age. These are formed on a bony cord, and are not shed. Another question asked is, What is the difference between an antelope and a gazelle? This is not so easy to answer, as there appears to be no definite distinction. Smaller and more lightly built forms are, as a rule, called gazelles.

Africa is the home of the Antelopes, far more being found there than anywhere else in the world. There are a few in Asia, none in Oceania and, strange to say, none in either North or South America, if we exclude the Pronghorn, which, strictly speaking, is not an antelope, but belongs to a separate family

having no relations anywhere. It is the most truly American mammal known, more decidedly so even than the Virginia and mule deer. One of its peculiarities is that the horns are placed directly above the eyes, are shed annually and have each a small branch or point. These prong-horns used to be very numerous in the middle west, but not east of 95° longitude, and from the more southerly part of Canada to Mexico. They were slaughtered in such quantities that they were almost exterminated. Thanks to careful protection, there are a few thousand in Canada, and perhaps 12,000 or 13,000 in the United States.

The number of known species and sub-species of antelopes is great. There are about 170 in Africa alone.

We will begin with the Eland, the largest antelope of all. These grand animals weigh upward of three-quarters of a ton and stand up to 6 feet at the shoulder—that is, the giant eland, the larger and much rarer species. Male and female have horns which attain a length of as much as 40 inches. They are more or

SHY KUDU

Imposing spiral horns distinguish the kudu, a rare species of antelope. The males are especially shy, and are off in a flash at the approach of danger. They wander in groups of two or more in mountainous African scrub country as seen in our photograph.

less straight, and have a slight spiral twist. The colour of the females and younger males is a soft sandy fawn; the males on reaching maturity become a curious bluish-grey. On the head of the male there is often a mat of very dark hair between the eyes; under the neck is a loose skin or dewlap, from which hangs a fringe of coarse hair. The range of the eland is over a wide area of Central and Southern Africa, where they roam the plains in large herds. The giant eland, which is very rare, is found west of the Nile in the Provinces of Mongalla and Bahr el Ghazal, also in Senegambia.

Perhaps the next in point of size is the Greater Kudu, considered to be the most impressive antelope of all. It stands 4 feet 3 inches in height and carries truly magnificent horns. These are gracefully spiral, with a length of nearly 6 feet and with a marked ridge starting at the base and going almost to the tip, following the curve all the way. Females have smaller horns, when they have any, but usually they are hornless. The colour of these kudu is fawn, turning to grey with age, and the sides are marked with vertical white stripes, which continue into the light-coloured mane that runs all along the spine. Under the throat there is a dark fringe which seems to complete the beauty of these fine animals. Unfortunately they are so rare that few people get a chance of seeing them in their wild state. Their range is limited to certain restricted areas where they live among

rough, scrubby mountains. They are known in some districts of Central Africa and in the hill regions of Kordofan and Kassala in the Sudan and southwards.

A rather smaller form of the kudu is not nearly so rare. Instead of being more or less solitary, they go in small herds, and frequent more open, sandy country.

Of the so-called Harnessed antelopes that is, those which have white vertical stripes on various shades of chestnut to fawn colour—the finest is the Bongo, that rare and beautiful dweller of the thick forest, of either bamboo or mixed trees. Its range is extremely restricted. In Kenya it is found in the Aberdare Mountains and on the mountain slopes, usually at elevations of from 8000 to 10,000 feet; in the South Belgian Congo, in a very small area and in the country bordering on the Gulf of Guinea. In each of these districts the

bongo is classified as a more or less distinct geographical race.

The colour of these large antelopes is very rich chestnut, with clearly defined, white, vertical stripes, about twelve in number, a white band on chest and small white markings on nose, sides of jaws and lower lip, also on legs and ears. The horns are massive and very graceful, carried by both sexes, and conspicuous for the ivory-white tips. Their length is about 32 inches, while the height of the animal itself is well under 4 feet. This is quite justly regarded as perhaps the most beautiful of all the antelopes, but, being extremely shy and very rare, it is, unfortunately, seldom seen.

A small and peculiar member of the harnessed group is the Sitatunga. It stands just over 3 feet in height. Only the males carry horns, and these are spiral, 28 inches long, measured straight, and 35 round the curve, and resemble those of the kudu. The colour is greyish-brown, with the characteristic vertical stripes but scarcely discernible. The coat, unlike that of most antelopes, is long and soft, but the greatest peculiarity is the extraordinary length of the hoofs, which have been developed to enable them to walk in the swampy ground which is their natural home. Their distribution is very local, and they are perhaps most common in the marshland of the upper White Nile and near the great lakes.

There are several varieties of those handsome antelopes, the Bushbuck, which range from Abyssinia to West Africa. They stand between 30 and 33 inches in height, and all have the characteristic chestnut colour. They carry several distinct white stripes, as well as some spots on the flank. The horns, carried only by the males, are up to about 14

Two bull waterbucks are about to test the power of their horns and to engage in a contest
which will secure the affection of the doe for the winner. The horns often measure up to

inches in length, and are twisted into bold spiral curves. The Abyssinian variety is lighter in colour and has white stripes on the flank. Those of the West Coast are the darkest.

The Forest-loving Nyala

The Nyala is a bush- or forest-loving antelope, about 3½ feet in height, having horns rather like those of the bongo, being spiral, with a length of 30 inches round the curve. These are carried only by the males. The general colour is a deep grey in the males, while the females and young are a dull reddish-yellow. All have the white bands round the body and haunches. The males have long dark hair hanging from the throat and on the sides and belly. These antelopes are found in Zululand to the Sabi River and in a

small area in Nyassaland.

A rather common and very beautiful type of antelope is the Oryx, which is conspicuous for its long and more or less straight, sharply pointed horns, which reach a length of 4 feet or more and are carried by both sexes. The form called Beisa is the best known, especially in Kenya, where it can be seen in large herds. The colour is a curious light dove tone, with conspicuous black markings on the front legs, side, face and ears. It is decidedly gregarious, and frequently goes in the company of several other species, such as the hartebeest, Grant's gazelle, and even giraffe.

Very closely related is the Fringe-eared oryx, which, as its name implies, has long, fringed ears, strongly marked with black. This is neither as common

STRENGTH

three feet in length. As the name suggests, waterbuck are found in places where there is an abundance of water. The common species has an elliptical white ring on the flank.

nor as gregarious as the beisa. Then there are the White oryx of the Sudan deserts, the Gemsbuck of southern areas and largest of the family, standing 4 feet in height and having horns about 4 feet in length, the Beatrix and, closely allied, but a different genus, the Addax, a desert liver standing about 38 inches in height and having horns, not straight but double curved, about 28 inches long, measured straight, and 36 following the curve. They are found in the more northern part of Africa from Dongola and Senegal northward

Roan and Sable Antelopes

The Roan and the Sable antelopes, closely related to one another, are two of the larger and finer of the family and belong to the oryx group, though very different in appearance. The roan stands 4 feet 9 inches in height, is greyish-brown to warm roan in colour, with the front and sides of face black. It has long, coarse hair under the neck and a stiff mane from back of ears almost to the rump. The ears are tufted and rather long. Both male and female have horns which are rather goat-like in form, curving backward and having a length up to 34 inches. Their range includes most of Africa south of the Sahara, though in the extreme south they have been exterminated as wild animals.

The Sable is a very handsome antelope, though smaller than the roan and is of much more striking appearance, with its coat of shiny black relieved by white markings on the face, and completely white under-parts. On the back is a stiff

ONE OF THE MOST GRACEFUL OF

Full of the joy of life is the impala, one of the most graceful of antelopes ; and one of the pleasant sights that Africa affords is that of a herd playing or running. They are to be

ANTELOPES: THE BEAUTIFUL IMPALA

seen in most parts of the continent, and even in the vicinity of large towns. They usually frequent open, scrubby country permitting of free movement, rather than forest districts.

HARTEBEESTS AT THEIR DRINKING-HOLE

Called "the sentinels of the veldt", hartebeests are the most alert of antelopes and give warning of danger to other animals. With them beasts of many other kinds live together in harmony and it seems to be the hartebeests' special duty to guard them.

mane down the neck to behind the shoulders. The male stands 44 inches at the shoulder and the female 36 inches. The horns, like those of the roan, are of goat-like shape, but much longer, being sometimes as long as 50 inches in the male, while those of the female are much shorter. They curve backward very gracefully, and are strongly ridged around most of their length. Their range is north of the Transvaal to Tanganyika, where they are occasionally found in fair-sized herds.

The Waterbuck form a distinctive group of rather heavy type of antelope in which only the males carry horns.

One group is the strictly local species

called Mrs. Grey, the most handsome of the family. This is found on the banks of the White Nile, from Malakal southwards. Occasionally travellers on, the great river have the good luck to see a herd of these rare antelopes and admire their beauty. In colour they are deep chestnut brown, or chestnut, according to age, with a white patch on the shoulders, while the ears also are white. Their height is about 38 inches. Unlike the other waterbuck, the horns have a graceful double curve, and are about 33 inches long. The White-eared Cob is a somewhat smaller form found in the Sudan.

The Common waterbuck found in places where water is abundant is named *ellipsiprymnus*, from the elliptical white ring round the flank, a conspicuous pattern when the animal is running away. Unlike most antelopes, it is rather heavily built, and covered with longish, coarse hair. The males carry very fine horns, nearly 3 feet long, slightly lyre-shaped and strongly ribbed. In habit they are inclined to go in small herds, though this is not always true, as pairs or groups of three or four are quite common. But as a rule when in herds the females always predominate. The Sing-sing is a much more reddish variety, and has a white patch on the rump instead of the circle. In general appearance it reminds one of the red deer. It is common in the Sudan and Uganda and in many other parts. Owing to the fact that the meat of the waterbuck is not at all good to eat, these animals are not in danger of being killed off. The natives use the horns for musical instruments—so called!

Not far removed from the waterbuck group, and about the same size, is the Reedbuck. It is, however, much more lightly built and more graceful in its movements. Only the males carry horns, which are about 16 inches long, and curve backward and then forward and outward. In colour they are more or less uniformly fawn, lighter on the underparts. Distinct features are the nearly bare patch below the ear and the softness at the base of the horns. They go in small groups, keeping to a great extent to the

BRINDLED GNU ON THE SAVANNAH

This is one of the three species of gnu or wildebeest, an unusually ugly member of the antelope family. The photograph was taken in the savannah country of Mozambique. The habits of the gnu are in accordance with its appearance, for a herd will deliberately try to frighten an intruder though without intent to cause real harm.

SPRINGBOKS AT THE GALLOP

Startled by the roar of a plane, a herd of springboks (emblem of the Union of South Africa) careers across the Kalahari Desert. Aptly named, the springbok can clear the most difficult obstacles with ease and with the elastic springing motion here seen.

vicinity of water. When startled they give a curious whistling sound. They are widely distributed in various forms or sub-species, some of which, like the Bohor, are smaller than the main type.

The Gerenuk is a distinctive type of gazelle, and is sometimes called the giraffe antelope, on account of its remarkably long neck. They are very delicately built, with extremely thin legs. Their colour is a sandy fawn, which matches the sandy ground where they are usually found in small herds, often far from water. Some people say they never drink, and certainly to see them at a water-hole must be such an uncommon sight that, so far as the writer is aware, no photograph has ever been made of them drinking. They feed on small leaves and twigs, and in order to reach the upper ones they have to stand on their hind legs,

much as goats do, so it is in that position that they are most often seen. Only the males have horns, and these are not much over 14 inches long. The range of these strange little antelopes is restricted to suitable dry country, chiefly in Somaliland, Kenya and parts of Tanganyika.

In its movements there is certainly no more graceful animal than the Impala, or Palla, which fortunately is so common that it may be seen by anyone travelling in the parts of Africa where it lives. Even in the vicinity of a large town like Nairobi they may be seen in quite good-sized herds, though not as far north as the Sudan. The colour is rich, almost chestnut fawn above, and very pale underparts. Only the males have horns, and these are lyre-shaped, about 20 inches in length. It is noticeable that in the herds, which are sometimes quite large, the number of females greatly predominates, even to as much as twenty to one. They frequent almost any sort of country, open or scrubby, but not, the writer thinks, the thick forests, and one of the most beautiful sights in Africa is to watch a herd playing or running. They seem filled with the joy of life as they go bounding about in a most extraordinary manner, jumping to unbelievable heights.

The very beautiful little creature, Grant's gazelle, is one of the commonest. It is found in many parts of Africa and, though small—being only 34 inches in height—it has the longest horns of any of the gazelles. They are up to 30 inches in length and spread to as much as 26 inches, or even more. Most of their length is strongly ridged around, and they are most gracefully curved. The horns of the females are much smaller. Their colour is sandy-fawn above, with a black stripe along the sides and vertically up the flank, also on the face. Underparts are white, this colour following by the side of the black up the flank and making the animal conspicuous. In some districts, however, the strong contrasting colours are lacking, and, instead, the fawn and the white come together without the intervening black. This is most noticeable in the northern part of Kenya. They are distinctly gregarious in habit, going together in large herds as a rule, with more females than males.

Types of Springbok

Thomson's gazelle is similar to the Grant's, but smaller. The two species frequently go together. Their horns are very much smaller and less noticeable. These are a form of the springbok, or springbuck, of South Africa, and closely allied to the addra found in the Sudan.

Well named "the sentinels of the veldt" the Hartebeests are the most alert of all antelopes, and seem to take unto themselves the task of guarding other animals.

Sentinels of the Veldt

They are rather like caricatures, with their strangely elongated faces and narrow heads, made all the more so by the extension of the skull that forms the pedicles carrying the horns. So the front view of a hartebeest is peculiar, particularly as the ears, so often held horizontally, are in a line with the lower bend of the horns. These horns, carried by both male and female, are about 25 inches long, are heavily ribbed and curve first sideways and then up and back. There are several species of hartebeests more or less similar, according to their locality. Their average height is about 52 inches, and the colour of the common Kenya variety, Coke's, is lightish fawn above, much lighter or almost white below with a light patch on the flank. Jackson's hartebeest is very much darker, especially on the face, which is rich purplish chestnut, this colour merging into the rest of the body tones. This is found in the Southern Sudan and from there for some distance south into Kenya. Neuman's hartebeest is very much like the former, also found in the Sudan, and another species is the Tora, which frequents the more easterly part of the Sudan. Very closely related is the Tiang, a dark variety belonging to the Sudan and East Africa, and this has a very close cousin called the desert tiang from Kordofan. All hartebeests are strictly gregarious, and have the same strange method of running, which consists of a series of stiff-legged jumps. With the hartebeests are usually found many kinds of other animals.

It is hard to believe that the strange and even grotesquely ugly Gnu, or wildebeest, can belong to the usually graceful antelope family. It is certainly the ugly duckling of the family. Its name, given, the writer believes, by the Boers, suits it well, for its face is thoroughly evil, with its curious tufts of coarse black hair and the very peculiar flattened nostrils. They seem to take a real pleasure in frightening people.

They travel in large herds, and are common in certain districts, particularly in the Serengeti Plains of Kenya, but the greatest concentration is, the writer believes, in the Great Crater of Ngora Ngora, where the many thousands remind one of the vast herds of bison on the plains in North America long years ago. They do, in fact, look like the bison, especially when running. A newcomer to Africa is apt to become badly frightened when a herd of these wildebeests play their usual trick by charging full speed towards the intruder and then suddenly, when 100 or 200 yards away, stop in a line, like a troop of cavalry. They look dangerous, but it is all bluff, and after giving a few loud snorts, they all turn about and gallop away as fast as they can. The newcomer is left mopping his brow and congratulating himself on his narrow escape! Their range is from south of the Sudan southwards. The three forms of species are the common brindled, the white-bearded and rare white-tailed.

Miniature Antelope

The Klipspringer is one of the smaller types of antelope, standing only 1 foot 9 inches in height, with 5-inch horns carried only by the males. Its colour is a golden-grey, and the hair thick and wavy, of curious texture. The most remarkable feature of this miniature antelope is the wonderful agility it displays in jumping among the rocky places it selects for its home, often at elevations of 10,000 feet

Largest Asiatic Antelope

Of the Asiatic antelopes the most noticeable and largest is the Nilgai, which stands 4 feet 8 inches at the shoulders. The male is dark grey, and the female, which is somewhat smaller, is more tawny in colour, and both have a white patch on the throat. Only the males have horns, and these are about 9 inches long—absurdly small in proportion to the size of the animal. They detract greatly from its appearance. Its home is in India.

The Indian antelope or Black Buck is by far the most handsome of the Asiatic antelopes, though it is small—only 2 feet 8 inches high. The beauty of the long, spiral, twisted, 28-inch horns and the striking colour make it a conspicuous animal. The upper part of its body is black, with a patch of chestnut back of the neck, while the underparts are white. The female is less beautiful, being fawn colour and not having horns. They live in the open plains of India, and are said to be among the fastest of animals.

The Four-horned antelope or Chika-rah is found in India and Tibet. It is just over 2 feet in height, but is noticeable because of the strange fact of its having four horns instead of the conventional two. It is related to the large nilgai.

A strange antelope, classified as a separate genus, is the Saiga. It is the ugly duckling of the Asiatic antelope, because of its greatly enlarged puffy nose. It stands about $2\frac{1}{2}$ feet in height and is found in South-eastern Europe and in Western Asia.

THE RARE BONGO

Many species of antelopes, such as the white-tailed gnu, the sable antelope and the greater kudu, are dwindling in numbers, and among them is the bongo, shown in the above photograph in its native haunt, the jungle country of West Africa.

Polar Bear

Moth

Stick
Insect

Tiger

Starred Lizard

Partridge

VARIED EXAMPLES OF

Much of nature's camouflage consists in a protective pattern such as the stripes of the tiger, the dappled back of the deer, the wings of the moth and other examples shown above. With

CAMOUFLAGE IN NATURE

pattern goes protective coloration—the white coat of the polar bear, the changing coat of the chameleon. Some insects, such as the stick insect, imitate the shape of twig and leaf.

consist of small bony projections in the giraffes, and in the deer take the form of solid branched antlers which are shed every year and grow afresh out of the skull the following season. The cattle, sheep, goats and antelopes have quite a different type of horn, which thus unites them into one natural group and distinguishes them from other types of ruminants. This type of horn consists of a solid core of bone which is a permanent part of the skull, and covering this is a hollow sheath, which is the horn proper. Such horns are permanent, as distinct from the temporary antlers of deer, and the sheaths are not normally shed during the lifetime of the animal. Thus we get the term "hollow-horned ruminants", though, strictly speaking, the horns are not hollow, as the sheaths are more or less filled by the bony cores.

Wild Ancestors of Farm Cattle

The familiar cattle of our farms are the descendants of wild ancestors, though their exact origin lies shrouded in the mists of antiquity. The first historical evidence we have of wild cattle in Europe comes from the writings of Julius Caesar in the first century B.C., when the Romans were extending their dominion over the known world. In attempting to subdue the barbarians on the northern borders of their domain, the Roman legions encountered wild cattle in the Black Forest of Germany. These oxen were of gigantic size, being 6 feet high at the shoulder and some 10 feet in length. The bulls were exceedingly powerful and ferocious; it is said they could never be tamed and the Romans greatly feared them. They were certainly captured alive, however, for during the early period of the Roman Empire gigantic bulls, to which the name "Urus" was given, were made to provide spectacles in the arena, where yellow-haired giants from their native land fought with them.

Aurochs and Celtic Shorthorn

The German name for this formidable creature was "Aurochs", and it is by this name that it is usually known at the present day. On the European continent the Aurochs survived until a much later period than in Britain, and we read of it being encountered by the first Crusaders on their route through Germany in the eleventh century, when it was hunted for food and sport. It seems to have lingered in Poland long after it had died out elsewhere, and the last Aurochs cow is reputed to have been killed there as late as the seventeenth century.

At some remote prehistoric period the Celtic tribes of Gaul had domesticated another breed of cattle, very different from the Aurochs, although it is regarded as merely a variety of the same species. This was a small animal about 4 feet high, with short horns and red in colour. It is known as the Celtic Shorthorn. When the Celts invaded Britain they brought these little cattle with them, and the invading Romans at a much later date found herds of these tame cattle, which provided food for their legionaries. At a later period still came the invading Saxons, driving the Romano-British tribes and their little cattle to the west and north, and bringing with them larger cattle with long horns, derived undoubtedly from their native breed. Thus our domestic cattle appear to have originated from a mixture of these two breeds, though the ancestry of the Celtic Shorthorn is obscure.

The most direct descendants of these

CATTLE OF THE HIGHLANDS

In some of the remote districts of Scotland cattle of this type still remain in a semi-wild state.
This photograph of an impressively horned group was taken in the Ben Nevis district.

ancient wild or semi-domesticated oxen are considered to be the so-called Park Cattle, remnants of which still exist. These are known to have originated from herds of wild cattle which roamed the wooded country of Southern Scotland or Northern England in the thirteenth century. Long before the Reformation, herds of these cattle were confined in parks belonging to certain ecclesiastical establishments, and it seems probable that white individuals were selected for this purpose and the herds kept white by killing off the coloured calves that were born. This practice has been continued right up to the present day. The purest breed are supposed to be the Chillingham cattle, which are now white, with black muzzles and the inside of the ears red. Red and black calves are frequently produced, however, and if these were not killed off it is probable that coloured

Members of the famous Cadzow herd are seen lying in the shade of ancient oaks, the remnants of the Caledonian forest, which was probably their original habitat. Such

MAGNIFICENTLY HORNED NATIVES OF AFRICA

There are several types of native African cattle, and these are peculiar and distinguished from Indian cattle in their horns, which are exceptional, both in their length and thickness. This striking feature is well seen in this picture of Watussi cattle in East Africa.

ROUND-UP

Once roaming freely in vast herds over the plains of North America, the bison, some-times inaccurately called "buffalo", has been greatly reduced in numbers, being slaughtered

OF BISON

for meat and hides until as recently as the end of the war of 1914–18. *Since then, bison have been preserved in the United States and Canada. This is a scene in Alberta.*

of the enclosure of Chartley Park in 1248. The present breed is not pure, but in size and form they are probably the nearest approach to the Aurochs in existence. Black calves are frequently produced, which tends to show that this was the original colour.

Cattle of the East

In India and the East generally quite a different type of cattle is found. These animals are distinguished by the presence of a prominent hump on the withers, large drooping ears and enormous dewlaps. Another characteristic is the voice, which is merely a grunt, and the colour is usually some shade of grey, cream or white. These cattle are commonly called Zebu by Europeans, but apparently not by the Indians. They were extensively used as draught animals throughout Asia, Egypt and East Africa, and are of a very quiet and gentle disposition. As no wild species at all resembling the zebu is known to have existed within historic times, it is evident that these humped cattle were domesticated at a very early period, undoubtedly long before anything of the sort was attempted elsewhere. We know that many thousands of years ago the highly civilized Egyptians had tame humped cattle, which served them as beasts of burden and givers of milk when alive, and provided meat, leather, horn and bone when dead. This was at a period when the Neolithic inhabitants of Western Europe were little better than savages, still using crude weapons and tools of bone and flint. They were merely hunters at this period, with no domesticated animals; but we know that they did succeed in slaughtering the Aurochs, because skulls have been found transfixed with stone axe-heads.

There are several types of native domesticated cattle in Africa, but these differ from those of India by having enormous horns of exceptional length and thickness.

The largest of the wild oxen now living is the Gaur, a magnificent animal found in India, Burma and Malaya. Old bulls sometimes reach a height of 6 feet at the shoulder and a length of $9\frac{1}{2}$ feet, thus approaching the extinct Aurochs in size. The general colour is black or dark brown, with light-coloured legs, the hair being short, soft and glossy. The convex ridge on the forehead and massive curved horns somewhat flattened at the base are other characteristic features. The Gaur frequents hilly districts and is nocturnal in habits, feeding by night and hiding in the jungle by day. It is by nature shy and retiring, and avoids the vicinity of human dwellings, but can be formidable when at bay.

A close relative of the Gaur is the Gayal, or Mithan, which was at one time thought to be merely a domesticated variety, but is known to exist in a wild state in the hills of North-east India.

The Banteng, or Java Ox, is found in Burma, Siam, Malaya, Java, Borneo and Sumatra, and is extensively domesticated by the Burmese and Malayan peoples. Its most distinctive characteristic is the large white patch on the rump, and the fact that while the adult bulls are black, the cows and calves are reddish-brown. The lower parts of the legs are white, as in the two previous species, and the general habits are very similar.

Native Ox of Tibet

The Yak is the native ox of Tibet, its home being the high mountain plateau from 14,000 to 20,000 feet elevation.

BUFFALO BULL

Buffalo were introduced into the North-west tip of the Northern Territory of Australia from Timor, in the early nineteenth century, when they provided meat and milk for the early outposts. They have remained in this comparatively well-watered district.

In the wild state it is a very wary animal, haunting the most inaccessible places, and difficult to approach on account of its keen scent, though its sight is poor.

The Yak has been domesticated in Tibet for unknown ages, and is the universal beast of burden, as well as the main source of food and clothing for the inhabitants of this desolate region. Yaks have extraordinary strength and endurance; they delight in freezing temperatures and rough country, while the poorest wiry grass suffices for their food. Thus they are essential for journeys at high altitudes in Central Asia, where no other animals could survive.

The grunting voice of the yak is one of its peculiarities; while its humped shoulders, long hair and low carriage of the head resemble the bison more than the typical oxen. The wild animals are always black; but domesticated individuals vary from black, through brown, to white.

Bison are distinguished from other members of the cattle tribe by the massive development of the head and fore-quarters compared with the hinder part. This appearance is accentuated by the great growth of shaggy hair on the head, neck and shoulders, while the hind-quarters and lower part of the back and sides remain smooth. The horns are comparatively small and curved, and set low down on the sides of the head, while the muzzle is short and blunt.

In earlier times bison have ranged over most of Europe, and were extensively hunted in Poland as late as the middle of the seventeenth century. Two hundred years earlier they were so numerous

DWELLERS IN THE BARREN LANDS

Musk-oxen, of the type here shown in the North-west territory of Canada, inhabit cold and desolate regions, ranging in herds from Greenland to Alaska and feeding on moss and other scanty growths. They are related to the Asiatic goat-antelopes.

HARDY YAK OF CENTRAL ASIA

The yak is the animal-of-all-work in Central Asia. It serves as beast of burden, provides food and clothing, and is hardy enough to survive freezing temperatures and the roughest conditions. It is essential for travelling at the very high altitudes of Central Asia.

in some regions that peasants were sometimes run down and trampled to death by stampeding herds. During the war of 1914–1918 the European bison were extensively slaughtered for food in the regions they still frequented and driven from many of their natural haunts. At the close of the war the bison were on the verge of extermination. The truly wild race in the Caucasus had practically died out, and all that remained were a few small herds that had been preserved in the Lithuanian forests by the former Russian Government. A European Bison Society was formed to encourage the preservation of this noble animal and attempt to save it from extinction.

The American Bison, commonly but erroneously spoken of as "Buffalo", is a larger animal than its European relative

and darker in colour. It is the only ox indigenous to the American continent.

Less than 100 years ago this great beast existed in incredible numbers over vast areas of North America, and was the main source of food and clothing for the native tribes of the prairie regions. Although the great prairies of the west were the bison's natural home, it was not confined to the open country. Its original range started almost at the Atlantic coast, through a dense forest region, across the mountains to the prairies along the Mississippi, to Texas and Northern Mexico, and over the Rocky Mountains to Utah and Idaho. Thence it ranged northwards into Canada, through Alberta and British Columbia, to the bleak shores of the Great Slave Lake. It has been estimated by competent authori-

H   (W.L.)

ties that at least 60,000,000 bison existed at this period.

It was the coming of the white man that sealed the doom of the bison, though it seems incredible that such vast numbers could have been reduced to the verge of extinction within so short a period. For unknown ages the Red Men lived on the bison without appreciably reducing their numbers. Then came the white man, who not only took to hunting the bison himself, but supplied firearms to the Indians. The slaughter seems to have started in a comparatively small way about 1730, and during the next hundred years the bison were driven away entirely from the Eastern United States and also from the country to the west of the Rocky Mountains. Then from 1830 onwards the gradual spread of civilization attracted an ever-increasing body of hunters, the demand for so-called "buffalo robes" increased, and hundreds of thousands of animals were killed systematically for their meat and hides. The completion of the Union Pacific Railway in 1869 had the effect of cutting the great herd in two, and from then onwards began the most abominably wasteful and ruthless slaughter. Immense numbers of bison were killed for their hides only; some merely for their tongues, which supplied a newly established canning factory. The carcasses of these animals were left to rot, and the stench of their remains poisoned the air for miles.

Doom of the Bison

The year 1875 saw the end of the herd to the south of the railway; only a few thousands escaped into the wilds of Texas, where they were gradually hunted down. The northern herd was said then to number 1,500,000, and the Sioux Indians in Wyoming, armed with modern rifles, played a great part in its final destruction. The hunters became alarmed at the great reduction in the numbers of the "buffalo" about 1880, and being determined to get what they could while there was still time, a rush was made from all sides during the winters of 1881-2 and 1882-3. Further expeditions set out in the autumn of 1883, only to return empty-handed; the great herds had vanished for ever.

Bison and Buffalo

Some 300 or 400 settled in Yellowstone National Park, where they were protected by the U.S. Government, but every individual outside the park was killed. A larger remnant survived in Canada, some of which are preserved in Banff National Park; while a still greater purely wild herd exists in the uninhabited wastes of the north-west. These latter are what Canadians term "Wood Buffalo", being a somewhat smaller animal than the great beast of the prairies.

We now come to the true buffaloes, which differ greatly in form from the bison, to which the name is universally misapplied in America. They are heavily built animals, but without the humped shoulders and great mass of hair of the bison. They are further characterized by the large ears, short necks, broad muzzles and large horns flattened at the base.

The Cape Buffalo is the largest and most powerful, and said by hunters to be the most dangerous animal in Africa if wounded or angry. The black hair is very thin and scanty, and aged individuals are often more or less bare. The massive horns are a prominent feature of this animal, as they are flattened at the base and expand to form a kind of cap over the

ON FOREST-CLAD HEIGHTS

Frequenting high regions and most abundant in British Columbia are the Rocky Mountain goats, a species intermediate between goat and antelope. The photograph above was taken in the beautiful country of one of the great Canadian national parks.

ROCKY MOUNTAIN SHEEP

This photograph was taken in the Banff National Park, Alberta, Canada. The "big-horn", or Rocky Mountain sheep, is aptly so-called, having massive curved horns. It is thoroughly at home in mountain country, ranging to a height of 12,000 ft. in summer.

top of the head. The range of this buffalo extends from the Cape to the Equator, while a smaller variety is found in Abyssinia. Apart from man, the lion is the principal enemy of the African buffalo. The Short-horned buffalo is a smaller species, of a red or yellowish colour, and with much shorter and less massive horns. It is found throughout West Africa, and a distinct variety occurs in the Congo.

Indian Buffalo

The Indian buffalo still exists in the wild state in the swampy grass jungles of India, but has long been domesticated and introduced throughout Burma and Malaya, as well as westwards to Turkey, Egypt and Italy. The massive horns are very long, and usually curved backwards, and the head is longer and with a narrower muzzle than in the African species. It is extensively used as a beast of burden by the native races of the East. Its most notable characteristic is its fondness for water, in which it is always ready to stand or lie almost submerged. For this reason it is often called the water-buffalo.

Smallest of the ox tribe is the Anoa, a small animal not much over 3 feet in height. It appears to be related to the buffaloes, but also shows characteristics of the antelopes, and may be regarded as intermediate between these two groups. It is an inhabitant of the island of Celebes, in the Dutch East Indies. This animal is black in colour, and in general form resembles a young Indian buffalo. The sharp-pointed, backward-pointing horns are only about 10 to 12 inches long, triangular at the base and perfectly straight. It is thought that the Anoa is a survivor from a race of primitive antelope-like buffaloes, from which other members of the group may have evolved.

There is really little scientific difference between sheep and goats, which are all classified into one sub-family, called the *Caprinae*. The typical sheep have massive horns, much curved in a spiral form down the sides of the head; in the goats the horns are more erect and much less curved. Sheep also have peculiar "tear glands" just below the eye, and glands in each foot between the toes; goats never have glands on the face or the hind feet, while the glands on the front feet are sometimes absent. Male goats always have a strong characteristic smell, and usually a beard on the chin, while these features are absent in sheep. The above are the characteristics which distinguish typical sheep from typical goats, but there are exceptions and intermediate species, so that it is difficult to draw a hard and fast line between them. The fact is that the sheep (genus *Ovis*) seem to pass imperceptibly into the goats (genus *Capra*), while the goats—through the group of antelope-goats, including the Chamois—pass imperceptibly into the antelopes.

Wild Sheep

The origin of our domestic sheep is uncertain, but they are thought to be derived from several species of Asiatic wild sheep, perhaps with an admixture of Moufflon, which is the only wild sheep still existing in Europe. There are no native wild sheep in the British Isles at the present time, though remains from the Norfolk "Forest Bed" deposits show that a large type of sheep existed during the pre-glacial period. There still exists a race of feral sheep on the island of Soay in the St. Kilda group. These are supposed to have originated from domesticated sheep left there by the Vikings, and their descendants have remained perfectly

LOOK-OUT IN THE ALPS

On a rocky height in the Berchtesgaden Alps, the agile chamois surveys the surrounding country. Celebrated for its nimble movement and surefootedness, it is the most graceful of all the wild goats. The short, upright horns with hooked tips are a prominent feature.

wild on this uninhabited islet for about 1000 years. These sheep have brownish-coloured wool and curved horns, but are only about half the size of any good modern breed. They have obviously degenerated through their restricted range and continual inbreeding, and reverted very much towards their wild ancestral stock in other respects.

The only surviving wild sheep of Europe is known as the moufflon, which in many respects resembles our tame sheep and is probably one of their ancestors. The moufflon is about the size of a domestic sheep, with the same type of head, a characteristic sheep-like expression and a similar bleat. The horns, however, are much larger than in any tame breed, and the general colour is dark reddish-brown, with light under-parts. As with all wild sheep, the outer coat is hair-like, but a thick undercoat of wool is developed for the winter. The moufflon is now restricted to the islands of Corsica and Sardinia, where it is to be met with only in companies of five or six individuals. There is much fighting between the rams during the mating season in December and January, and the successful males become leaders of small parties of ewes. The lambs are born in April and May, either singly or twins, as with tame sheep, and are very soon strong and active enough to follow their mothers anywhere over the mountains. Wild moufflon have been known to consort with tame sheep and even to interbreed with them, so the two animals must be very closely related. In its native mountains, however, the moufflon is an extremely wary beast and most difficult to approach. It also possesses excellent protective coloration, and will deliberately seek the shadows of rocks and bushes when alarmed, thus becoming practically invisible from a distance. The animals inhabiting the two islands appear to have developed into distinct races, because the females of Corsica possess small horns, while the Sardinian ewes are hornless.

The Smallest Wild Sheep

Similar in general form, but smaller, is the Red Sheep of Cyprus. This is the smallest species of wild sheep, the rams being only about 26 inches high at the shoulder. It is a graceful animal, of a general reddish-brown colour, with light underparts and white markings on the face and rump. It frequents the pine-clad slopes of the Cyprian mountains.

A much larger animal of similar form is found in Asia Minor and Eastern Persia, known as the Armenian Sheep. The colour in this case is reddish-yellow, with the usual white markings.

There are several closely related species of wild sheep found in the mountains of Central Asia, of which the Urial is one of the most notable. The urial is a somewhat goat-like animal, because of the ruff of long hair on the throat and chest of the rams, and the horns are more spreading and less closely curled than in other species. It is the only wild sheep found in India, but has an extensive range over the mountains of the Punjab, into Northern Tibet, Afghanistan, and westwards into Persia.

The giant of the sheep tribe, the Argali, found in the mountains of Mongolia, Tibet and Southern Siberia, is a handsome animal, standing some 4 feet high, thus being as big as a donkey and larger than the smallest members of the cattle tribe. The argali is notable for its massive curved horns, which are normally about 40 inches in length and 17 inches in girth at the base; up to 48 inches with a girth of 20 inches have been recorded. The colouring follows the general pattern of most wild sheep, being greyish-brown with light underparts, and white on the rump, throat and chest. The rams of the Tibetan argali have a ruff of white hair on the throat and chest, but this is absent in the Mongolian race. In Tibet this sheep ranges craggy mountains up to 15,000 feet; but the Mongolian variety does not seek such desolate regions, frequenting thinly wooded country with mountains up to 4000 feet altitude and open valleys.

American Bighorn

The American "Bighorn", or Rocky Mountain sheep, is one of the best known. It is, however, an extremely shy and wary creature, and exceedingly difficult to get even a sight of in its native haunts. It frequents the mountainous regions of Western America and Canada, its range extending from Mexico northwards as far as Alaska. The bighorn is a slightly smaller animal than the argali, though the horns are equal in size, and thus appear larger in proportion to the sheep itself. The bighorn is a wonderfully expert climber, scaling rocks and leaping precipices with almost goat-like ability and ranging up to an altitude of 12,000 feet or more in summer. The Yukon grey and the white Alaskan sheep are considered to be merely varieties of the bighorn, and the Asiatic Kamchatkan sheep is regarded as the same species.

SCENE IN THE ROCKY MOUNTAINS

Sheep and goats which roam the mountain-sides have become amazingly sure-footed, picking their way from rock to rock with blithe disregard of the sheer drop below. The photograph of Rocky Mountain sheep, above, was secured only after hours of climbing.

The only representative of the sheep tribe found in Africa occurs in the Atlas Mountains. It is commonly known as the Barbary Sheep, and is called the "Arui" by the native inhabitants. It is a large goat-like animal, with its massive horns much less curved than in most other wild sheep. The most notable feature is the great mane of long hair which the rams have on the throat, chest and fore-legs, also the tail is much longer than is usual in sheep, and thickly haired. The colour is reddish-fawn, which tones admirably with the limestone hills the sheep frequent, and they are expert at hiding themselves in barren country where concealment would seem impossible. They are usually seen singly or in quite small groups, and show great skill in finding a living in these regions where both vegetation and water are so scarce.

Closely allied to the Barbary sheep is the Bharal, or Blue sheep of Tibet. The winter coat is grey, and is the reason that the animal is called "blue"; but in summer the colour is brown, with black markings on the face, chest and legs, and a black line along the sides.

Tur of the Caucasus

Very similar in appearance to the bharal is the Wild Goat or Tur of the Caucasus, which is, indeed, sometimes called the Caucasian Bharal. It has, however, sufficient goat-like characters to be regarded as a goat, and placed by zoologists in the genus *Capra*. There are three closely related varieties of tur inhabiting the Caucasus, those of the eastern and western areas being the most distinct. The Spanish wild goat is allied to the turs, and frequents the Pyrenees and other mountainous and rocky tracts of Spain and Portugal.

The Ibexes are rather large goats, one of whose peculiarities is that the hind legs are longer than the front legs, so that the back tends to have an upward slope from front to rear. The term ibex is often applied by sportsmen to the Spanish wild goat and others that are not entitled to it. The large erect horns with numerous corrugations or bosses are a notable feature of these animals.

The Large-Horned Ibex

The Alpine ibex no longer exists in a wild state, though it has been preserved in some of the Swiss valleys and in Northern Italy. The Himalayan ibex is a larger animal with longer horns, a thick beard and a dark ridge of hair along the back. It has a very extensive range, being found on all the mountain ranges of Central Asia. The Arabian ibex is a similar animal found in parts of Arabia, Egypt and Palestine, and another species occurs in Abyssinia.

The Persian Wild Goat, or Pasang, is found in Crete, Turkey, Persia and Afghanistan as far as India. It haunts rocky country up to about 12,000 feet. The Markhor is notable for its upstanding, spirally twisted horns and the thick black beard, which is extended to form a ruff on the throat, chest and shoulders. It is a native of the Himalayas.

The last few animals to be considered seem to be intermediate between the goats and the antelopes. Three of these borderline creatures are called Tahrs; they have no beards, and no hair on the end of the muzzle, which is moist, this latter being a character of the antelopes as distinct from the sheep and goats; also there are no glands on the feet. The horns are very short, broad and almost meeting at the base, and curved sharply backwards to a point. The Arabian tahr is the smallest of the goats, being only 2 feet high, but the Himalayan tahr is a large animal of over 3 feet.

Chamois

The Chamois is better known by name than most of the other animals mentioned in this chapter. It is, indeed, the most graceful of all the wild goats, and its great agility on the rocks and the terrific leaps it takes are wonderful to see. Though once abundant in the Swiss Alps, it is now rare in that country. The chamois is more numerous in the Apennines, the Pyrenees and the Carpathians, though each of these ranges has a race peculiar to the locality and differing somewhat from the Alpine chamois. The short, upright horns with strongly hooked tips are a prominent feature. The idea that the chamois is solely an alpine animal is mistaken, for its chief haunt is the wooded country on the lower slopes, and it is only the more adventurous males that venture on to the snowfields and glaciers above the timber line

The Rocky Mountain goat is another of these intermediate creatures, and, in spite of its name, is probably more antelope than goat. It is about the size of a domestic sheep, and notable for its thick white coat and shining black horns. Apart from the Bighorn sheep, the Rocky Mountain goat is the only animal of its tribe found in America. It is a somewhat stolid and dull-witted beast and easily stalked once the hunter has climbed to the high regions it frequents. It is most abundant in British Columbia.

The Serow and the Goral are Asiatic "goat-antelopes" possessing some characteristics similar to the last species, though quite different in appearance.

Finally there are two curious anomalous creatures to be mentioned: the Takin and the Musk Ox.

The Takin is quite unlike any other members of this family, being a clumsy, heavily built animal with a rather bovine appearance. Its body is yellowish fawn in colour, with a black head and a blunt, hairy muzzle. The horns are black and thick at the base; they are curiously shaped, growing at first straight out sideways, and then being turned sharply upwards and slightly backwards. The takin is a native of the Mishmi Hills of Eastern Tibet and Assam; but little is known of its habits in the wild state, and the few individuals that have been captured alive have proved dull and uninteresting in captivity.

Musk Ox

The so-called Musk Ox used to be regarded as intermediate between the sheep and the oxen, as indicated by the generic name *Ovibos*. At the present time, however, it is considered to be nearly related to the goat-antelopes of the takin group. It is an animal of ancient lineage, and its fossilized remains have been found even in the British Isles, which it appears to have inhabited during the glacial epoch. Its present range is from Greenland, across Northern Canada to Alaska, inhabiting the most barren and desolate regions imaginable. The horns are reminiscent of those of the African buffalo, because their expanded bases form a hard cap over the head; the horns then droop downwards behind the eyes, the ends curving up and outwards. The musk ox has a coat of long, shaggy hair and a thick undercoat of fine wool as a protection against the arctic conditions. These animals go about in herds.

THE MOUNTAIN WATCHER

The large and heavily corrugated horns are typical of the ibex, a large type of goat, here seen silhouetted against a background of beautiful mountain scenery. The Alpine ibex has declined from a purely wild state, though it has been preserved in some Swiss valleys.

READY FOR ACTION

Prepared to whisk off up the tree like lightning is this grey squirrel. Unlike the red squirrel, it is a destructive animal and efforts have been made to cut down its numbers.

CHAPTER FOURTEEN

RODENTS AND THEIR ENEMIES

by RAY PALMER, F.R.E.S., F.Z.S.

Numbers, depredations and value to Man. How rodents gnaw. Squirrels and Marmots. Jumping rodents. Rats and Mice. Voles and their relatives. Swarming and migration. Mole-rats and Gophers. The Porcupine. Hares and Rabbits. The Weasel Family.

THE rodents, including some of the most familiar of all animals, are the most numerous in both species and individuals of all the orders of mammals. Rats, mice, squirrels, rabbits, guinea-pigs, porcupines and beaver are the best-known forms. Some of the most abundant rodents, such as rats, mice and voles, are serious pests, and the destruction they cause costs many millions of pounds annually, while millions more are spent in keeping their numbers in check. Other rodents provide valuable fur, and some are farmed on a large scale for this purpose; others again, such as rabbits and hares, are useful as food, though the wild rabbit can be a serious pest; while guinea-pigs and tame rats are extensively utilized to valuable effect in biological experiments.

The main characteristic of the rodents is the chisel-like teeth in the front of the jaws. In most cases there are only two of these large incisor teeth in each jaw, the exception being the rabbit family, which is unique in having a smaller second pair of teeth placed *behind* the large incisors in the upper jaw. Thus the lower incisor teeth, of which there is only one pair, close into a groove formed by the two pairs in the upper jaw. For this reason the members of the rabbit family are called "double-toothed rodents", and the others "single-toothed rodents". Further, the lower incisors continue growing throughout the life of the animal, and are constantly ground down against the upper pair. Thus, if these teeth should be injured so that they do not meet properly, they may continue growing unchecked and form great curved tusks projecting over the top of the animal's head. In most cases, however, rodents with deformed teeth do not live long enough for this to happen, but come to an early end through starvation.

Rodents also have a peculiar form of mouth, by means of which the upper incisor teeth are enclosed in a pocket formed by the hairy skin of the face, which folds inwards and joins up behind them, opening externally by a vertical slit extending downwards from the nose. This can easily be seen by examining the

237

ANYTHING FOR ME?

A red squirrel looks in at the window where it has become a regular visitor in search of food. Intelligence and friendliness are suggested by its appearance, though it remains a creature of the wild. It is now comparatively rare in populous districts of Britain.

mouth of a rabbit, and no doubt serves to prevent the entry into the mouth of large pieces of undesirable material such as wood splinters, and other inedible substances. Its function can be seen by watching a tame rabbit feeding, sorting the food over with lateral movements of its lips and rejecting undesirable portions.

Rodents have a world-wide distribution, being found everywhere with the exception of the extreme polar regions, though South America seems to be the headquarters of the tribe.

The squirrels and related animals— such as marmots—form a very large group. The Red squirrel has unfortunately become comparatively rare in the more populated parts of Britain, and the bolder and more ubiquitous Grey squirrel has been blamed for this disappearance. The grey squirrel is a most destructive little beast, though its numbers have been considerably reduced by official action. Both kinds of squirrel build large nests of twigs in tall trees, store up caches of nuts for the winter and hibernate, at least partially, during the severe weather.

In North America, Siberia and parts of Eastern Europe are found a number of closely related animals, known as Ground squirrels or Chipmunks. As will be evident from their name, the ground squirrels are mainly terrestrial in habits, though they can ascend trees if they so desire, but have nothing like the agility of the true squirrels. In addition to nuts, they also eat roots of various kinds, corn and insects. Chipmunks are most abundant in North America. They are migratory, and wander about the country in search of food. Where food is found in abundance in the autumn, there the chipmunks establish their winter quarters; they lay up stores of nuts and beech mast and go into hibernation in holes in stumps or in the ground, a number usually sleeping together in the same hole. These animals have large cheek pockets in which they can carry food to their store-places. Another species, the Gophers of

North America and the Susliks of North-east Europe and Northern Asia are closely related to the ground squirrels; they differ, however, in inhabiting open plains and burrowing in the ground in large colonies. They have more carnivorous tendencies, and will kill and eat other small rodents, as well as devouring birds' eggs and young.

The Marmots also belong to the squirrel family, and representatives are found in Europe, Asia and America in open or mountainous country. The

NUTS FROM THE WINTER STORE

Prudently, the red squirrel has collected a supply of nuts in a cache and now that winter has come it draws upon its reserves. If the weather proves severe it usually retires into a partial hibernation.

WINTER COATS

The mountain hare is seen in the white coat to which its summer coat of greyish-brown changes with the coming of winter, thus making it less conspicuous against a snowy background.

Prairie marmot of America is the best known, and is confined to the dry, open prairies. In some places the ground may be riddled with their burrows. Outside each entrance is a heap of earth that has been thrown out in digging, and the animals use these as look-out posts, and constantly sit bolt upright on their mounds staring around them. Each burrow may contain about a dozen individuals. Should danger threaten, the sentry gives the alarm by a shrill chirping whistle and the whole party bolts underground. The little burrowing owl and the rattlesnake are often unwelcome tenants of the marmot's burrows, and feed on the young of their unwilling hosts.

Beaver, which are among the largest rodents, are dealt with in another chapter; so here we will only mention that there are two species—the well-known Canadian beaver, colonies of which are now on the increase due to Government protection, and the lesser-known European beaver, which is now nearly extinct.

That delightful little creature the Dormouse is not really a mouse, but is more like a distant relative of the Squirrels. It is of arboreal habits, and not uncommon in parts of Southern England, being particularly partial to hazel plantations and old high hedges that contain plenty of hazel bushes. It has a comparatively thick and furry tail, large bright eyes, fur of a light reddish-fawn colour, fading to yellowish underneath, and with a white patch on the chest and throat. In the autumn the dormouse builds a globular nest of grass, leaves and moss, usually low down in a dense bush or hedge, though the author has found them 5 or 6 feet from the ground. It gets fat on an abundant food supply in the autumn, and then retires to its nest, where it spends five or six months in the deep sleep of hibernation. Being purely nocturnal in habits, even in the summer the dormouse spends the day in sleep, and it is sometimes possible to hear a sleeping dormouse snoring in its nest, and so detect its presence.

The best known of the jumping rodents are the Jerboas, of which there is a number of species. These are characterized by the enormously developed hind legs and tail, and their manner of leaping along kangaroo fashion. The Kirgiz jerboa of Central Asia is one of the largest, being 7 inches long without the tail, which is nearly twice the length of the body. Nocturnal in habits, jerboas hide by day in holes in the ground. The speed with which these little creatures can travel is said to be faster than that of a galloping horse. One of the smallest species is the Afghan jerboa, which is only $3\frac{1}{2}$ inches long, with a 7-inch tail.

The so-called Jumping Hare of South Africa is a much larger and more thickset animal, being some 48 inches in total length, of which slightly more than half is composed of the thick and bushy tail. The solitary representative of this group in America is the Jumping

BRER RABBIT

There is only one species of wild rabbit, whose main characteristics are perhaps too well known to require much description. A gregarious animal, it is distinguished from the hare by living in burrows, as well as by its shorter legs and ears, and its smaller size.

CHIPMUNK IN QUEST OF FOOD

Caught by the camera among the pine-cones, the chipmunk crouches close to the branch in an effort to hide. Also called ground squirrels, chipmunks are mainly terrestrial in habits and do not climb trees with the agility of the tree squirrel. They abound in America.

SLEEPY MARMOT

This rotund creature has been disturbed during the period of hibernation and looks a little cross about it. Marmots are members of the squirrel family, living in burrows which often contain a dozen inhabitants. They are found in Europe, Asia and America.

Mouse, a little creature of 3 inches with a 5-inch tail.

The Gerbils, although resembling jerboas very much in their habits and manner of leaping, really belong to the mouse tribe, and differ—particularly in their feet and teeth—from the other jumping rodents. They are elegant little animals, about the size of a rat, and with long hind legs.

The common members of the Rat family are too well known to need much description. Farmers, householders, store-keepers and shipowners all over the world are only too familiar with the depredations of these destructive and prolific rodents.

The most injurious of the lot is undoubtedly the Brown rat, which seems continually to increase despite the constant warfare waged upon it by traps, poison, gas and various other means. It has been estimated that the rat population of Britain is nearly double the number of the human inhabitants.

During the seventeenth century and earlier the great pest was the Black rat, itself an earlier immigrant from the East. This species was prevalent in Europe generally, and, in addition to the destruction it caused, was a serious menace on account of its carrying the germs of the plague or "Black Death".

Fierce Invader from the East

Meanwhile the brown rat, which flourished in temperate Asia, began to invade Europe from the east. In Western Europe it first appeared about 1716, and was found in England by 1728. This newcomer was a larger and fiercer animal, hardier and more adaptable; also more at home out-of-doors, fonder of burrowing and a more omnivorous feeder. Within fifty years it had become the predominant species, and by 1850 the black rat was on the verge of extinction. This species has one advantage over its brown relative, however; it is a better climber, more agile, and therefore better adapted to life on a ship. Owing to this numbers survived in various ports.

Rats begin to breed at the age of four months and at all seasons of the year. There may be five or six litters a year, each containing from eight to a dozen young, but there is great mortality at every stage, particularly in the young.

The House mouse is very like a rat in miniature, and, like the rat, has followed man all over the world, and, notwithstanding continual persecution, contrives to exist in undiminished numbers.

ROCK-RABBIT FAMILY

The hyrax or rock-rabbit has been identified with the "cony" mentioned in the Bible. This domestic group, which seems to have obligingly posed for the photographer, lives in holes among rocks in Africa. The hyrax, not a true rabbit, is related to hoofed mammals.

Although called "house mouse", this little rodent is even more abundant in outbuildings and farmsteads, and finds a cornstack an ideal home—until threshing time! Rats and mice do not get on well together, and where numbers of rats are present there are usually few mice.

In fields and gardens the place of the house mouse is taken by a much prettier but equally destructive little creature— the Long-tailed Field-mouse, or Wood-mouse. It is easily distinguished from its grey domestic relative by its light brown fur, white underparts and feet, large prominent eyes and long tail. This mouse is particularly troublesome in a garden, eating seeds and bulbs of all kinds, being specially fond of peas. In the autumn it gathers a supply of seeds, nuts, haws, etc., into some snug retreat, and these provide food for its periods of activity during mild spells in the winter, as it only hibernates fully in severe weather.

Light-Weight of the Wheat-fields

Our third British mouse is comparatively scarce and little known, and found chiefly in the southern countries. This is the Harvest mouse, the smallest of British mammals with the exception of the Pigmy Shrew. So light is its weight that it can climb up a wheat stem without bending it. It differs from other mice in feeding during the daytime. In the early part of the year the food is very varied, including all kinds of vegetable matter and a large proportion of insects; but in late summer and autumn corn of all kinds and various seeds are devoured.

The nest is a closely woven, globular structure without any definite entrance, the mice merely pushing aside the fibres to leave or enter from any part of the nest.

The Voles differ from mice in their short tails, rounded heads with blunt muzzles, and small ears largely hidden by fur. Field voles cause much damage to crops in some districts, and now and then great plagues of voles occur, causing immense destruction. Such plagues are no doubt due to the destruction by game-keepers and others of the voles' natural enemies, such as the owl, kestrel, stoat and weasel. After a period of such abnormal increase, the voles die off quickly through famine or disease, assisted by birds and beasts of prey, and are thus reduced again to their normal numbers.

The Bank vole is slightly smaller than the field vole and brighter in colour, being bright chestnut above and white beneath. It frequents woods and hedge-banks rather than fields, but otherwise its habits are similar. In captivity the bank vole will soon become tame and makes an interesting pet.

A much larger creature is the Water vole. It is often mistaken for a rat and, in fact, most country people still call it the "water rat". The water vole is really an animal of most inoffensive habits, and its food consists mainly of the succulent stems and leaves of various plants that grow in and near the water. The holes made by this animal in river banks must be familiar to everyone, also the "plop" with which it dives when alarmed.

The Prolific Lemming

The Lemmings are closely related to the voles, but are larger animals of heavier build and with very short tails. They are found in Northern Europe, particularly Scandinavia. Normally dwelling in high mountains, the lemmings breed to such an extent that every few years their territory becomes over-populated and a famine results. Then a great migration starts and they begin to move down to lower levels. It may be one or two years before this vast horde reaches the cultivated districts, and during this time birds and beasts of prey congregate on the outskirts of the migrating host and thrive on such easily obtained prey.

Hamsters are animals of very similar type, but larger, being over a foot in length, while a lemming is about 5 inches. The hamster is abundant in parts of Europe and Northern Asia.

The Musk rat, or Musquash, is a North American member of the vole family, though larger than any other. The valuable fur is dark brown and thick, very similar to that of the beaver. The total length of the animal is about 22 inches, of which some 10 inches is tail. The tail is remarkable for being flattened sideways, almost hairless and covered with scales. Being thoroughly adapted for an aquatic life, its food consists of the stems and roots of water plants and grasses, mussels and fish. Musk rats make extensive and elaborate tunnels in the banks of lakes and rivers. They have been bred for their fur in England, and some have escaped and established themselves in the banks of certain rivers, where they have done much damage by their burrowing, and to adjacent crops.

The Toothy Mole-Rat

The strange-looking Mole-rats of Africa and Asia are characterized by the enormous development of the lower incisor teeth, which project from the bottom jaw to meet the upper teeth in such a way that they are always visible. The mole-rats are of subterranean habits and have only rudimentary eyes and ears, but, unlike the true moles, are vegetable feeders. The most curious members of

this group are the little Sand rats of Somaliland. They are only about the size of mice, but practically naked, with no visible ears and tiny eyes that hardly function. They make extensive burrows in the sand, and never come to the surface.

The Pocket gophers of America also belong to this family. They are rat-like animals with powerful claws for digging and the usual great teeth. The Kangaroo rats and Pocket mice are allied to this same group in having external cheek pouches, but in other respects appear very different. The kangaroo rats resemble the jerboas in general form and habits, and are mainly found in arid desert regions of America to the east of the Rocky Mountains. The pocket mice are similar in form and habits, but are tiny creatures not more than 2 inches long.

Armour of Quills

The Porcupine is a large animal of somewhat pig-like form, and characterized by its remarkable defensive armour of quills. There are two distinct types, one being confined to the western hemisphere, and the other to the Old World. The American porcupines usually have prehensile tails and are arboreal in habits. In the Brazilian porcupine the tail is particularly long and tapering, and the animal spends all its time in trees, sleeping during the day and waking up at sunset to feed on the foliage and bark of the trees in which it lives. The Mexican tree porcupine has so much black hair that the short, stiff spines are hidden.

The much better known Canadian porcupine is a larger and altogether different animal. It has a short, broad tail, which is not prehensile, but used as a weapon, the porcupine when annoyed striking sideways and inflicting severe

LONG-TAILED FIELD-MOUSE

This flashlight photograph was taken at midnight in November, in a Hertfordshire wood, the wood-mouse, as it is also called, having come to feed on bait. A pretty but destructive little animal, its depredations are troublesome in the garden in summer.

"AN APPLE A DAY . . ."

A bank vole, three months old, nibbles an apple as large as itself. This frequenter of woods and hedge banks quickly becomes tame and makes an interesting pet. It resembles the field vole but is brighter in colour, chestnut above and white below.

wounds by means of the short, strong quills, which are left in the flesh of its enemy and gradually work their way inwards. The body quills are much longer than in the tree porcupines, and are white with dark tips. Normally the quills lie flat, directed backwards, but when the animal is alarmed or annoyed it can erect its quills, hedgehog fashion, and partially roll up, so that few animals ever venture to attack it. Though not completely arboreal, the Canadian porcu-

pine is an excellent climber, and spends much of its time in trees. It is largely nocturnal, but not completely so.

The porcupines which inhabit the Old World never have prehensile tails, are terrestrial, never ascending trees, and are purely nocturnal in habits. One of the most familiar is the Crested porcupine, found in North and West Africa and parts of Southern Europe.

Of the spineless rodents which are considered to be distant relatives of the porcupines, the only one we need mention is the Coypu, or Nutria. These are something like enormous rats in general form, except for their blunt muzzles, and are about 2 feet in length, without the tail, which is about half the length of the body. The long brownish fur has a dense undercoat of great softness, which makes the skin valuable. In habits the coypu somewhat resembles the beaver, and is found in lakes and rivers over the greater part of South America.

The Common Chinchilla is a pretty little creature about 10 inches long, with pearly-grey fur of remarkable softness, and a long, bushy tail. It lives at high altitudes in the Andes in Chile and Bolivia, in barren and desolate regions where vegetation is scarce. Its home is a burrow in the soil or a crevice in the rock, and it darts about with lightning rapidity up and down the rock faces and in and out of crevices. Its food consists of moss, roots and grass, the quest of which, in such barren country, often means travelling long distances. There are several other species of similar habits, of which the Viscacha may be mentioned, this being an inhabitant of the open pampas of the Argentine. It is strikingly marked

DORMOUSE SLEEPING

The dormouse sleeps for half the year and spends most of the day curled up in its nest. At dusk it hunts for nuts and berries which it stores up in its resting-place. The photograph shows one which has evidently, by its comfortable proportions, had a successful autumn's forage.

by a white stripe over the top of the nose and along the sides of the face, and lives in colonies in burrows in the ground.

The best known of the Cavies is the familiar Guinea-pig, which has been so long domesticated that its exact origin is doubtful. It is thought, however, to have been derived from a wild species found in Peru, which was domesticated by the Incas before the Spanish conquest. The true cavies are without tails, are mostly small animals of uniform colour and are found only in South America. The Dutch introduced the guinea-pig to Europe in the sixteenth century, and it became known in England about 1750.

The Patagonian cavy has long legs, which give it a somewhat hare-like appearance. It reaches a length of about 30 inches, and stands over a foot in height. It also has large upstanding ears and a short tail.

The largest of all living rodents belongs to this group. It is the Capybara, or

ENEMY RODENT

Constant warfare is waged by gas, poison and traps on the brown rat, here seen, though its numbers show no signs of diminution. It has supplanted the black rat, the scourge of Europe in the Middle Ages, and outnumbers the human population of Britain by two to one.

NATURE'S DEFENSIVE ARMAMENT

The porcupine is provided with quills which come into an upright position when attack is threatened. There are two distinct types—the common or crested porcupine being shown above. This animal is nocturnal in its habits. The photograph was taken in Kenya.

Carpincho, 4 feet long and weighing nearly 100 lbs. In size, habits and voice these animals bear a great resemblance to pigs, and are thus often spoken of as "water-hogs" by the inhabitants of Argentina. They are never found far from the river banks, and are more at home in the water than on land.

The Agoutis are rather elegant, long-legged rodents, very abundant in Brazil and other parts of South America, and have very much the appearance of a Mouse Deer. The common species is about 20 inches long, and brown, with a pale line along the back and bright orange hair on the hind quarters. They are chiefly forest dwellers of nocturnal habits, and, like other rodents, are vegetarians, sometimes doing much damage to sugar plantations.

The Paca is a similar type of animal, but with shorter legs and characterized by having rows of light-coloured spots along its body. It is found in the northern part of South America as far as Paraguay.

Hares and rabbits are too familiar to

SKUNK

A relation of the weasels and badgers, the skunk of North America is easily recognized by the strongly marked stripes of white in its black fur and the bushy black-and-white tail. It is, of course, noted for the unpleasant odour by which it keeps enemies at bay.

GAMEKEEPER'S PROBLEM

The stoat is one of the gamekeeper's problems for it wreaks havoc in his preserves. It makes off with and stores up pheasants' eggs, and keeps hares and rabbits in its larder.

need any detailed description of their general form. There are some thirty species known, and they are almost all found in the northern hemisphere.

The hares, of which the common Brown hare is typical, are solitary animals, mainly of nocturnal habits. They do not burrow in the earth, and their only home is a resting-place known as a form. This is usually a concealed spot flattened out in grass or thick herbage, or a sheltered place among rocks. To such a form the hare returns to rest during the day after its nightly wanderings; but it is essentially a nomadic animal—a gipsy—and each hare may have a number of such camping places and move from one to the other as the fit takes it. The nest made by the female

for her litter is merely a form more carefully hidden than usual, and the young, which are born covered with fur, with open eyes and able to run almost at once, lie in the open forms for about a month. At first the young leverets are all together, but after a few days the doe finds a separate form for each one and visits them for suckling at night. There are two broods in a year. March is the great month for the courtship of hares, and on moonlight nights great fights take place between rival bucks, which stand erect on their hind legs and box each other with their front paws. The great speed of the hare when running is well known, and the gait is always a series of leaps. Hares and rabbits cannot walk, and even the slowest movements of these

WEASEL PEERS FROM ITS LAIR

For its size there is no more savage animal in the world than this snaky little creature, which measures only about ten inches in length. It can worm its way into the runs of rats and mice, hunts its prey by scent and will even fly at the throat of man.

animals are in the form of leaps, or hops.

The Mountain hare, also known as the Blue hare or Varying hare, is found in upland and mountainous country over a large part of Europe and Asia. Its summer coat of greyish-brown changes in the autumn, through varying shades of mottled grey, to pure white in winter to match the snow-covered country it frequents. It is common in the Highlands of Scotland, the Hebrides, Scandinavia, the Alps, the Pyrenees and the Caucasus. A distinct variety, known as the Irish hare, is found in the mountains of Ireland.

A number of American species exists, and the "Jack Rabbit" of America is really a hare. This animal—more correctly called the Prairie hare—is famed for its "spy-hops", when it leaps several feet into the air to get a view of the surrounding landscape.

There is only one species of rabbit; whose original home was along both the

European and African shores of the Mediterranean. It was introduced to the British Isles, probably in prehistoric times, though the Romans are often credited with its introduction. The rabbit differs from the hare sufficiently to cause modern zoologists to place it in a separate genus. It has shorter legs and ears, is smaller, slower and less powerful in every way. It is gregarious, living in burrows excavated in the earth, and the young are born blind and helpless, and almost naked. Rabbits have been introduced by man into various other countries, but nowhere with such disastrous consequences as in Australia and New Zealand, where great efforts have been and are still being made to keep the pest in check. All the numerous varieties of tame rabbits are descended from the original brown wild rabbit.

Many of the smaller carnivores are included in the Weasel family, which are animals with elongated bodies and

STOAT IN WINTER GARB

The stoat, or ermine, shown above, is a fierce member of the weasel family, preying on rabbits, hares, birds and smaller creatures. Its white winter coat, in which it is called ermine, is due to climatic conditions, pure white fur coming from Northern Europe.

comparatively short legs. The Weasel is the smallest and commonest British species: a snaky little chestnut-brown creature, some 7 or 8 inches long, with a short tail. The Stoat is a much larger animal somewhat darker in colour, with a longer and more bushy tail with a black tip. The stoat in its winter coat is also called the Ermine, this change being influenced by climatic conditions. Except in Scotland and the north of England completely white stoats are rare in Britain, some brown patches usually being left. Thus pure white ermine furs are obtained from Northern Europe.

Both stoat and weasel are extremely ferocious and formidable beasts for their size. Their food consists of rats, mice, voles, rabbits, hares, birds and eggs. In the case of the larger prey, such as rabbits, only the blood is sucked. Rabbits when chased by a stoat soon become terrified and paralysed, apparently by the scent given off by the pursuer, and sit still and scream until bitten and killed.

A much larger animal is the Polecat, which is now rare in most parts of England, though still found in small numbers in Scotland, Wales and the Lake District. It is about twice the size of a

SMALL BEASTS OF PREY

A marten (top left) was photographed in the north of Britain, where, however, it is extremely rare. Lower left is the polecat, also a rare specimen, photographed in Wales. Larger than the weasel and somewhat darker in colour is the stoat (above) seen weaving its way across a field. Its summer coat is reddish-brown above and yellowish-white below.

I

(W.L.)

BADGER LOOKING OUT OF ITS EARTH

Largest of the weasel tribe is the badger, a shy animal, nocturnal in habits. In spite of its retiring disposition, it can bite savagely when provoked, and although it subsists on a mainly vegetarian diet, it will supplement this at need by preying on small animals.

stoat, and more formidable. The ferret is a domesticated race of polecat.

A still rarer animal, so far as Britain is concerned, is the Pine Marten. In body size it is scarcely larger than the stoat, but has a bushy tail 12 inches long, which makes it look bigger. A few martens still exist in the wild mountain regions of the British Isles, but they get fewer every year, and the species is on the verge of extinction. There are various other kinds of martens in Europe and America, of which the Sable is well known for its valuable fur. The Mink is another related animal found both in Canada and Northern Europe.

A more distant relative of the weasels which has taken to an aquatic life is the Otter. This is a much larger animal than any of the foregoing, having a total length of about 45 inches and a weight of some 20 lb. It has the long body and short limbs of the weasel tribe, but the toes are webbed and the tail enlarged into a long and powerful "rudder". The head is also much more rounded and the eyes placed higher up. Otters are quite abundant on most of the larger rivers, fish being their staple food, which they pursue and catch with wonderful dexterity. If unable to get fish, otters will kill rabbits, water birds and poultry.

The Common otter occurs throughout Europe, parts of Asia and North Africa. The American Sea Otter and Canadian Fisher are related animals.

OTTER—RAPACIOUS BY LAND AND WATER.

The otter is as rapacious in the water as its relative the weasel is on land. Though its staple diet is fish, which it catches in expert fashion, it finds rabbits, water birds and poultry equally acceptable, and it often makes marauding expeditions on solid ground.

BEAVER AT WORK

The beaver cuts down trees for food, eating the bark. It favours certain of the deciduous varieties and is ready to tackle anything, from small saplings to the most mighty trees.

CHAPTER FIFTEEN

THE INDUSTRIOUS BEAVER

by A. RADCLYFFE DUGMORE.

Beaver as tree-feller. How the Beaver's "lodge" is made. Why it builds dams. Its engineering skill. How its labours benefit man.

"WORKING like a beaver." How often do we hear that remark, and how few realize how apt it is, for no wild animal works harder, or with so much intelligence and effect.

First, Beaver cut down trees for food. They are vegetarians, and eat tree bark, berries and various roots, such as those of the water lily and yellow spatterdock. The trees most sought after, and in order of preference are the deciduous varieties: birch, poplar, maple, alder, ash and various others. Those felled vary in size from mere saplings to mighty trees over 9 feet in circumference. The length of time taken in cutting down a tree varies greatly, and, as a sample, we may say that a 7-inch birch would take about one night. Some people consider tree-cutting as the greatest work performed by these small animals, but in fact it requires less intelligence than most of their other tasks.

The story goes that the beaver controls the direction in which a tree will fall and invariably drops it towards the water, whether lake or stream, whereas, as a matter of fact, it has no such control. There is a very simple explanation for

this seemingly wonderful feat: a tree growing on the bank of a river or lake has its greatest development of branches towards the light—that is, the open space of the water—and, when cut, naturally falls in that direction. Once a tree is felled, the next task is to cut off the branches and divide these into suitable lengths for carrying or rolling. Beaver never try to carry anything that is too large. They judge exactly what is a convenient size.

Next to food comes the question of housing or shelter for the long, bitterly cold winter months of the North. In an emergency the beaver's lodge or house may be made on a river bank, or he may make use of a burrow excavated in a suitable place, but the properly constructed lodge is the final aim when a colony is started. This may be on an island, either natural or made by the beaver, or occasionally on a bank. In appearance it is a rough-looking pile of sticks, logs and sod, the size varying from 8 to 10 feet to nearly 40 feet in outside diameter. These larger lodges usually house more than one family. Inside there is a cavity or chamber with a fairly

261

smooth, vaulted surface. There are two levels or floors. One is only a couple of inches above water-level. This is the dining-room, and contains one, two or three entrances to the tunnels leading under water. The second level is several inches higher, and is floored with peeled sticks or shredded wood, if possible cedar (this being unlikely to harbour insect pests). There are no windows such as are shown in some old drawings, and no outlets except the under-water tunnels. In the centre of the roof there is a flue or chimney of interlaced sticks free from sod or earth; this is for ventilation, and allows the vitiated air to escape. The method of building is probably as follows.

First the site is selected, then a burrow is made, more or less in the centre, leading out to a point at least 4 feet under normal water-level. A mass of sticks and sod is piled on this site, after which the beaver goes up one of the tunnels and with his teeth cuts away the necessary cavity or room. After that more and more material is added to the outside, sticks, logs and even stones and sod being used, but care is taken not to obstruct the chimney. When winter is due, after the first hard frost, the whole edifice except the outlet or chimney is coated with mud, which freezes hard and forms a perfect protection against attacks by any enemies except man. If the plastering is done

ENGINEERING FEAT OF THE BEAVER

From these forest-clad slopes on the Rio Grande, Colorado, beavers have gnawed the barrage of logs which now dams the river. The beaver's house or lodge is seen on the right in the background.

feet long, the height varying from 2 feet to as much as 12 or 15, or even more, and such structures contain thousands of tons of material. The dam may be in a straight line or curved up or down stream, or even in the form of an **S**. There is no rule governing its shape, and the material differs according to the conditions; but it usually consists of sticks and logs, up to 8 or 10 feet in length, on the lower side, and sod or earth on the upper or steeper side. Stones are also used, sometimes quite large ones. The result is a strong, water-tight dam. A spillway usually occurs near the course of the stream.

The size of the resulting pond may be only an acre or so in extent, or several hundreds, or even thousands of acres. During the winter, when the pond is frozen to a depth of 2 feet or more the beaver are imprisoned, or rather confined to the lodge and to the under-water area, which is covered over by a barrier of ice. When the beaver feel the need for exercise, they simply go for a swim, and when they are hungry they come out to the wood supply which is piled up in the water near the lodge (and fastened to the bottom by some method not yet understood by us). Then they cut off a branch or twig and take it through the tunnel into the lodge, where they can eat the bark in comfort, after which the peeled stick is pushed out into the pond to be used next season for building material. Before the beaver begins his tree-cutting operations, he clears a pathway to the

before the frost, there is risk of its being washed away by rain, but the beaver avoids making this mistake.

Now comes the question of maintaining a constant level of water, and this is of paramount importance, because only by this means can the mouths of the tunnels be kept concealed and unwelcome visitors such as foxes, lynx or other of the beavers' natural enemies be kept at bay.

In order to accomplish this there is only one satisfactory method. A pond must be made. Hence the building of the famous dams. These dams are not small, trivial affairs, as some people imagine, but serious engineering feats on a very large scale. Some of the dams are over 1000

TIME FOR RETIREMENT

This beaver seems to be casting a last look round before taking to its winter quarters. When the pond is frozen over it will be confined to the snug lodge and underwater area.

water, dragging or carrying the logs or sticks to the water and swimming with them to the lodge, when he adds his load to the wood pile. Besides the main dam, it is a common custom to build one or more secondary or subsidiary dams, so that the water in these smaller ponds shall protect the base of the main structure against freezing.

Formerly beaver were found all over Europe (except Ireland), in Asia as far as the Euphrates, and in America northwards from Mexico. To-day they are found chiefly in the Northern United States and Canada, and there is one colony near Arendal in Norway. The European beaver is so like his American

cousin that it is difficult to tell them apart. The weight of a full-grown beaver varies from 40 to 60 lb., and its most notable features are: sharp teeth, faced with hard enamel and backed with soft dentine, so that they automatically sharpen themselves with wear; large webbed hind feet, which are used for swimming (the animals being largely aquatic); and a large, flat, scaly tail, used for balancing when standing erect and for slapping the surface of the water as a danger signal. It is *not* used as a trowel.

A strange feature of the beaver is the castoreum, a substance found in the glands below the pubis. This was used by the ancients for medicinal purposes, and is still so used in Canada. This substance was supposed to cure every known ill, including headaches, deafness, abscesses, epilepsy, colic, toothache, sciatica, pleurisy, tuberculosis and even madness.

The beaver is perhaps the only wild animal which has done work of direct benefit to man. This may seem to be a surprising statement until we look at the country which has been inhabited by these animals for countless ages. Large tracts of fine land, level and rich, farmed or wild, can be found in the Northern United States and Canada, whose fertility is due to the work done by the little engineers long ago. Let us imagine a valley clothed with forest composed largely of deciduous trees, a peaceful spot in the wilds. Through this valley a stream runs, small or large, according to the season. A pair of beaver, in search of a place to found a new colony, come to this valley and build a dam on the stream. Before long the autumnal colours of the trees are reflected in the quiet waters of a beaver-made pond. At first the dam is small, but as the colony increases in size and more lodges are built, the dam is extended and the pond becomes larger. As years go by the supply of trees close to the water becomes depleted, so again the pond is enlarged to bring the water nearer to the desired food supply. Sometimes it may be necessary even to dig canals in order to reach the trees, and these canals or ditches may be anything

ADDITION TO THE WINTER STORE CUPBOARD

This remarkable close-up shows a beaver cutting off an aspen limb to add to its storage pile of winter food which is piled up in the water near its lodge. The coarse outer hair, well shown in this photograph, keeps the water from an inner coat of soft fur.

ADDING TO THE DAM

The materials of which the beaver builds its dam may often contain thousands of tons of material, consisting of sticks and logs on the lower side and a sod of earth on the upper side, though stones also are sometimes used. The length of the dam may be as much as a thousand feet.

up to 1000 feet in length, for the beaver requires their protection against many enemies. Perhaps the pond will be occupied for many years, and during all that time the decaying vegetable matter from the surrounding hills is washed down by rain and melting snow, and so finds its way to the pond. By the levelling action of the water, all this forest loam is spread evenly over the whole bed of the pond. Then comes the time when the supply of food-furnishing trees is exhausted, and the beaver has to seek fresh country and start all over again. The colony divides itself into families, each of which goes to a different place, each lot starting its own village. When this happens, the dam, no longer kept in constant repair, soon disintegrates and allows the water to escape, so the pond, however large it may have been, dwindles in size with the passing of time, till nothing remains of it, and again the stream flows along its original bed. The action of the wind, frost and sun soon dries this expanse of what at first is a swamp, and before long it becomes covered with rich grass, rich because the soil is as fertile as any soil can be. If a prospective settler, roaming the country in quest of a suitable place to start a farm, has the good fortune to find this old beaver meadow, he soon has a flourishing farm. Thousands of acres on the richest farms of North America have owed their existence to the labours of the humble beaver.

ANT-EATER OF TROPICAL AMERICA

This photograph of the ant-eater was obtained in Gatun Lake, Panama. The fore-feet are provided with long claws which enable the ant-eater to dig up ants and termites.

CHAPTER SIXTEEN

SOME OF NATURE'S CURIOSITIES

by RAY PALMER, F.R.E.S., F.Z.S.

Insect-eaters and their ways. A natural parachutist. Dwellers underground. Nature's pincushion. Small beasts in armour-plate.

MANY of the most curious and interesting of the smaller mammals are found in the order *Insectivora*. This includes some apparently very diverse types of animals; the chief common characteristic is indicated in the name of the order—their food consists solely of insects and other small creatures, such as worms and slugs, with a few exceptions where fruit is also eaten. The only other mammals that are purely insect-feeders are the bats, which are distinguished by having wings, though the teeth of the groups are similar.

The insectivores are small mammals, and usually of nocturnal habits. A notable feature is that they do not walk on the toes only, like most familiar animals, but more or less on the whole of the foot. The great majority are further characterized by numerous sharp-pointed teeth and exceptionally long, pointed snouts, the ends of which are flexible and protrude some distance in front of the lower jaw.

A curious creature which seems to occupy an intermediate position between the bats and the insectivores is the Cobego. This vegetarian is found in Malaya,

Java and Sumatra. It has extensive folds of skin along the sides of the body which connect the fore and hind legs and tail. This forms a kind of parachute, by means of which the cobego can make long, flying leaps from tree to tree.

Tree Shrews differ from most of this order in being strictly arboreal in habits and being active by day. Their food consists mainly of insects, but they also eat fruit, their upper molar teeth being specially modified for this purpose. In general appearance tree shrews resemble squirrels, and the Malays use the same word for both animals. They are not related to squirrels, and are easily distinguished by their long, pointed snouts. Tree shrews consist of some twenty species, and are found in parts of India, Malaya, the Dutch East Indies and the Philippines. They are intelligent, and though living mainly in trees, at times they enter houses, where they behave with great familiarity, running about unconcernedly, getting on to tables and stealing food whenever they can.

Jumping shrews, or Elephant shrews as they are called, owing to their exceptionally long snouts, are purely

269

DWELLER UNDERGROUND

The mole usually remains below the earth during hours of daylight, but in times of scarcity may come up in search of food. Water, also, is of vital importance to him.

ground-dwellers. The most distinctive feature is their habit of leaping like jerboas or tiny kangaroos, and they have greatly developed hind legs for this purpose.

Whereas tree shrews are purely oriental, jumping shrews are confined to Africa. There are many species, ranging all over the continent from Algeria in the north right down to South Africa.

Moles and Desmans resemble shrews in their long, flexible snouts, with skulls and teeth of similar form, but they are adapted either for burrowing in the earth or for swimming.

The Common mole is widely distributed over Europe and Asia. The development of the front feet into great shovel-like paws, together with the powerful and sensitive snout are excellent equipment for its life underground. One of the mole's most notable features is the dense black, velvety fur. This is set vertically in the skin, and can be stroked in any direction, like the pile of velvet. Thus earth does not cling to it, and the mole can move backwards when necessary without discomfort.

Moles lead a life of intense activity, feed voraciously, and are very pugnacious. Their food consists mainly of earthworms, but leather-jackets and various other insect larvae and slugs are also eaten. The mole is also carnivorous when it gets the chance, and will eat any kind of raw meat in captivity. It needs quantities of water, and its burrows usually have openings near ponds or ditches, by which it frequently comes above ground at night to seek water and food and fight rivals. On such occasions it frequently falls a prey to owls or foxes.

During very dry weather moles may sometimes be found above ground during the daytime; they have come up to seek water, or to scour the country for food when worms are scarce, and may have found the surface of the ground so hard that they cannot readily dig in again. On one occasion the writer found a mole above ground on a very hot day after a prolonged drought. This was during a field meeting of a county Natural History Society, and the members stood around watching the mole. The writer suggested that it was probably making a desperate search for water, whereupon a lady member of the party said, "I wonder if I could give it a drink". She filled the cup of her vacuum flask with water and poured a little on the ground in front of the mole's nose. This was quickly sucked up, and then the mole rushed around in a perfect frenzy, looking for more. So the cup of water was held in front of it and the mole drank without hesitation, resting its front paws on the edge of the cup and putting its head down inside as the water got low. It continued drinking for several minutes, then, its thirst appeased at last, it turned away and in a more leisurely manner began seeking for a place to dig. It was carried to soft earth beneath some bushes, where in less than half a minute it had disappeared beneath the surface

Moles do not pair, and breeding is promiscuous. Males seek the females in the early spring, at which time they make straight surface runs which throw up the earth in ridges. If two males meet during the breeding season they fight with great ferocity, usually to the death, such combats taking place above ground. Once a mole is injured and starts to bleed, death seems inevitable.

Making a Mole-hill

In making deep tunnels the mole has to get rid of the excavated earth; it therefore makes holes upwards at intervals, pushes the soil along to the hole, and throws it out by means of quick jerks of the head. In this way the familiar mole-hills are formed. In preparation for the young the mother throws up a much larger heap of soil, beneath which she prepares a snug nest of dried grass and leaves. There is only one litter a year, averaging four young.

JUMPING SHREW OF SOUTH AFRICA
The rock elephant shrew is noted both for its long, flexible snout, here seen twitching at a great rate, and its extraordinary agility. Sometimes it curls up and rolls itself along instead of leaping in kangaroo fashion.

HEDGEHOG WITH YOUNG

*The female produces her young in July or August, varying in number from four to eight.
They are born with the rudiments of the armament which characterizes their parents.
The spines both resist attack and enable the hedgehog to fall from a height without harm.*

THE THREE-TOED SLOTH

These arboreal mammals travel along branches by means of their incurved claws, though these, if the animal is forced to the ground, make walking difficult. Another curious feature of the sloth is its ability to turn its head right round without moving the body.

A curious type of mole in North America is the Star-nosed mole, so called from the peculiar ring of appendages surrounding the tip of the snout. The exact function of these appendages is not known, though they would appear to be sensory organs. This mole differs also in having a tail nearly as long as the body. In all moles the eyes are rudimentary, being very minute and buried in thick fur; their powers of sight are no doubt limited to distinguishing light from darkness.

The desmans are clearly allied to the moles, but are aquatic in habits, their feet being adapted for swimming and not for digging. They have long, flexible snouts, very like those of the elephant shrews, and long tails; their reddish fur is dense and thick, like that of an otter. They are much larger than moles, being about 10 inches long in the body and the tail over 6 inches.

True shrews are all small animals of rather mouse-like form, and are frequently mistaken for mice. Closer inspection, however, reveals long, sensitive and flexible snouts, and fine, sharp-pointed teeth, which are totally distinct from the gnawing teeth of a mouse. Another curious feature of these little beasts is that their teeth are stained with a reddish colour, so that this group is sometimes spoken of as Red-toothed shrews. They are further characterized by long tails evenly haired throughout, large ears—though greatly concealed by fur—and small eyes. Their voice is a series of high-pitched squeaks.

When the Shrew starves

Like the mole, shrews live a life of intense activity. They have a voracious appetite, and constantly hunt for food. If food is not obtainable, a shrew starves to death in two or three hours. The common shrew is said to eat twice its own weight of food every day.

GREAT ANT-EATER

Above is seen the South American ant-eater in search of food. Its mouth is small and toothless but a tongue some twelve inches long shoots out and catches its insect meal.

Shrews are more frequently seen dead than alive, being found lying about on paths and open places in late summer and autumn. There is still something of a mystery about this annual mortality, and the probability is that they die at the end of the summer from old age. The average life of these tiny mammals apparently does not exceed 12 or 14 months. On the other hand, it is known that cats, and probably other animals, kill shrews, but they do not eat them.

The Pigmy shrew is much smaller than the common species, and considerably rarer, except in Ireland, where it replaces the common shrew entirely. It has the distinction of being the smallest British mammal, and is probably the smallest in the world; it measures only 2¼ inches, including the tail.

Our third species is the Water shrew, quite different in appearance, being much larger, and black above, with white underparts. It haunts the banks of streams and rivers, seldom being found far from water, and feeds on insects and small crustaceans, such as fresh-water shrimps, both on and below the surface. As the water shrew dives, air-bubbles cling to the fur and give it a silvery appearance; with these air-bubbles clinging to it the fur never gets really wet.

Allied to this group are Musk shrews, which are about the size of rats, some being as much as 6 inches long exclusive of the tail. They take their name from the possession of glands which give out a strong, musk-like odour.

Although classed among the insectivores, the Hedgehog is really omnivorous. Little that it finds during its nightly wanderings comes amiss to it; insects, larvae and worms are certainly devoured in large quantities, so are the eggs and young of ground-nesting birds, frogs and toads, and any mice or other small mammals that can be caught; vegetable matter also is eaten occasionally. The hedgehog is known to kill snakes, biting its victim near the tail and then rolling up promptly, while the snake strikes again and again, injuring itself on the spines of its captor. When the snake is exhausted, the hedgehog cautiously unrolls, bites its prey into several pieces and proceeds to devour it greedily. Both grass snakes and adders are dealt with in this way.

The hedgehog has a somewhat piglike face, a sensitive nose and small weak eyes, while its brain is poorly developed. Powerful muscles enable it to roll into a ball, with erected spines, whenever alarmed, and in this position the soft underparts, head and feet are completely protected. It is also a good climber, a somewhat unexpected accomplishment.

In the autumn hedgehogs seek dry beds of leaves, holes in banks and hedge bottoms where there is some protection from the weather; here they roll up and

NATURAL ARMOUR-PLATE

A curious feature of the armadillo is the coat, which is composed of plates of horn joined in flexible bands. The sharp edges of this armour are employed to lacerate the flesh of reptilian enemies. A nocturnal animal, the armadillo lives in a burrow in the daytime.

go to sleep. They become quite cold, and the heart-beats almost cease until warmer conditions in the spring cause them to resume activity. The young are born in late summer, with rudimentary spines that are soft and white, but develop into an efficient protection by the spring.

The only other spine-bearing insectivores are some curious primitive creatures called Tenrecs, which are found in Madagascar. Some greatly resemble hedgehogs in appearance, being covered with stiff bristles or weak spines, and have the power of rolling up.

The Common tenrec, which belongs to a distinct family, is the largest of the insectivores, being 16 inches long.

The nearest living relations to these queer animals are the Solenodons, found in the West Indies. They do not possess spines, but resemble tenrecs in the formation of the teeth, which show them to be of very primitive origin.

The last family of insectivores consists of the South African animals commonly called Golden moles, though they are not at all closely related to the true moles. They are termed "golden" because of the metallic lustre of their dark fur. In form they are somewhat similar to moles, and spend their lives below ground. The front feet are specially adapted for digging, but quite differently from the true moles, as the digging power depends on the enormously developed two middle claws.

Toothless Species

Some curious animals belong to a group scientifically called *Edentata*, which signifies "without teeth". This designation is not strictly accurate, as only a few species are entirely toothless; but none of them has any front teeth or incisors, so the name must be interpreted in this restricted sense. The cheek teeth, where present, are of primitive form.

The Sloths are confined to the primeval forests of South America, and are entirely arboreal, rarely if ever descending to the ground. Their feet are armed with enormous powerful curved claws, with which they cling upside down to the great trees which form their home. These animals are vegetarians, and mainly nocturnal in habits, spending the day asleep, rolled in a compact ball suspended from a branch by all four feet. Their fur often has a greenish tinge, which is caused by green algae which grow on the hair in the warm, damp atmosphere.

Terrestrial Animals

The Ant-eaters are terrestrial animals, and most resemble the sloths in the strong curved claws of the front feet, but are otherwise very different in form. The Great ant-eater is a strange-looking beast about 4 feet long, excluding the tail, which is very large and bushy. The hind feet are of normal form, and lie flat on the ground like those of a bear; but the sloth-like front feet are deformed by the great claws, so that the ant-eater has to walk on its knuckles with the toes turned under. The most remarkable feature of this animal is the head, which is very small and greatly prolonged into a tapering snout, with nostrils at the tip and only a very small mouth-opening through which the long tongue can be protruded. The food consists of both ants and termites, and the purpose of the large claws is to dig into the nests of these insects, which are then licked up with the long tongue coated with viscid saliva. The great ant-eater ranges all over the swampy forest regions of tropical America.

PANGOLIN OF SUMATRA

This ant-eater resembles the armadillo in having a coat of armour, but in the pangolin it overlaps in a series of scales. These are strong enough to resist even a revolver bullet.

Of very similar habits is the Aardvark, or Ant Bear, of Africa. This is a particularly ugly, almost hairless creature, with a long tongue and elongated snout rather like those of the true ant-eaters, and also powerful claws for digging out termites. Aardvark is a Dutch name applied to this creature by the Boers, and means "earth pig".

The Armadillos are distinguished from all other mammals by having an armour of bony plates covering their bodies. These plates are joined by flexible skin, so that some kinds can roll up into a ball with the head and legs drawn in. There are a number of species, which vary greatly in habits. Some feed entirely on insects, while others are omnivorous and include both vegetable matter and carrion

in their diet. The true armadillos are confined to South America and the name, of Spanish origin, suggests armour.

The Scaly ant-eaters, or Pangolins, resemble the armadillos in having a complete coat of mail, but this is composed of overlapping scales in the reptilian fashion, and these animals are distinguished from the armadillos also by their long, thick tails. There are several species, found in Africa and parts of Asia. They live in burrows in the ground and feed on termites. The African species are partly arboreal, and will often rest with their long tail and body wrapped completely around a branch. Little is really known about the habits of these strange creatures, and they are probably not at all closely related to armadillos or ant-eaters.

BLACK TERN FEEDS ITS YOUNG

This amazing photograph shows the little black tern, hovering above the young bird. The black tern is migratory and passes in spring and late summer over south-eastern England.

CHAPTER SEVENTEEN

A WORLD SURVEY OF BIRD LIFE

by OLIVER G. PIKE, F.Z.S., F.R.P.S., M.B.O.U.

Grouping of bird families. Perching birds. Brilliantly coloured birds of the Tropics. Birds of prey. Parrots. Pigeons and Doves. Sea birds. Game birds. Ducks and Geese. Long-legged birds. Water birds. Ocean birds. Penguins. Flightless birds. Migration.

BIRDS are to be found in every part of the world. They are vertebrates with a blood temperature of 103° F., while that of mammals is 98° F. They may be distinguished from all other animals by their clothing of feathers. There are in the world, roughly, 25,000 different vertebrates or backboned animals, and about 10,000 of these are birds which are placed in the class *Aves*. This is divided into *Orders*, the orders into *Families*, the families into *Genera*, and the genera into *Species.*

About half the known species of birds are grouped into the largest order, *Passeres* or perching birds, and included in this are crows, birds of paradise, finches, larks, tits, warblers, the beautiful little sun birds, the African weaver birds and swallows.

The Crow family is large and diverse, containing many species which are a contrast—owing to their brilliant plumage—to the sombre raven, crow and rook. They are found all over the temperate zone, with allied species in Australia. The Raven, the largest of the family, has from time immemorial been a bird of ill omen, for it has all the characteristics around which superstition might gather. It is sombre in plumage, dismal in voice, solitary and wild of habit. It is essentially a carrion feeder, although hardly any food comes amiss to it.

This large bird has been accused of many bad deeds, such as killing lambs, but it is not nearly such a marauder as the carrion and hooded crow. The true raven is distributed all over Europe, in West Siberia, Armenia and east as far as Afghanistan, while there are allied forms in Iceland, Greenland and North America, India, Tibet and Australia.

The carrion and hooded crows often inter-breed, and some ornithologists regard them as races of one species.

Jackdaws, magpies and jays are so well known in all parts of the northern hemisphere that no description is needed. All are wonderfully inquisitive—in fact, all members of the crow family in all parts of the world are attracted by bright or unusual objects, and all may easily be tamed. The writer once had a jackdaw that had perfect freedom, living in the

279

garden, but often entering the house. Its great delight was to sit on the carriage of the typewriter, and it would actually try to sleep while typing was in progress!

If we can credit birds with intelligence, the crows appear to be the most advanced. Several of the problems which they have to face seem to have been carefully considered. One example must suffice. Several species of crows in all parts of the world are fond of shell fish, which they pick up on the sea-shore, but the shells of these are hard, and too tightly closed for the bird to get at the contents, so they carry them to a great height, then drop them on to the rocks beneath, so cracking open the shells.

In India and other Eastern countries crows become a nuisance, for they are always on the look-out for an opportunity to steal food, and as they are quite fearless of man, they will enter open windows to snatch food from the tables.

A handsome member of the crow tribe is the Chough; it is about the same size as the jackdaw, but its curved crimson beak distinguishes it. Closely allied forms are found all over Europe in localities suitable for nesting. The Alpine chough is found as far east as the Himalayas. On the dreary sandy wastes which stretch from Bokhara to Eastern Tibet, where one would think food was almost absent, the curious Desert choughs are found.

THE CRY FOR FOOD

A baby blackbird clamours for the dainties which the mother bird is accustomed to bring. Snails, grubs, insects and fruit are among the items of diet. Several hundred garden pests a day are destroyed by each blackbird to satisfy its appetite and that of its young.

CLIFF DWELLER

The Cornish chough is seen on a ledge of the cliff where it has its nest. This bird is now rare, the peregrine falcon partly accounting for its decrease in numbers.

In this large family of perching birds we find some of the most brilliantly coloured species. The Birds of Paradise have been well named, for the plumage of many specimens is gorgeous beyond description. Their haunts are in the Malay Archipelago and in the great wild island of New Guinea, but, like the majority of birds clothed in fine feathers, they have no song. When we come down to hard facts, we find that these wonderful birds are, after all, just gaudily coloured crows, for they are closely related to the latter. It was the early Malay traders who first gave them the name of God's birds; later, the Portuguese called them sun birds, and the Dutch birds of paradise.

There is very little difference as regards structure between the birds of paradise and the bower birds. Both will prepare patches of ground on which they can display their wonderful colours and perform fantastic dances before the females. The golden bird of paradise of New Guinea is really a bower bird. Its plumage is a blaze of orange and gold, with jet-black quills and tail. Some of these birds build elaborate bowers which are really display playgounds, and have nothing to do with the nest proper, which is often quite an ordinary affair. One of the most notable species is the Gardener bird of New Guinea. The male of this species builds a conical hut around a sapling, makes a flat lawn of moss in front, and on this places a weird assortment of brightly coloured insects, flower buds and other brilliant objects which it has collected. A great Australian naturalist has stated that "without exception, the bower-building birds of Australia are the most extraordinary and interesting group of birds found in the world".

The Oriels, another group of brightly plumaged birds, follow closely after the birds of paradise. The Golden oriel occasionally appears in Great Britain, but is frequently met with in Europe generally, Africa and Madagascar. All species are usually of a startling yellow colour, with black wings, a contrast so distinct that the bright plumage is shown to the best advantage.

The Family of Finches

The family of Finches comprises a large number of smaller birds with strong conical beaks well adapted to their particular food, which consists of seeds and a miscellaneous diet. They are generally characteristic of the Old World, although in Northern America there are many beautiful specimens among the linnets, buntings and grosbeaks. The commonest bird in the family is the Sparrow, which is found all over Europe with the exception of parts of Italy and the extreme northern parts of Norway, Finland and Russia. It has been introduced into several countries, including America and Australia, where, increasing beyond anticipation, it has

become a nuisance. Many and varied means have been employed to get rid of it, but, strange to say, the most effective check it has received abroad has been the popular use of motor-cars in place of horses. The dung on the roads gave these birds a good supply of winter food, especially in the cold northern parts of the countries which they inhabited. Cars have done more to keep them within reasonable numbers than traps and poison.

The finches, especially the Goldfinch, have always been popular cage birds in all countries, and they become very tame. The writer once placed a newly caught Redpoll in a cage. A few days later it escaped, but it was found that the bird returned to its cage from the open country, for the food placed there.

Varieties of Sparrow

Spread over the North American continent there are many birds in this family called sparrows, some of them with beautiful plumage, such as the White-crowned sparrow and the male of the White-throated sparrow. There are also sparrows with delightfully pleasing little songs, and several species which are most useful to the agriculturist.

The Crossbills are so called owing to the mandibles crossing each other, giving the bird a strange appearance. At first glance it looks as though it would be impossible for a bird with such a strange bill to pick up food, but it can take the smallest seed in the tips of its mandibles, split off the husk, discard this, and take the heart of the seed. Also the powerful crossed beak is useful for splitting open the pine cones to get at the hidden seeds. All the crossbills found in Europe, Asia and America are, as a rule, inhabitants of northern climes, where they frequent

A VARIETY OF NESTS

Varied and often curious are the nests of birds. The female hornbill is sealed into a hole in a tree by the male which brings it food. The swift binds its nest together with saliva. The jackdaw collects a diversity of stolen objects. The weaver bird skilfully weaves a long bag-shaped nest which hangs from a tree. These and other curious nests are illustrated above.

SKYLARK SINGING

The skylark sings for six or seven months of the year, as early as 2 a.m. in midsummer and after darkness has fallen at night. The joyous song, so often praised by poets, is surpassed only by that of the nightingale. The colour af the skylark is a sober brown.

conifer forests. The Common crossbill of Europe is one of the first birds to nest. Eggs have even been found in January.

The wild Canary, a native of Madeira, the Azores and the Canary Islands, is another popular bird in this family, but the wild species is sombre-coloured compared with the brilliant-coloured birds which have been produced by selective breeding and crossing with many gay plumaged finches.

The Larks (family *Alaudidae*) are generally distinguished by the long, straight claw of the great toe and are good songsters. The Skylark, so well known in Europe generally, is represented by allied races in North-west Africa, most of the Mediterranean islands, right across Asia, Persia, Afghanistan, China and Japan, while it has been introduced to Australia. The Bushlark is an Australian species with a pleasing song.

Wagtails and Pipits are closely related to the larks. The wagtails are essentially birds of the Old World. They are all easy to distinguish, owing to their habit of moving their tail up and down. All are exceedingly graceful birds. Especially is this noticeable when they are searching for insects on the leaves of water-lilies.

The lovely Sun-birds belong to this order, and must not be confused with the Humming-birds, which many of them resemble. Although the apparent colours of both sun-birds and humming-birds are exceedingly brilliant, there is really a great difference. With the sun-birds the colour is due to actual pigment in the feathers, while with the majority of the humming-birds the colour is due to the prismatic surfaces of the feathers. In certain lights an individual bird may one moment appear to be clothed in the most brilliant feathers, and the next to be a dull brown bird.

A GENERAL FAVOURITE AMONGST BIRDS

The redbreast, a member of the thrush family, is popular because of its friendly and fear-
less character. It has a pleasing song, which can often be heard even when snow is
on the ground. Its nest may be found in such unexpected places as an old kettle.

BIRD OF PARADISE

The birds of paradise, originally so called by the Dutch in the Malay Archipelago, are the most gorgeous of birds, though they have no song. They are, in spite of their gaudily coloured appearance, related to the crows.

The sun-birds are found chiefly in the Old World, inhabiting the whole of Africa, Palestine, India, the Malayan Islands and northern Australia, where, however, only one species is found. These lovely little gems of birdland resemble the humming-birds in many of their habits, but instead of hovering in front of flowers to extract the nectar, they settle on the blooms, and also capture many insects.

Another popular family of birds in the order *Passeres* is that of the Thrushes. The best known is the Song-thrush, for this bird and closely allied species are to be found all over Europe, where their loud and musical song is a feature of the spring. The range of this bird reaches right across Europe to mid-Siberia, and as far south as Iraq and Persia. Other members of the family found in Europe are the Missel thrush, Fieldfare, Redwing and Blackbird. North America has over a dozen species. One of these—Wilson's thrush—has a particularly beautiful song, which, heard at sunset, has been likened to the jingling of a golden chain.

The Warblers

The Warblers (*Sylviidae*) constitute a very large family of small insect-eating birds, many of which have sweet songs. They are found all over the eastern hemisphere, and in North and South America. The Garden warbler and Blackcap are two of the best singers which nest in Europe. It is difficult to estimate the amount of good these small birds do; to the farmer and fruit-grower they are invaluable, for during the whole of the nesting season they capture myriads of insects harmful to crops.

The family of Titmice is spread all over the northern parts of the world, with a few species in Africa. All are sprightly, perky little birds, many seeming to prefer the company of man, building their nests near his dwellings. Although small, they are some of the most useful birds, for, like the warblers, they devour enormous quantities of injurious insects. The well-known Blue tit will often rear sixteen young, and during the period of feeding them she and her mate will destroy not less than 30,000 caterpillars, all captured within 100 yards of the nesting site. It is easy to imagine what devastation would take place in the countryside if it were not for the insect-eating birds.

In North America many of the tits are known as Chickadees, named after their

JEWEL OF BIRDLAND

Humming-birds are noted for the brilliance of their colouring, due to the prismatic surface of the feathers catching and breaking up the light. They have marvellous vision and in spite of their beauty a fierce temper. Above is shown a handsome specimen.

UNDESIRABLE GUEST

A tree pipit feeds a young cuckoo. The young parasite, already grown to great proportions, has all the appearance of bullying its foster-parent, whose own progeny have been sacrificed to the cuckoo's demands and are doomed to perish by the intruder in the nest.

cheery note. On the coldest and wettest days the chickadees may be heard.

Swallows and Martins (family *Hirundinidae*) are to be found throughout the world, and are a wonderful migratory species, for they fly enormous distances between their summer and winter quarters. All are insect-feeders, capturing their food while on the wing.

Closely allied to the swallows come the Swifts, birds with long, pointed wings, and capable of flying long distances at great speeds, and of spending practically their whole time in the air. The gorgeous humming-birds which have already been mentioned are really marvellously developed flower-haunting swifts. They take the place in the New World of the sun-birds of the Old World. Their wonderfully coloured plumage, which seems to radiate the most brilliant metallic hues, is shown to the best advantage while they hover in front of a tropical bloom, with their wings moving so rapidly that they are almost invisible, while all the time they give out the characteristic humming note.

In the order *Picariae* are many strange and brilliantly coloured birds of the tropics, such as the Toucans, Hoopoes, Bee-eaters, the grotesque Hornbills, the Kingfishers and Goat-suckers.

Although the toucans and hornbills have a strong superficial resemblance, there is no real relationship between the two groups. The toucans are found in

KINGFISHER WITH MINNOW

The kingfisher, conspicuous by its brilliant blue-green back and chestnut breast, is represented in all parts of the world. Nesting in the bank of a river, it feeds on fish for which it plunges into the water. It ingeniously constructs its nest from fish-bones.

WOODPECKER AT NESTING-HOLE

The nest of a woodpecker is a hole excavated in a tree-trunk. By tapping the bark it removes insects and larvae from the crevices. Above is shown the lesser spotted woodpecker, a small bird with distinctive black and white bands across back and wings.

South America. Most are of brilliant hues, which, together with an enormous beak, give the birds a strange appearance. They live chiefly on fruit, and although the massive bill looks clumsy, the bird shows surprising cleverness in picking up small raisins with the tips of the mandibles, and tossing them into the wide open beak, where such minute particles of food appear to be lost. The majority of toucans are small birds, ranging in size from a thrush to a pigeon, but the Toco, the largest of the species, has a measurement of about 2 feet from the tip of the beak to end of the tail.

The hornbills, which belong to this Picarian order, are found in Africa, India, and throughout the Malayan region as far south as New Guinea. They are birds of a most grotesque appearance, and although the beak is enormous, it does not present quite such an unbalanced appearance as that of the largest toucan. The hornbills are, however, bigger birds. The Rhinoceros hornbill, found in India, has the strangest appearance of all the species, for casual observation shows it to have apparently two beaks, one above the other, but this is a feature of most hornbills, and is a casque or helmet above the beak proper. It was this bird which suggested the ancient myth of the phoenix.

Hornbills have strange nesting habits. Evidently the male does not trust his mate, for he takes very good care that she shall not desert her duty during the

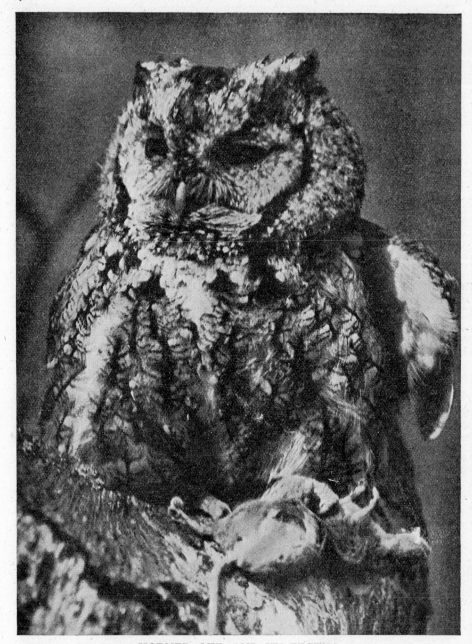

HORNED OWL AND ITS VICTIM

Fearsome in appearance is this member of the owl family, creature of barns, towers, ruins and woods, as it grips in its talons the rodent on which it is preparing to feast. It will eat every part of its victim, tail, fur, bones, until not a scrap is left.

period of incubation. The eggs are laid on wood chips at the bottom of a hole in a forest tree. Directly the last egg is laid, the male collects quantities of mud, and seals up the entrance, leaving only a small hole. This is just large enough for the imprisoned female to insert the tip of her large beak. Her mate now feeds her assiduously with a variety of food, fruit, carrion and insects. Directly the young are hatched, the mud wall is broken and both parents join in feeding them.

The Kingfishers

The kingfisher (family *Alcedinidae*) forms a well-marked group represented in all parts of the world. The majority feed on fish, although some of the tropical forms exist on insects and earthworms. The Laughing Jackass of Australia is a large, aberrant kingfisher, its food consisting of lizards, insects and snakes.

The Goat-suckers or Nightjars are another group of birds with a strange appearance. They have flattened heads, very small bills, and enormous mouths, with a gape extending to behind the eye. All are wonderful examples of camouflage, and when settling on the ground or certain trees, are almost invisible.

The nightjar is found all over Europe, with allied species in Asia and Africa, while there is a species in North America —the Whip-poor-will. The goat-suckers were given their name owing to the mistaken idea that they sucked the milk from cows and goats in the pastures. Although the birds are often seen fluttering round cattle, their objective is simply the insects that worry the cattle. Thus they are of the greatest assistance to the farmer. Mistaken ideas of such behaviour have caused the destruction of many useful birds and mammals.

Cuckoos (family *Cuculidae*) are widely distributed throughout the world, and within the limits of the family we find birds of widely varying habits. Many species build nests, while some rely upon other birds to incubate their eggs and rear their young. The common European cuckoo is too well known as a harbinger of spring to need any description. The myth that she lays her egg on the ground, then carries it to a selected nest with her beak, is now well exploded, for it has been proved by photography, and careful observation on hundreds of occasions, that the cuckoo lays her egg direct into the selected nest in the normal manner.

The order *Striges* contains the Owls, which are well distributed in all parts of the world. They are easily distinguished from most other birds of prey by their eyes, which are directed forward, so as to confront an observer, also by their large heads and short necks.

Types of Owl

The Eagle owl and its close relative the Great-horned owl of America are the largest of the species. The former is found all over Europe, with allied races extending to China and Japan and as far south as Persia and Tibet. The most widely known of the owls is undoubtedly the White or Barn owl, distributed over the best part of the globe. It is one of the most useful birds to the grain-grower, for one pair nesting in a barn will destroy thousands of rats round about.

Many look upon owls as large birds, but there are several exceedingly small species. The Pigmy owl of North America is about the size of a sparrow, but, although so small, it has a ferocious disposition, and will attack and kill birds twice its size. Its call is a half-

RED-TAILED HAWK AND VICTIM

With a stony glitter in its eye, the red-tailed hawk prepares to devour the bird it has brought down and into which its cruel talons are fixed. The accurate and lightning descent with which it has swooped through the air has instantaneously killed its victim.

BUZZARD AND COOPER HAWK

Flapping its wings, by whose broad, blunt character it may be recognized, the buzzard assumes an air of defiance (above). It makes a mewing cry as it circles above hills and cliffs. (Below) The cooper hawk poises over the garter-snake which it has captured.

HIS MAJESTY

The crowned eagle is seen in this photograph returning to the eyrie, with some portion of its kill. He is awaited by a family as ferocious looking as himself. The majestic beauty of the

THE EAGLE

wing-spread indicates why the eagle has so often been adopted as a national device from ancient times to our own. The large nest, which is constructed of branches and sticks, is typical.

SOMBRE GATHERING

Hyenas of the feathered world, these vultures have congregated near a dead or dying animal on the plains of India. The large, ugly birds detect the carrion on which they feed by sight rather than by scent, and when one is seen to swoop down, dozens more will follow. They are useful scavengers.

spoken whistle—*Cook-cook*—and is easily imitated; when uttered, all the small birds in the immediate neighbourhood will quickly cluster together and give out loud warning notes.

The order *Falconiformes* contains the powerful, rapacious birds of prey, and the Vultures. The latter are large birds which frequent the warmer climates. They are essentially carrion feeders. On the ground, when gathered around a dead horse or other large animal, they have a repulsive appearance, but they look majestic when on the wing as they sail round, high up over mountain or valley. The Great Griffon vulture is a resident in most parts of Southern Europe and Asia. The American vultures are quite distinct from those of the Old World, but all are useful scavengers, and in many parts are rigorously protected.

Eagles are found the world over, except in New Zealand. The Golden eagle, the best known of the family, is resident all over the northern part of the world, breeding as far north as 70°. This large and handsome bird served as an emblem of ancient Rome, and contributes largely to modern heraldry. The Wedge-tailed eagle of Australia has the honour of being one of the largest of its species. Its flight is even more majestic than that of the golden eagle.

The Sea eagles are found in nearly all countries of the world, with perhaps the exception of South America; they are a

MOURNING DOVE

Pigeons and doves have been overpraised for the constancy of their affections. Thus, the note of the mourning dove is not one of lament for a lost mate, as it is popularly supposed to be. This photograph of a mourning dove on the nest was taken in America.

large and powerful species. In the British Isles a war of extermination has been waged against the Great White-tailed eagle, which is now only seen as a passing visitor, but it breeds in Iceland, and its range extends across Europe as far north as 70°, and across Russia, and south, to Iraq and Turkestan.

The " Noble " Hawks

The Falcons are quite recognizable by their long, pointed wings. They were known to the old falconers as the Noble or Long-winged hawks, and were favourite birds of the chase, owing to their great strength, boldness and spirit in attack. The Peregrine falcon is of world-wide distribution, and is one of the greatest bird-hunters. It will strike down birds far larger and heavier than itself, such as pheasant and wild duck. The writer has often wondered if these birds love the chase. He remembers watching a pair of these falcons circling in front of a giant sea-cliff, with thousands of puffins and other sea-birds wheeling around. Now and again one or both of the peregrines stopped in its flight, put its head down, and dived at a terrific speed on to some luckless bird. After striking it down, the hunter soared upwards to join its mate, only to repeat the performance a few minutes later. It seemed as though the birds were killing for the sake of the sport, for they did not trouble to retrieve their prey.

Many species of falcons are found distributed over the world. The large Ger-falcon is a northern species, nesting in both the Old and New Worlds. In contrast to this large and powerful species, we find, in the Himalayas and the Burmese countries, small falcons not more than 7 inches in length.

Many of the most brilliantly coloured birds in the whole world are found among the Parrots (order *Psittaci*). They dwell in the warmer countries, but are mostly represented in the Australian region, and South America. There are none in Europe, none in Asia excepting India, none in Africa north of the Tropic of Cancer, and only one in North America. The South African Grey parrot is world-renowned for its talking powers. Six ·families of these gaudy birds are represented in Australia, ranging from the delightful and affectionate little Budgerigar to the large black Cockatoos measuring 26 inches in length. The thirty or so species of parrots found in the Amazon region are clever mimics, but they cannot compete with the African species. All are long-lived.

Pigeons and Doves

Pigeons and Doves (order *Columbae*) are very widely distributed over the world. The most interesting species found in Europe is the Rock dove, for this represents the stock from which all the domesticated birds have been bred by artificial selection. A family in this order contains three extinct species: one, the Dodo of Mauritius, disappeared about the year 1693. This and another extinct species, the Solitaire, were flightless, which no doubt contributed to their rapid extinction.

One of the most remarkable instances of extinction is that of the Passenger pigeon of North America. It was last recorded in a wild state in 1898, and the last remaining specimen died in captivity in 1914. This was the end of a species that used to be found in immense flocks that darkened the sky for hours on end as they flew to their feeding places.

The order *Lariformes* contains a large number of birds which spend their lives on or close to the sea. The Black-headed Gull is an exception, for in recent years it has become almost a land bird. During the winter months very large numbers fly inland where they congregate in and around towns and other inhabited places; they even settle on bird-tables placed in gardens. They are found all over the northern parts of the Old World, extending south in the winter as far as Abyssinia, Persia and India. Another common species is the large Herring gull, one of the most accomplished bird robbers to be found on the coasts. The writer was once approaching one of these birds with his camera, but before he got within range it left its nest, walked to the nest of a neighbouring herring gull a few yards away, and devoured all three eggs; but when it returned to its own nest, it found that another herring gull had cleared that up! This gull is found all over Europe, Asia, parts of Africa, India, China and in the Americas.

The Terns may be distinguished from the gulls by their smaller size, more graceful flight and long, pointed wings. They are a widely distributed family, being found on the coasts of most countries of the world. They nest in large colonies close to the sea, sometimes so close to the water that a high tide will swamp their nests. One well-known haunt, known as Wide-Awake Fair, is on Ascension Island. Here many thousands of birds lay their eggs. On an adjacent island it

THE TAKE-OFF

Much in the same fashion as a sea-plane, the beautiful water bird, the diver, or loon, skims along the surface of the water when it is about to rise in flight. Its wings flap at the same time in order to give it the necessary momentum, as seen in this photograph.

ROBBERY IN THE WILD

This is the crucial moment of an outrageous theft. The skua has alighted in the middle of a colony of penguins. With great speed it darts at a nest, snatches an egg and is about to make off with it, ignoring the horrified protest of the penguins gathered round.

was estimated that 100,000 terns had their nests on a tract of sandy shore of about 100 acres. On many of the small island paradises of the Great Barrier Reef, and others on the eastern side of Australia, terns make their nests on the flattened tops of giant *Pisonia* trees, overgrown as they are with creepers. There is an interesting partnership between the terns and the trees. The fruit of the tree is covered with a sticky substance which adheres to the plumage of the birds, and they carry the seeds to other islands to form new plantations.

The Skuas, closely allied to the gulls, are the robbers of the sea. They fly in the company of gulls, constantly robbing them of their food. The Great skua is a bold bird, never failing to attack any creature, human or otherwise, that approaches its nest. The author has often seen skuas accompanying flocks of gulls, apparently at peace with them, but directly a gull captures a fish or other food, the robber pounces on it, and usually succeeds in robbing the owner.

Auks, represented by the Little auk, Razor-bill, Guillemot, and the comical

WHEN THE TIDE

Wherever there are wide sandy bays and weed-covered shores, large flocks of waders are to be found. There are many species but they all look much alike, with their long legs

IS GOING OUT

and slender beaks, as they run along the margin of the tide in their search for food. This photograph, which shows a typical group of waders, was taken in California.

looking Puffin, are found chiefly in the northern hemisphere. They live in colonies, those of the guillemot and puffin consisting of immense flocks. One famous haunt of the latter is on the lonely island of St. Kilda, where hundreds of thousands have their nests on the grassy slopes of the great cliffs.

Plovers and Waders

The Plovers and Waders are represented by a very large number of species in all parts of the world. The best known of the plovers is the Lapwing or Green plover, which may well be termed the most useful of all the birds found in the northern part of the Old World. The Golden plover is another well-known species of the same regions.

The waders are an extensive group which frequent the coasts and marshes everywhere. They are distinguished by a slender and elongated beak, while many have long, slender legs. On suitable stretches of the coast throughout the world, where there are wide sandy bays and rocky, sea-weed-covered shores, very large flocks of waders are encountered. There are several hundred species, many looking very similar as they search for food on the margin of the tides. From a distance the large flocks, as they rise together to wheel round to another spot, resemble flakes of falling snow.

The game birds (order *Gallinae*) are ground birds, and include the Pheasant and their allies. They are found in all parts of the world. There are many interesting species in this order which stand out owing to their remarkable habits. One well worth mentioning is the Brush Turkey of Australia, a member of the mound-builders, sometimes called "scratchers". These birds take the place of the pheasant of the northern hemisphere. The brush turkey is one of the few birds that appears to retain the reptilian characteristic of not sitting on the eggs. Instead, these are laid in huge mounds of sand, earth and rotting vegetation, which, owing to the heat generated, form a natural incubator. The mound is made by the male bird. Some of these mounds have been found to weigh 7 tons. When the young hatch they have their wings fully feathered, and are able to fly directly they leave the mound. Also they look after themselves, and are quite independent of their parents.

The wild Jungle Fowl of India, the bird from which our domestic fowls have originated, is included in this order. The Red Grouse also should be mentioned, for it is the only species restricted to Britain, although of late years it has been introduced to other countries.

Geese and Ducks

The Geese, Ducks and Flamingoes of the order *Anseres* have representatives in all countries. The best-known goose is the Grey Lag-goose, the bird from which our domesticated form has sprung. The Mallard or Wild duck is considered to be the most popular of the ducks. The common flamingo is found in Europe, Asia and Africa. In appearance, with its long, flexible neck and long, stilt-like legs, it is one of our strangest birds. On some of the African marshes these birds congregate together in their hundred thousand, and with their pure white, crimson and black plumage make one of the most amazing sights to be seen in the bird world.

The long-legged birds of the order *Herodiones*—the Storks and Herons— are represented in all parts of the world,

RETURN TO THE NEST

The gannet's nest is made of seaweed and grass and placed on the ledge of a rock. This sea bird breeds in very large numbers on Lundy Island and on the Bass Rock at the entrance to the Firth of Forth. It lives on fish, swooping down on them from a height.

THE STATELY POISE

*The long, flexible neck of the flamingo falls naturally into varied and graceful curves
and a group of them together, standing in water on long, stilt-like legs, is most decorative*

OF THE FLAMINGO

in appearance. They are distributed in Europe, Asia and Africa, and the huge flocks with white, crimson and black plumage make a truly amazing spectacle of bright colour.

PARTY OF PENGUINS

These remarkable birds breed in lonely spots in the Southern Ocean. Their legs are enclosed in the skin of the body and their walk is slow and clumsy. They are gregarious, assembling in great rookeries, and explorers have found them remarkably fearless.

PENGUINS SWIMMING

Clumsy on land, the penguin is quite at home in the water and its wings, useless for flight, are excellent paddles : they are worked alternately, the feet acting as rudder.

The common white stork is a familiar sight in many European villages, and the common heron is found all over the Palaearctic and Ethiopian regions. The lovely Egrets which nest in large colonies in many parts of Europe, Africa and Australia have been sadly thinned in recent years by plume hunters. Man's cupidity and woman's desire for ornament at one time seemed to have doomed these birds to extermination. The elegant plumes are collected in the nesting season, and thousands of the parents have been slaughtered by hunters, leaving the young to die of starvation.

The Pelicans, Cormorants and Gannets are birds which in the nesting season congregate in vast flocks. All are fish-eaters, and are the most accom-plished and industrious fishermen of the sea. The pelicans are of almost world-wide distribution, and their great bill gives them an ungainly look. The Australian species is one of the largest of the tribe, and is practically identical with the "pelican of the wilderness" mentioned in the Bible.

The gannet is a bird of the North Atlantic. It is estimated that the world population of this large sea-bird comprises 167,000 breeding birds, of which 109,000 nest around the coast of Britain. The Australian species is very much like our northern bird.

The Petrels (order *Tubinares*) are true ocean birds. A few species are to be found on the northern seas, the Fulmar petrel being the best known, but the

PELICANS

Their large bills give the pelicans a somewhat ungainly appearance, though they are well adapted for catching fish. Like the cormorants and gannets, to which they are related, pelicans are accomplished fishermen, the pouch beneath the bill accommodating the prey.

CONVERSATION PIECE

These graceful members of the heron tribe which are called egrets are mainly found in the southern States of U.S.A. and in South America, though a small species is also found in Europe. The feathers, known as ospreys or aigrettes, are dorsal plumes.

ALBATROSS

The albatross is distinguished by possessing a wider wing-spread than any other extant bird. Of the fifteen species in this family, the largest, the wandering albatross, though

majority are found in the vast spaces of the great Pacific Ocean. The small storm petrels, known to sailors as Mother Carey's Chickens, are a familiar sight on the southern seas. The petrels nest in colonies. The fulmar petrel and a closely allied Australian species gather together in enormous numbers, some of the colonies numbering 50,000 pairs.

The several species of Albatross belong to this order. They are essentially birds of the open ocean. Largest of the family, the Wandering albatross has an enormous wing-spread reaching 14 feet from tip to tip. The majority of these birds are found south of the Equator.

The Grebes and Divers (order *Pygopodes*) are water birds found chiefly in the northern parts of the world, both on the sea and on inland lakes. The handsome Great-crested grebe is perhaps the best known of the grebes. It is a clever diver, and is distributed all over the eastern hemisphere. It is yearly extending its range.

Those strange birds, Penguins (order *Impennes*), take the place, in the southern seas, of the divers of the north. They are birds well adapted to a life on the sea, for they are flightless, and spend their whole time on land and water. The Emperor penguin is the largest of the species. Some, such as the Adele penguin, nest among the ice and snow of the Antarctic. The whole colony will sometimes be buried under a foot or more of snow, but appears to emerge none the worse for the experience. In all their breeding haunts

IN FLIGHT

weighing only sixteen pounds, sometimes possesses a wing-spread of fourteen feet. It sweeps before the most furious gales with arrow-like swiftness and unflagging power.

they congregate in enormous colonies.

The large flightless running birds, such as the Ostrich, Cassowaries and Emus, are all birds of the southern hemisphere. The largest is the ostrich, which stands 8 feet high, and is the largest existing bird.

Among the birds of the world there is always a great movement taking place, especially in the spring and autumn of each year. Migration is chiefly a movement between the winter and summer area. In the northern hemisphere birds come north for nesting purposes, while in the southern hemisphere they move south. Food plays an important part in these movements, for those birds which come to Europe for nesting purposes, move south again in the autumn when

their summer food supplies fail. The same applies to birds which fly south in the southern hemisphere, for they again travel north with the approach of winter.

In the nesting season the majority of birds have been observed to live in well-defined territories, and it has been proved beyond all doubt that these travellers return to the same haunt season after season. Take the nightingale as an example. It will fly north from Africa to woods in Europe, and when it reaches the selected spot, we find that during the whole of the period of nest-building, incubation and feeding the young, one pair of birds will live inside a tract of woodland about 3 acres in extent. The same applies to resident birds, which travel only short distances. Many birds

SECRETARY BIRD IN FLIGHT

This giant crane, the secretary bird, has been disturbed by a gunshot. It was not the intended victim, however, for these birds are included on the protected list.

which nest in the north will fly but. 100 or 200 miles south with the approach of winter, returning to their northern territories with the approach of spring. The great golden eagle may have a territory extending over several square miles. Others, such as gannets, puffins, petrels, terns and rooks, settle down for nesting purposes in colonies, but each colony still keeps to its territory, as all birds do during the breeding season.

The great distance some birds travel and the unerring manner in which they find their way over continents and seas, many flying by night, is one of the mysteries of migration, and has never been satisfactorily explained. Swallows which have been ringed in Britain in the summer have been recovered in South Africa. Many other marked birds have been found at vast distances from their breeding quarters. All appear to follow well-defined air routes. Many young birds travel several weeks in advance of their parents, while the young of the European cuckoo fly south weeks after.

Another strange fact is that birds which nest in the north temperate region will, when they fly south, travel to the temperate tracts of the southern hemisphere. Enormous distances are covered. The Curlew Sandpiper is an example; it nests inside the Arctic circle, but after it has reared its young will fly south as far as New Zealand. More amazing still is the flight of the Arctic tern, for it nests inside the Arctic circle, then, when it has completed its duties, flies south to the coast of the Antarctic, some 10,000 miles away.

FLIGHTLESS RUNNING BIRD

This photograph was taken in South Africa and shows the ostrich in movement. This handsome flightless bird attains a considerable speed, raising its wings at the beginning of a run, and then holding them close to its sides, in order to lessen resistance to the air.

CANADA GEESE

This photograph was taken in North Carolina and shows the characteristic V-formation in which geese fly. Canada geese winter in North Carolina, though their principal breeding

IN FLIGHT

ground is on the shores of Hudson Bay. From this region they move south in the autumn in a cross-country wave of migration. Their common flying speed is 40 to 50 miles per hour.

AUSTRALIA'S NATIVE "BEAR"

The koala, shown in the above photograph, is one of Australia's unique animals, a marsupial in spite of its popular description as native bear. It lives in the gum-trees.

CHAPTER EIGHTEEN

ANIMAL LIFE OF AUSTRALASIA

by DAVID SETH SMITH, F.Z.S., M.B.O.U.

Queer creatures of the Antipodes. Why pouched mammals still survive. Kangaroos, Wallabies, Opossums and Wombats. Flying Fox, Dingo and Tasmanian Devil. Egg-laying mammals: Platypus and Echidna. Australasian snakes and reptiles. Some exotic birds.

PERHAPS the most interesting fauna of all is to be found in Australia. Here is the home of the mammals known as marsupials, their title coming from a Latin word meaning "a pouch". The majority of Australian mammals belong to this queer species, ranging in size between that of a deer and a mouse. Then there are the unique duck-billed platypus and the echidna, mammals which lay eggs.

Why are mammals that carry their young in pouches confined to Australasia? The answer lies in prehistoric times, when pouched animals were distributed over a great part of the world, as fossil remains have shown. They were, in fact, the most numerous of the mammals. It seems beyond doubt that at that time Australasia was joined to Asia and that land fauna could move from one region to another without difficulty.

Gradually the mammals which are not marsupials (known as placentals) began to get the upper hand, with the exception of Australia, where they were represented only by small species.

The pouched mammals began to disappear from most parts of the world before the placentals. Only in Australia were they safe and without rivals; whilst one group managed to survive in America.

Most people, asked to name a typical Australian animal, would unhesitatingly reply, "Kangaroo". This quaint-looking beast is, of course, of the marsupial (or pouched) order.

It was first described in 1773 by the explorer Captain Cook, who had seen some in what is now North Queensland. One legend has it that "Kangaroo" comes from a native phrase meaning "I don't know", given in reply to the white man who enquired the name of this strange new animal.

At all events the quaintness of the kangaroo has always fascinated young and old alike, although it is not generally known that the group contains some distinct varieties which feed on plants, insects, and flesh.

A feature of the marsupial tribe is the helplessness of their young at birth. The newly born kangaroo, for instance, is

L

BLACK WALLABY AND YOUNG

The wallaby, of which there are several species, is a small type of kangaroo. The young wallaby in our picture is sufficiently advanced to pop its head out of the maternal pouch and look with interest at the surrounding grass on which it will presently venture out.

TREE-CLIMBING KANGAROO

Adapted to tree climbing is this kangaroo, having large and strong forelegs and sharp, well-developed claws. It descends a tree slowly and with dignity, tail first. Tree kangaroos inhabit Australia and are also found in the forests of New Guinea.

only about 1 inch in length—a powerless little morsel of flesh. The only parts perfectly formed are the front legs and claws. With these the newly born kangaroo manages to climb through its mother's fur to her pouch, there to become firmly attached to one of her nipples. In this position it remains for three or four months while milk is automatically pumped into it by muscular action (it has no power of sucking).

When perhaps four months old the baby has become covered with fur and becomes detached from the former source of nourishment. It is then able to pop its head out of the pouch, and, greatly daring, to venture out and nibble tender blades of grass. At the slightest sign of danger it will scuttle back to the snug security of its mother's pouch.

The largest of present-day kangaroos are the Great Grey (known as the Forester because of a preference for partially-wooded country), which once roamed Eastern and Southern Australia, and the Red kangaroo of dryer districts.

In days gone by the great grey was very numerous, being often met with in packs of up to fifty. Being a grass-feeder, it was slaughtered wholesale by the sheep-farmers, and now its numbers are sadly reduced. The Grey of the West, which is distinguished by a black face, and the Kangaroo Island kangaroo are related.

HIGH JUMP

The ability of the kangaroo to cover the ground in a series of jumps is strikingly shown in this photograph, the great development of the long hind legs giving it a mighty thrust forward. The hind legs provided with single sharp claws also serve as a powerful weapon.

FLYING OPOSSUM

Squirrel-like is the flying opossum, here shown. The membrane which extends from front to hind legs serves as a parachute and enables it to glide through the air from one tree to another. Unlike the American opossum it feeds entirely on vegetation.

The red fully equals, if it does not exceed, the grey kangaroo in size, and a fully grown male is a grand animal, its colour varying between chestnut, sand colour and bluish-grey, while the throat is rich pink, the legs and stripes on the face being white. It favours the more central districts not less than about 500 miles from the coast.

The large male kangaroos often indulge in boxing with one another. Standing very upright, supported by the long hind legs and the tail, they spar together in the typical boxing attitude. Sometimes one will strike forwards with the hind legs, when the long toenails may cause serious injury to the opponent, but, as a rule, the boxing is an expression of harmless play. Male reds have often been trained to box with human opponents, and have sometimes put up a very creditable performance.

The Wallaroo (*M. robustus*) is a rather thick-set, heavy kangaroo with coarse hair, varying in colour from greyish or blackish-brown to red. It frequents the hilly or mountainous districts, those in New South Wales being of the typical greyish colour, while those in central and western districts are generally red.

The smaller species of kangaroos are generally termed Wallabies, and there is a large number of species, all of which live near brushwood, to give them some

PLATYPUS—EGG-LAYING MAMMAL
*An extraordinary mixture is the rare platypus, with its duck-bill and webbed feet.
Neither fish nor fowl, it spends most of its life in streams, on whose banks its eggs are laid.*

protection from their enemies the dingos, foxes and eagles, of which the fox is the most destructive. Space will only allow of the mention of a few of these charming small kangaroos. Their range extends over practically the whole of Australia, Tasmania and New Guinea.

One of the most beautiful of the typical wallabies is Parry's wallaby of the northern parts of New South Wales and Queensland. It is a slender, graceful animal with soft, silky fur of a bluish-grey colour, with white legs and stripes on the face. The Black-gloved wallaby of South-western Australia is bluish-grey above and has yellowish underparts and black feet, while Bennett's, of Tasmania, has much thicker fur and is hardier than

most of the others, and thrives well in England, the young showing their heads out of their mothers' pouches about June, by which time they are probably fully six or eight months old. Wallabies are comparatively tame animals.

Specially adapted for life amongst the rocks are some half-dozen species of Rock wallabies in which the tail is used to balance the animal as it leaps from rock to rock, the feet being roughened to prevent slipping. These animals live in holes in the rocks by day, coming out at night to feed. The largest of the genus is the Yellow-footed rock wallaby of South Australia, which has long, silky fur, grey above and white below, with a conspicuous white stripe running from the shoulders along the body to the hips.

Tree kangaroos are modified for climbing, their fore limbs being larger and stronger than those of other kangaroos, while their claws are very sharp and strong. They climb trees with the greatest of ease, and may be seen feeding on the leaves of the topmost branches. Two species—Lumholtz' tree kangaroo and Bennett's tree kangaroo—are found in Queensland, while several others inhabit the forests of New Guinea. It is a strange sight to witness kangaroos perched high amongst the branches of trees, with their long tails hanging down. They return to the ground tail first and with a slow and deliberate movement.

Opossums, or Phalangers, of Australia must not be confused with the American opossums. The latter are carnivorous in tastes and have scaly, rat-like tails. The Australian opossums are thick-furred, bushy-tailed, arboreal marsupials which feed entirely upon vegetation.

The Common, or Silver-grey opossum ranges over the greater part of Australia, where the eucalyptus trees provide its food and shelter. It occurs in Tasmania, too, but there it carries a thicker coat, black or very dark brown specimens being keenly sought after for their fur. These animals sleep in hollow tree-trunks or limbs by day, climbing to the upper branches after dark. Although formerly

ONE OF NATURE'S FANTASIES—THE ECHIDNA

The echidna or ant-eater, with its tube-like beak, its five-toed feet and spines like a porcupine, is as quaint as the platypus and resembles it in being an egg-laying marsupial possessing a definite pouch in which the eggs are hatched and the young reared.

BABY WOMBAT GOES FOR A WALK

Pausing at the mouth of the burrow in which it lives, the mother wombat, accompanied by its young, has an air of sluggish contentment. It somewhat resembles the European badger, and is a strict vegetarian. Its coarse fur is black or brown.

extremely common, the many thousands that have been shot or trapped for their skins have greatly reduced the numbers now existing. It has been introduced into New Zealand, where it has thrived. A near relation is the Short-eared opossum of Eastern Australia which is somewhat larger, but with shorter ears.

A favourite sport in Australia is to shoot or attempt to shoot opossums by moonlight. The shooter stands with the tree, a giant eucalyptus, between him and the moon, and if he is lucky, he may see what looks like a slight bulge in the trunk which moves upwards. But as soon as he raises his gun, the chances are that this will have disappeared, the animal having moved to the other side, and so become invisible. The writer witnessed one such hunt in which the shooter, after expending much ammunition, secured only one animal, while the writer failed to spot even one 'possum. It is a sport that requires very good eyesight.

KANGAROO RAT, RING-TAILED OPOSSUM AND TASMANIAN DEVIL
The kangaroo-rat (about the size of a rabbit) has the pose of the kangaroo itself and carries its young in a pouch (top left). The ring-tailed opossum (top right) is similarly a pouched animal. The Tasmanian devil is aptly named. It kills for the sake of killing.

THE SAVAGE AND HANDSOME DINGO

Although treated with much affection by the natives with whom it leads a semi-domesticated life, the dingo, Australia's wild dog, is considered a pest in the Commonwealth and various States have been compelled to put a price on its head.

Flying opossums are often known as "Flying Squirrels", on account of their squirrel-like habits. They are nocturnal, and very active after dark, not only in climbing, but in gliding from one tree to another by means of their flying membrane, which extends from wrist to ankle. Well-known representatives of this group are the Squirrel flying opossum and the Lesser flying opossum, which is regarded as a most desirable pet.

Then there is the Ring-tailed opossum comprising several races, of which the common species extends throughout the eastern districts of Australia. It is clothed in soft, woolly fur, varying in colour between rufous and grey, and has a prehensile tail.

Many large nests have been seen by the writer, composed of leaves and strips of bark and built by these pretty opossums at no great height from the ground. The tree selected is generally a small one, and a good shake to the stem usually causes the sleeper to dart quickly away.

The Koala, or native bear, is one of Australia's most prized animals, though in former days it was ruthlessly persecuted, and in some districts completely wiped out. It is in no way related to the bears, though it has perhaps a slight superficial resemblance to them. It is a trustful, slow-moving, tree-climbing marsupial, with a thick, woolly grey coat, large round ears and an indiarubber-like nose. It lives in the gum-trees and feeds upon their leaves. One young one is born at intervals of two years, being carried in its mother's pouch for perhaps nine months and then on her back. The eastern parts of Australia are its home.

It has seldom been seen in European Zoos, though a couple were successfully brought home to Britain by a sailor who had fed them throughout the voyage upon gum leaves.

Somewhat resembling the badger of Europe in its nocturnal and burrowing habits, though more strictly vegetarian in diet, is the Wombat, a short, thickset animal of between 3 and 4 feet in length. The fur is coarse and the colour various shades of black and brown. The common species occurs in New South Wales, Victoria and South Australia, while closely related species, or races, inhabit Tasmania and South Australia.

The Bandicoots

The Bandicoots are burrowing animals, the largest of which is about the size of a rabbit. The pouch has its opening at the back. Their diet is more or less omnivorous, consisting of worms, insects, roots and other vegetable products. There are several species inhabiting Australia, Tasmania, New Guinea and the adjacent islands, one of the best known being the Short-nosed bandicoot, a stoutly built animal with coarse, yellowish-black hair and a thin, rather short tail. It is destructive to crops in the southern parts of Australia and Tasmania, as it burrows under the roots, destroying the plants, as well as eating any worms and grubs that it may find. The comparatively large Rabbit bandicoot of Central, South and Western Australia is a pretty animal with long, silky fur and ears like those of a rabbit.

Tasmanian Wolf

The largest of the carnivorous marsupials is the Tasmanian Wolf, known in Tasmania as the "Tiger", because of the stripes on its body. It is about the size, with much of the appearance, of a small wolf. These animals, which are now very rare, remain in caves by day, coming out to hunt their prey after dark. This formerly consisted mainly of wallabies and bandicoots, but the attacks by "Tigers" upon sheep have led to efforts to exterminate them.

Another troublesome though very interesting carnivorous marsupial is the Tasmanian Devil, which is rather like a small bear, black, with white on the chest, a large, ugly head and very powerful jaws. Its habits are much the same as those of the Tasmanian wolf, and its numbers have been greatly reduced for the same reason. Four young are reared at a time in the mother's pouch.

A friend of the writer's kept some of these strange creatures in an enclosure in a garden in Hobart, and young ones were successfully reared. These grew up to be quite tame, and even friendly.

The most abundant of the carnivorous marsupials are the Dasyures, or native cats, of which there are several species

YELLOW-BILLED SPOONBILL ON THE NEST

*This bird is an Australian species of a family related to the storks. With its broad, flat
bill it is able to sift small animals from the mud of ponds and river shallows.*

inhabiting the greater part of Australia, Tasmania and New Guinea. They are about the size of domestic cats or smaller, with pointed noses and ears, and long, slender bodies. The usual colour is brown, or black, or grey, covered with white spots. They are most active climbers, and capture many birds, which, with small mammals, constitute their principal diet. They are sometimes very destructive to poultry. Five young are reared at a time in the mother's pouch.

This does not exhaust the long list of the marsupials, but space permits of only the mere mention of the pouched mice, the Jerboa pouched mice, the rare Banded ant-eater of Western Australia, and the very interesting and rare marsupial mole of Central and Western Australia.

Most unique of all the Australasian animals are the *monotremes* or Egg-laying mammals, the most primitive of all mammals. They consist of the Duck-billed platypus found in the eastern parts of Australia and Tasmania, and the Echidnas or Porcupine ant-eaters of Australia, Tasmania and New Guinea.

An adult platypus is about 24 inches in length from beak to tail-tip, covered with thick fur of a blackish-brown colour. It is provided with a flattened bill like that of a duck, though, in life, of the texture of indiarubber, and a broad tail. The feet are webbed, and it spends most of its life in the streams and rivers, feeding upon worms, insects and small shell-fish. Its burrow is formed in the bank, and at the end of this the female constructs her nest of grass and leaves, and in it deposits her two or four eggs. These are joined in pairs, and are of a leathery texture, like those of reptiles.

The amount of food required by these animals is very great, as with other worm-eating animals, such as the mole. A platypus that was successfully kept for some years in Australia taxed its owner to the utmost to supply sufficient earth-worms and such-like. The first platypus to be raised in captivity was born at the end of 1943. Up to the present all attempts to transport a living specimen to Europe have failed, though one was exhibited outside Australia for a time. This was in the United States.

The echidna is an ant-eater, furnished with a long snout and worm-like tongue, its body covered with stout spines. It lives in holes, which it digs with its powerful claws amongst rocks. It possesses a definite pouch, in which the eggs are hatched and, as with the kangaroo, the young are reared.

The more ordinary type of mammals is represented by bats, rats, mice and the dingo dog, though this is perhaps not really indigenous; and around the coast are seals and dugong. Rudyard Kipling's delightful "Just So" stories familiarized many of us as children with the existence of the Australian "Yellow Dog Dingo". To the Australian farmer the dingo is something more than a nuisance. Before the introduction of sheep it preyed

MATING DANCE OF THE LYRE BIRD

Most famous of Australian birds is the lyre bird, so called from the resemblance of its plumage to the lyre. The mating dance here shown, and photographed from a hidden position some distance away, takes place within sight of the female birds.

The pups, which number from five to eight to a litter, are born about August in a cave or burrow.

Continuing our glance at the non-pouched mammals, there is quite a number of bats in Australasia, of which the large Fruit bats (also known as Flying foxes because of their fox-like faces and furry bodies) are the most conspicuous. Of these

TWO QUEER BIRDS
At left is the tawny frogmouth, a relative of the nightjar. Its name well describes its ugly features. Below is the bower bird, so called because the male builds a bower of twigs in which it dances and pays court to the female bird. The bower is often ornamented with feathers and shells.

chiefly upon kangaroos, wallabies, bandicoots and other native animals, but sheep are easier game, and the dingo is liable to meet its end from a well-placed bullet. Young ones can be handled and petted, and become as tame and affectionate as domestic dogs; when fully grown they are less trustworthy, and can never be relied upon not to worry sheep and poultry. The dingo's hair is rather long and of a tawny colour, lighter on the underside; the ears are pointed, and the tail rather long and bushy, and white-tipped. It hunts singly or in pairs, following its prey, which consists of any animal it can master, by scent.

LAUGH OF THE KOOKABURRA

The Australian kingfisher, laughing jackass or kookaburra, has a loud laughing cry familiar to all who know the Australian bush. Unlike the European kingfisher, it is often found far from water, and lives on insects, snakes and lizards, frogs, and birds.

THE HUIA

Australasia abounds in unusual birds and the huia is an example. It is found only in the neighbourhood of some mountain ranges in New Zealand. It has orange wattles, and a long white beak.

feeding on the fruit of a large fig tree growing just outside the window of the hotel bedroom.

There are a dozen or more species of insect-eating bats in Australasia, including Horseshoe bats, Tube-nosed bats, Pipistrelle and Long-eared bats, some of which are peculiar to the Antipodes, while others have a much more extensive range.

Upwards of a hundred species of true rats and mice are to be found in Australasia, excluding New Zealand.

Australian birds run into well over a 1,000 species. One of the most famous of them is the Lyre Bird of the south-eastern parts of Australia, a bird as large as a pheasant, related to the Passeres or perching birds. It builds a nest not unlike that of a wren, though larger. Its beautiful tail is distinctive.

The Birds of Paradise are mostly inhabitants of New Guinea and the nearby islands, though there are three species of Rifle birds and one Manucode belonging to this group in north Australia. It is a truly wonderful group of birds, characteristic of the densely wooded districts, and feeding upon the wild fruits. The males are, in most species, adorned with the most extravagant development of plumage, and this is brought into prominence during the nuptial display.

The Bower birds are of particular interest because of the habit of the male

alone there are more than a dozen species, whose habits are much the same in all. By day they hang in clusters to the branches of trees, looking like so many large dark-coloured pears, though every now and then one will unfold its wings and enter into a heated discussion with its neighbour. When darkness comes the whole party, of perhaps a hundred or more, fly off to some spot where they know the fruit upon which they feed is ripe.

One of their favourite fruits is a wild fig, but they are also only too fond of cultivated fruit, and do a great deal of harm in fruit-growing districts. The writer, when staying in an hotel in Brisbane, was awakened in the middle of the night by the squabbling and screams of a large party of these bats that were

bird of building a bower of twigs in which he dances while his mate is occupied with her nest. The bower and surrounding dancing ground are generally decorated with bright-coloured stones or flowers. There are several species in Australia and New Guinea, a well-known one being the Satin bower bird of the south-eastern parts of Australia. The adult male is deep blue-black with violet-blue eyes, and he always likes to collect blue ornaments with which to decorate his bower.

The Parrot Family

The parrot family is well represented in Australasia, including as it does the remarkable nocturnal owl parrot. A more repulsive variety is the notorious Kea parrot of New Zealand, which originally fed on carrion, grubs, fruits and seeds. With settlement, the kea came to feed upon offal from the slaughter-houses and this fondness for flesh has led it to attack live sheep, pecking through the flesh to the kidneys, for which it has a particular relish.

Others of the Australasian parrot family are the White and the Black Cockatoos, the Brush-tongued Parrakeets or Lorikeets, which feed mostly upon honey, and a large number of gaily-coloured parrakeets, whose principal food is the seeds of grasses and fruit.

Piping Crows, or "Magpies", with black-and-white plumage and very musical voices, are common, and great favourites both in the east and west, while another black-and-white bird, the Magpie Lark, whose cheerful call of "Pee-wit" is constantly heard, is common throughout the greater part of Australia.

The Kingfishers of Australasia are comprised in two groups—namely, those that feed almost entirely on fish and are seldom far from fresh water, and those that are to be found in the bush, often far from water, and whose food consists of grasshoppers and other insects, lizards, snakes, etc. To the first group belongs our European kingfisher, which is represented in Australasia by species with like habits and appearance. The Australian Blue kingfisher might almost be mistaken for the European variety, while the lovely white-breasted Little kingfisher of Northern Australia is probably the smallest of all. Of the Bush kingfishers, the best known and largest is the Brown kingfisher, Laughing Jackass or Kookaburra, whose loud laughing call is familiar to all who know the Australian Bush. Insects, lizards, snakes, frogs, small mammals and birds are its food.

The Honey-Eaters

The Honey-eaters form a large family of 100 or more species, of various sizes and colours but similar habits. Their food consists chiefly of the sweet juices extracted from the flowers of the various species of eucalyptus, their brush-like tongues being specially adapted for gathering this. One of the most beautiful is the Blood honey-eater, whose name describes its colour. It is commonly found in Queensland.

Allied to the honey-eaters are the White-eyes, small greenish or grey birds with white patches around their eyes. They have a wide distribution in tropical countries, and are well represented in Australasia. Then there are the Flower-peckers, Pardalotes or Mistletoe Birds, beautiful little creatures of various colours, which feed upon fruit, berries and insects, mostly collected at the tops of the trees, though some build their

DISTINCTIVE BIRD OF NEW ZEALAND

The apteryx of New Zealand, commonly known by its Maori name of kiwi, is almost without wings, and its long, sword-like beak is used to dig deep in the ground for worms.

nests in holes that are in the ground.

The family of Flycatchers is a very large one, well represented in Australasia, and in it we find those gems the so-called "Robins" and the Blue Wrens. Of the robins, the Flame-breasted, the Rose-breasted and the Pink-breasted are all to be met with in the eastern parts of Australia. The common blue wren of the south-east, with black and enamel-like blue dress and tail pointing to the sky, is represented in other parts of the continent by even more brilliant birds.

Of more than thirty birds of prey, best known is the Wedge-tailed Eagle, which ranges over the whole of Australia and Tasmania, preying mainly upon wallabies, bandicoots and rabbits, and in many respects resembling the Golden Eagle of Scotland. The White-tailed Sea Eagle occurs in Australia, Tasmania and New Guinea, and may sometimes be seen soaring high above hills and mountains, the sun shining upon the pure white of its under surface; and the White-headed Osprey frequents the coastal regions and lakes, building its huge nest of sticks and sea-weed upon some large rock or stunted tree, and plunging into the water to capture its finny prey.

The Boobook is the most common of the owls, being distributed over almost every part of the Australian continent, and its call, "Boo-book" or "Mo-poke", is familiar to every Australian. For a long time this call, heard nightly from dusk to

AUSTRALIAN BLACK SWANS

The black swan may be called a beautiful freak of nature. Though sufficiently distinctive of Australia to have become the symbol of New South Wales, it has been introduced elsewhere in parks and ponds for its ornamental character. It has a bill of bright coral red.

FRILLED LIZARDS IN THE NORTHERN TERRITORY

Like a scene from prehistoric times is this picture taken in the Northern Territory of Australia. The pleated membrane which forms the lizard's frill is expanded in anger.

dawn, was thought to be made by the Frogmouth, another common night-flying, somewhat owl-like, species, but related to the nightjars, as a result of which the boobook is generally referred to as the "Morepork".

Australia has its swallows and its swifts, which winter near the Equator, but spread all over Australia when spring approaches; but more characteristic of the Australian bush are the so-called Wood swallows, whose flight resembles the true swallows, though they have affinities with the shrikes.

The Grassfinches, or Weaving finches, are very numerous throughout the northern parts of Australia. All are beautiful, but the most brilliant is the Gouldian finch, in a coat of many colours.

Pigeons, too, are numerous, and include the Gouras or Crowned pigeons of New Guinea, of the size of turkeys, the gaily coloured Fruit pigeons, and a great many others that feed upon seeds and berries. The so-called game birds are represented in Australia by several species of quail and by the very interesting and primitive Mound Builders, of which the Brush- or Scrub-Turkey is the best known. The male of this species builds a huge mound of leaves, and in this the eggs are hatched by the warmth of the fermenting mass.

The only crane in Australia is the so-called Native Companion, and the so-called Wild Turkey is the Australian Bustard. Plovers and other waders form a large group, and the same may be said of the many sea birds and those of the rivers and lakes, such as the Pelican and the well-known Black Swan. Two remarkable flightless birds must also be mentioned: the Kiwi of New Zealand, a relic of past ages, and the splendid Emu, which ranges over the greater part of Australia, standing nearly 6 feet in height. Its only means of escape from its enemies being by the use of its strong legs, it is not surprising that this magnificent bird should be becoming scarce in districts where it was once common.

Reptiles and amphibians abound in Australasia—snakes, both harmless and venomous, crocodiles, terrapins, lizards, toads, and frogs. There are some hundred and thirty species of snakes

alone, of which about a hundred are venomous. Of the non-venomous ones the most important are the pythons, which inhabit the northern parts of Australia and New Guinea. Of these, the beautifully-marked Carpet snake, which reaches a length of 10 or 11 feet, and the spotted variety known as the Diamond python, are the best known. Their principal food consists of small wallabies, bandicoots and rabbits. In the rivers there are several harmless water snakes, though some have poison glands. The Green Tree snake is also harmless.

In the waters surrounding the rocky coasts are several species of sea snakes, distinguished by the flattened, paddle-shaped tails. The majority are highly

STUMPY-TAILED LIZARD

With its broad, blunt tail the stumpy-tailed lizard appears to have a head at both ends of its body, and was at one time described as a two-headed lizard. The way in which the hind legs are attached adds to the illusion. Fat is stored in the tail for winter food.

TURTLES IN NORTH-WESTERN AUSTRALIA

The marine turtles, including the green turtle which provides the celebrated soup, are regular visitors to the warmer coasts of Australia and deposit their eggs in the sand.

venomous, and some of them beautifully coloured—for example, the widely distributed Yellow-bellied sea snake.

Of the large number of venomous land snakes may be mentioned the common Brown snake, which has blackish bands throughout the length of its brown body, the Tiger snake, which is yellowish-brown with darker bands and favours dry country, and the common Black snake, with red underparts, which is found in dampish places in the eastern coastal regions. But most dreaded of all is the so-called Death Adder, which lies half hidden in the sand, where it may be trodden upon, with disastrous results. It occurs throughout the drier parts of Australia and New Guinea.

Crocodiles are very common in the rivers of Northern Australia and New Guinea, the most dangerous being the salt-water crocodile, which is widely distributed throughout the East Indies and the tropical parts of Australasia. The Australian long-nosed crocodile is not dangerous and feeds upon fish.

The marine turtles, including the celebrated Green turtle of turtle-soup fame, visit the warmer coasts of Australasia to deposit their eggs in the sand of the sea-shore, while the water tortoises, or Terrapin, are common throughout the rivers of Australia and New Guinea.

The long-necked terrapin, with flattened body and long neck, deposits its eggs in holes in the river banks of southern and south-eastern Australia. Allied forms occur in the north and west.

Lizards, large and small, abound throughout Australasia, where there are more than 400 species, ranging in size from the Monitors of 6 feet in length to the small Geckos of only a few inches.

Perhaps the most interesting of all is the Tuatara lizard of New Zealand, sole representative of a family now long extinct. It is confined to the small islands off the north-east coast and is protected. Of the monitor lizards, the Lace monitor of eastern Australia attains a length of 6 feet. If disturbed in the bush, it goes crashing through the undergrowth, like some heavy mammal, to the nearest large tree, which it climbs with the greatest ease, always ascending the side farthest from the observer, and quickly reaching a considerable height. The monitors feed upon any animals they can capture, and are very destructive in poultry yards, where they devour both birds and eggs.

The Skinks are rather flat-headed, stumpy lizards numbering some 100 species in Australasia, the best known being, perhaps, the Stump-tailed and Blue-tongued lizards. The Stump-tailed lizard has a wide range in Australia, but is absent from Tasmania, whereas the Blue-tongued occurs both in Australia and Tasmania. Both are sluggish creatures which may be easily captured.

The so-called Dragon lizards, with stout heads, large bodies and long, tapering tails, include the Bearded lizard, which is common to the whole of Australia. When frightened it opens its large mouth and extends its frill, though this is small compared to the huge frill of the true Frilled lizard of western and north Australia. But perhaps the most strange-looking of the lizards of Australia is the Moloch, Horned Dragon or York Devil of west and central Australia, covered with formidable-looking spines, though quite harmless.

CROCODILE OF NORTH QUEENSLAND

Crocodiles, like the saurian shown in this photograph basking on a rock, are very common in the rivers of Northern Australia, where the climatic conditions are suitably tropical.

WAR AMONG THE LIZARDS

The habits of lizards vary considerably but their ferocity can be extreme. This is a fight to the death between two rivals. The stronger of the two has turned its opponent over.

CHAPTER NINETEEN

LIZARDS AND SNAKES

by HORACE DONISTHORPE, F.R.E.S., F.Z.S.

Giant ancestors of the reptiles. Chief representatives of the class to-day. Peculiarities of the Lizard tribe. Poisonous lizards of the American deserts. The Unique Komodo Dragon. Characteristics of the Snakes. Their food and habitat. Pythons, Boas, and others.

THE simplest definition of reptile is cold-blooded vertebrate, unprovided with hair or feathers, breathing by means of lungs, and not undergoing any transformation.

Some reptiles are viviparous, others lay eggs. None of them ever undergoes metamorphosis, but are born, or hatched from eggs, in the perfect state, only growing larger as they get older.

The skull of a reptile is articulated with the first vertebra by a single bone end. These creatures are mostly long, and, with the exception of the turtles, covered with scales. The construction of the scales and teeth varies considerably in the different orders and species. Reptiles proper are now considered to include tortoises, crocodiles, lizards and snakes; the Bactrachia or Amphibia—frogs, toads, newts and salamanders—being placed in a different class.

The ancestors of reptiles made their first appearance in the carboniferous epoch, ruling supreme on the earth long before the appearance of man, millions of years ago. Many of the earlier orders have become extinct. They included great monsters, some being nearly 100

feet long. One of the dinosaurs must have weighed quite 20 tons; another great beast possessed a double row of large horny plates running down the middle of its back, and its tail was protected by long formidable spines.

The earliest forms of birds and mammals are descended from reptiles; they in their turn being descended from the bactrachia mentioned above; the latter in all probability having been developed from the fishes.

In the secondary period, fish-eating reptiles with paddle-shaped hands and feet made their appearance. Other forms possessed wing-like membranes which enabled them to fly in the air—the wings of some of these having a span of 18 feet.

With the exception of certain snakes, reptiles have more or less degenerated, and it would seem as if they were dying off. Their numbers, as well as their size, have become greatly reduced. The crocodiles are the largest representatives of the reptilian order now living.

All reptiles originally possessed four well-developed feet, with five toes to each. In some modern groups this is not the case; there is also a tendency to

MEAL OF FLOWERS

Sinister in appearance though they are, these two lizards, a blue-tongue (left) and a Jew lizard are only feeding on the petals of dandelions. The photograph was taken in Australia.

reduction in the size of the limbs, and there are some lizards with only one pair of limbs. In snakes and some lizards the limbs are rudimentary and are represented by no more than the merest vestiges.

The existing reptiles vary very greatly in size, and some species of both snakes and lizards are very small. Some 4000 species of reptiles are known at the present day, the class *Reptilia* being divided into five orders: *Rhynchocephalia* —the Tuatara lizard of New Zealand; *Chelonia*—turtles, terrapins, and tortoises; *Crocodilia*—crocodiles, alligators, and caimans; *Lacertilia*—lizards and chameleons; *Ophidia*—snakes.

Of the Lizards, one of the most interesting is the tuatara lizard, once abundant on the New Zealand mainland;

it is now confined to a few small islands off North Island and is strictly protected. It is the only living representative of a group of reptiles which have long become extinct, and may therefore be regarded as a first-class example of a "living fossil"!

A Living Fossil

In appearance it is very like an iguana, but differs from all other living reptiles in many important anatomical characters. The vestigial organ known as the pineal, or middle eye which can be detected in the brain of nearly all the vertebrates, including man, is very traceable in the tuatara lizard.

The colour of this reptile is dark green, with some white specks on the side. It is of a stout build, and sometimes measures over 2 feet in length. Spines extend from the back of the head to the extremity of the fairly short and flattened tail, and the body is covered with scales.

When the tuatara has excavated a burrow to live in, certain species of petrel share this habitation with it, all living together on quite friendly terms. The entrance to this dwelling, which is about 5 inches wide, is lined with grass. There is an inner chamber 1½ feet long, and the right side is nearly always inhabited by the lizard, its petrel guests occupying the left side. The tuatara treats the birds and their young with consideration, but it will on no account allow another of its own species to enter the burrow. Being nocturnal in habits, it does not leave its home until after sunset. Its eggs are white with hard shells, and are laid in the sand, where they take about thirteen months to hatch out.

Wide Range of Lizards

Quite 1500 species of lizards are known at the present day, differing widely in shapes, sizes, colours and habits. They inhabit all parts of the earth, except the polar regions; but are most abundant, and are found in greater variety in the

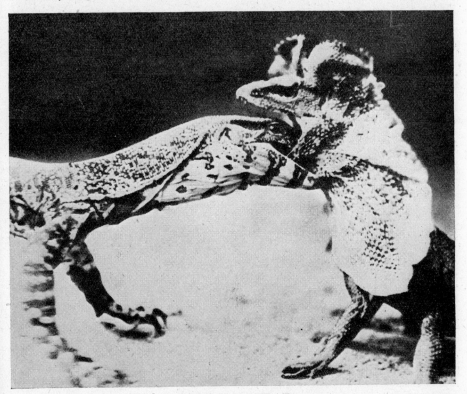

MORTAL COMBAT

Ferocious battle has been joined between this giant Australian monitor lizard (left) and the frilled-necked lizard. The monitor, commonly called a goanna in Australia, often attains a length of seven feet. It is agile in pursuit of snakes, birds and rabbits.

GIANT IGUANA

Above, an iguana is pictured in the Galapagos Islands, off the coast of Ecuador. There are many varieties of these tropical lizards of the Americas, one of the most interesting being the marine iguana. It is an expert swimmer and feeds on sea-weed, fruit and fungi.

CROCODILE'S MOST DEADLY ENEMY

The monitor is one of the largest of the lizards. One is shown devouring crocodile eggs, of which the species is particularly fond. They also chase and eat the newly-hatched crocodiles.

tropics. Some measure only 2 or 3 inches in length, but others, such as the celebrated Komodo Dragon, attain the length of 8 feet. They vary in colour from dull greys, browns and blacks, to the brightest greens, blues and reds.

The majority of lizards possess eyelids and ear-openings, and the senses of both sight and hearing are exceedingly well developed. Most of them are also equipped with four legs, with long toes, sometimes fitted with claws. Some, however, occur with only front legs, others with only back legs, and some again with no legs at all. The tongue is very variable—broad and short, and used only for tasting ; long and forked and used as a probe, or able to be extended rapidly to some length and sticky for catching flies and other insects. The teeth are also very variable. In the poisonous species they form poison fangs and are connected with a poison gland.

One of the most amazing peculiarities of the lizard tribe is the faculty some possess of casting off their tails when seized from behind. The rejected tail continues to move by reflex action, and keeps the attention of the enemy whilst the lizard escapes. The tail is not disjointed, but one of the vertebrae snaps clean across. This does not appear to cause the lizard any inconvenience, for a new tail at once begins to grow, which in time replaces the old one. Injury to the tip may cause the growth of two, or even three, new tails. The tail is sometimes armed with knobs, or spikes, and can then be used as a weapon. Those species which are equipped with a long, whip-like tail use it to lash and cut at any assailant which the lizard cannot reach with its sharp and powerful teeth.

Relations of the Snakes

Lizards are nearly related to the snakes, many details of their internal anatomy being very similar, in spite of the great difference in their external appearance.

There are tree-lizards, ground-

REPRESENTATIVES OF REPTILES LONG EXTINCT

Interesting as an example of the "living fossil" is the tuatara lizard, once common on the mainland of New Zealand but now limited to some of the smaller islands, this photograph being taken in the Aldermen group. These survivals are now strictly protected.

CHAMELEON CATCHES FLY

Two stages are here shown in the chameleon's pursuit of its prey. It has crept to within range, when, with lightning speed and unerring precision, it shoots out its tongue (above) and withdraws it (as seen at right) with the fly adhering to its sticky tip. The tongue is club-shaped and provided with a sticky secretion at its tip, whilst the narrow basal portion is composed of very elastic fibres. When not in use this basal portion is telescoped inwards and concealed from view.

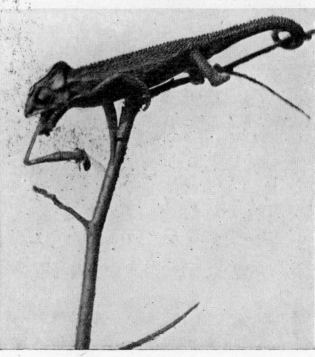

JAWS OF A VIPER

The open jaws of the viper reveal the wicked fangs through which the poison is ejected and the characteristic cleft tongue. The definite markings on the scales form a zig-zag pattern running down the back. The viper or adder is the only poisonous reptile found in Britain.

lizards, underground-lizards and water-lizards. Some are very rapid in their movements, and others are very sluggish.

Most of them catch living prey; the larger ones devour mice, frogs, other lizards, snakes, young turtles and crocodiles, fish, birds, and in fact anything they can overpower. The smaller ones live on worms and insects of all kinds. Some of the Iguanas of tropical America, which attain a length of 6 feet, prefer a vegetable diet. Only two species are known to be poisonous; one of these is found in West Mexico, the other in the South-western United States. Most lizards are quite harmless, though some of the otherwise peaceful species become fierce fighters and biters when annoyed. Some of the more gentle species can be easily tamed and exhibit a certain amount of intelligence when in captivity.

Most lizards lay oval-shelled eggs, which vary in number, and these they bury in the earth or sand to hatch in a few weeks. A few species, however, produce living young.

Lizards are frequently transported accidentally from land to land in ships and otherwise. Thus they are sometimes introduced into isolated islands and even towns. The writer once captured a black gecko which was sheltering in a bunch of bananas in a greengrocer's shop at Putney. It was a rare tropical species.

Handsome Gecko

Space will allow us to take only a glance at a few of the more interesting forms belonging to this large group of reptiles. The Geckos have the digits expanded and equipped with tiny pads and hairs; enabling them to climb up a pane of glass, or walk on a smooth ceiling. They are both harmless and

M

beneficial, as they catch numerous flies and other insects. These creatures are widely distributed and vary in size. The largest species, which measures 1 foot in length, is common in South-east Asia. It is very handsomely coloured, being light blue above, marked with large round orange and red spots. There is a small species confined to the Mediterranean region in Italy and Sicily.

The so-called "Flying Dragons" belong to another family. There are some twenty species known, confined to the Malayan region. They take long, sailing leaps from tree to tree. These "gliders" are often very brightly coloured, and look like beautiful butterflies as they float through the air. Their "wings" are formed by the outward extension of the ribs, which are connected by thin membranes of skin. When a leap is made the membranes spread out like fans, and the lizard is supported as if by a parachute. When at rest the membranes lie close to the creature's sides.

Frilled Lizard

The Frilled lizard of North Australia measures 1 yard in length and possesses a long and slender tail. It gets its name from the broad collar of loose skin round its neck, which forms a cape hanging from behind the head over the shoulders. This it spreads out like an umbrella when frightened or enraged, at the same time opening the mouth to its fullest extent and hissing in a venomous manner.

"Horned Toads" belong to the Iguana family. They are flat, squat and toad-like lizards, and are covered with many sharp spines, especially round the head. This spiny construction protects them from being swallowed by snakes. They inhabit

(W.L.)

HATCHING OUT

The camera has caught some baby milk snakes at the moment of hatching from their eggs, which were laid in a hole in the sand to be incubated by the warm rays of the sun. Some varieties of snakes lay eggs; while others bring forth their young alive.

the deserts of the United States and Mexico, and are harmless creatures. The largest species measures some 7 inches in length. It is able to squirt a thin stream of blood from the corner of each eye, with extraordinary suddenness, to a distance of 5 feet. This remarkable performance is, no doubt, intended to intimidate a foe in default of more effective means of defence.

The most helpless of all lizards is the Blind Worm or Slow Worm, which does not possess any legs, and looks like a snake. It is neither blind, slow nor a worm. It possesses small bright eyes, equipped with eyelids, and can move very quickly on occasion. This little legless lizard, a common British species, is quite harmless, and its food consists of small insects. The tail is extremely brittle,

and often breaks off when handled. Like many other innocent creatures, it is regarded with dread, and thought to be venomous by the ignorant who judge simply by appearances.

There are only two species of Gila Monsters, or Beaded lizards, which inhabit the deserts of Arizona and Mexico. They are called Beaded lizards, because their scales are bead-like in appearance. These are very poisonous animals. Their venom is powerful enough to kill a human being. They are heavy and bulky in build and possess a broad, flat tail abounding in fat. The colouring is very striking, consisting of a bright orange, or red, and black pattern—evidently warning colours. Gila monsters are sluggish in their movements, dragging the body slowly along the

KILLER OF THE EAST

Perhaps the most dreaded of the Indian snakes, a specimen of Russell's viper is shown above surrounded by young about three days old. Found in Ceylon, Burma and Siam, as well as India, Russell's viper is feared by the natives above all others.

ground, but if annoyed in any way they are able to move quickly enough and can bite very severely.

Their food is said to consist of the eggs of other lizards and snakes which they dig up out of the sand; in captivity they will feed on the eggs of hens.

The Komodo Dragon is the largest member of the Monitor family, growing to a length of over 12 feet. The only spot in the world where it occurs is the small island of Komodo in the Malay Archipelago. Komodos are very powerful beasts and can kill a fair-sized hog; being strong swimmers, they occasionally take to the sea. In captivity they become very tame and will devour chickens, and pigeons' or hens' eggs.

Before closing this brief account of the order *Lacertilia*, a few words must be written concerning chameleons. The five toes of their feet are so constructed that three of them are placed opposite to the other two, thus enabling them to grasp a branch, or any other support, very firmly. Their eyes can be moved in any direction independently of each other, and the tongue is exceedingly long and can be shot out very rapidly to a considerable distance. Their best-known and much-quoted peculiarity is the faculty they possess of changing their colour to match their surroundings. There are some fifty widely distributed species of this peculiar creature.

Characteristics of Snakes

Over 2000 living species of snakes are known. Their chief characteristics are the absence of ear openings, and movable eyelids. The entire body is covered with scales; the tongue is long, narrow and cleft, and the two halves of the lower jaw are capable of independent action. Snakes never close their eyes, which are covered with a transparent membrane, and vary in size and shape. The teeth also vary considerably in size, and so does their position in the mouth. Most snakes, on account of the structure of the jaws, are able to swallow their prey whole. The tail, which usually forms a quarter of the whole body, also varies a great deal. It may be flat and paddle-shaped for swimming, or round, and very prehensile, to enable it to grip the branch of a tree or other hold. A snake walks with its ribs, which are very numerous, and each is fastened to a section of the backbone. The joints which connect the section of the latter allow the greatest freedom of movement to the reptile. The tips of each pair of ribs are attached by muscles to one of the crosswise scales of the abdomen. The snake is able to move each of these scales independently, and thus they act as feet, and, being drawn backwards, push the animal's body forward.

Kinds of Food

About 250 poisonous snakes live on land. Some sea-snakes, which are mostly confined to tropical waters, are also highly poisonous. Not one-third of the living species, however, are known to be venomous, but there is a number of semi-poisonous ones which are unable to do much harm to man and the larger animals. Poisonous snakes put an end to the struggles of their prey with their venom.

The food of snakes is very variegated, consisting of insects, fish, lizards, other snakes, frogs, birds and their eggs, rabbits, rats, mice and other small mammals, and in some cases larger mammals. Any food is swallowed whole, and usually head

BOA'S POINT OF VANTAGE

These snakes, remarkable for their gorgeous colouring, are found in Central and South America, Madagascar and the West Indies. They belong to the family of the constrictors, like the python and anaconda, gripping their prey with their teeth and crushing it.

BATTLE OF MONGOOSE AND COBRA

In the top photograph the opponents prepare for a deadly struggle. The active and weasel-like mongoose is very often the winner, though, in the lower photograph, taken in southern India, the cobra had succeeded in wrapping its coils round its foe. Both died.

first, and alive. These reptiles are able to swallow extremely large morsels, on account of the very elastic condition of the two halves of the lower jaw and the loose construction of the bones around the throat and mouth. The teeth, being sharp and curved backwards, help to push the food down the gullet.

Snakes inhabit all sorts of localities: deserts, mountain tops, tropical forests, etc. Some live on the surface of the ground, others burrow in it; some live in trees, others in lakes and rivers; a few are to be found in the sea.

In many parts of the world snakes are treated as pets, and in olden days they were worshipped as gods.

ANGRY KING COBRA

The king cobra, or hamadryad, is one of the deadliest of the snakes. When threatening to strike, it raises itself about five feet and spreads its hood. Its bite can be fatal in a few hours.

One of the emblems of the Greek god of medicine, Aesculapius, was a snake coiled round a staff.

Now let us consider a few of the better-known and more interesting snakes ; and first we will deal with the Constrictors. These include the Boas, Pythons, the Anaconda, etc. They are mostly large in size, and of beautiful iridescent colouring. They grip their prey with the teeth and crush it to death by coiling round it when it is swallowed whole. Many of the largest species will attack a deer, and a python 20 feet long can swallow a fair-sized hog. Boas are found in Central and South America, Madagascar and the West Indies. They bring forth their young alive; whereas pythons lay eggs, and to incubate them the mother coils her body round them. Pythons are common in Australia, Asia, Africa and the Indian Archipelago. The Reticulated python is the largest snake, growing to a length of 32 feet, and a 30-foot specimen will be quite fifty years old. Its iridescent colouring, especially

DANGER SIGNAL

This "rattler" of ill-omen, photographed in Costa Rica, has adopted a threatening pose. The upraised tail makes the rattle.

Most people in England are acquainted with the Common Grass snake, which is marked with a yellow collar round the neck. It swims easily and catches fish and frogs in pond and stream. The writer once saw a grass snake in Windsor Forest, gliding along and carrying a frog which it held by the breast. Eventually it swallowed the frog head first. The female lays a string of eggs, which she hides in vegetable refuse, manure heaps, and such places where they are left to hatch.

Of the two other British snakes, the Smooth snake is rare and confined to the south of England; the writer has captured a specimen at Bournemouth.

when it has changed its skin, is most beautiful. Its food mainly consists of birds, and small deer, but it is capable of fasting for long periods.

The anaconda of South America is also a very large snake, as it attains a length of 30 feet. It matures quickly, reaching a length of over 17 feet in ten years. It is chiefly aquatic in habits, feeding on fish, birds and small mammals, which it constricts and swallows under water. This snake has been known to crush men in its formidable coils.

The Viper or Adder is the only poisonous British snake. It possesses a dark, V-shaped mark on the back of the head and a zig-zag pattern running down the back. Twenty-eight inches is the greatest length attained by this reptile. Country folk have been known to support themselves by killing adders and making and selling a viper-oil. It was supposed to be a cure for snake-bite.

Vipers feed on small birds, lizards and mice. They will enter keepers' lodges and cottages near their winter home and soon get rid of any mice that may be living there. The adder is viviparous and the young ones keep near their mother.

Rattlesnakes—so called because the horny segments at the end of the tail are loosely connected and when shaken by the reptile make a noise like a rattle—belong to the same family as the vipers. To make its characteristic sound the snake holds its tail up to vibrate it. It is most probably used as a warning.

There are some ten species of Cobras extant, living in India, China, Africa and elsewhere. The chief characteristic of these reptiles is the possession of a hood, which can be expanded and extended at will, and striking markings. These markings in the best-known, or Indian cobra are remarkable in that they resemble a pair of eyes, or perhaps a pair of spectacles. It is one of the most deadly of all serpents, and the annual death rate caused by its bite is very high.

The Hamadryad of India and other oriental countries is the largest species of cobra known, sometimes attaining a length of over 16 feet. It is extremely poisonous, and its bite will cause death in under six hours. Being quite fearless, it will attack at sight, and moreover will pursue its prey with considerable speed. Its food consists entirely of other snakes. Another very deadly snake which attacks anything that molests it is the Common Mamba of South Africa. Its food consists of birds, which it catches in trees.

WATER-SNAKE CLAIMS ITS VICTIM
Like a powerfully coiled spring released, this large water-snake has sprung from the shallows at a frog and seized it in its jaws. It will swallow its prey whole, though the frog has already become half-paralysed and ceased to struggle before being swallowed.

SWARMING CROCODILES ON THE WATER'S EDGE

*The natural home of crocodiles is in the water. When on land they remain near the shore,
often clustered together in large numbers, and ready to dive back if alarmed or attacked.*

CHAPTER TWENTY

CROCODILES AND OTHER REPTILES

by WALFORD B. JOHNSON, F.Z.S.

How to distinguish between Crocodiles and Alligators. Where various types are found. The Crocodile's remarkable camouflage and strength. Rearing baby Alligators by hand: their intelligence. Habits of Turtles and Tortoises: how the shells are constructed.

O F the existing reptiles, Crocodiles and Alligators are the largest and most specialized group. They are widely distributed throughout the hotter parts of the world, occurring in Africa, Tropical America, the southern parts of Asia and Northern Australia. They are much alike in their main broad characteristics and details. One is often asked, "What is the difference between a crocodile and an alligator?" The easiest way to tell one from the other is by the fourth tooth in the lower jaw. When the mouth is closed, this tooth fits into a pit in the upper jaw in the case of the alligator, and is then invisible, but in the crocodile there is a notch in the edge of the upper jaw which receives it, leaving it uncovered and still visible when the jaws are closed.

Best-known crocodiles are the Garial and the Mugger (two Indian species), the Nile and the Estuarine. The last named has a range from India and Ceylon to Northern Australia. In the New World there are the Mississippi Alligators and the South American

Caimans, closely allied to the alligators.

Reptiles are descended from amphibians which began life as fishes; for tadpoles are merely the fish stage of amphibians. Typical reptiles lay eggs, and some of these eggs, such as those of lizards and snakes, are contained in tough, leathery coverings reminding one of the shell-less egg which is sometimes laid by a domestic fowl. Tortoises and crocodiles lay hard-shelled eggs, which many people would assume, by their appearance, to be the eggs of birds.

Reptiles, if they have the luck not to figure in one of Nature's tragedies, seem to have the power of reaching great age with little or no sign of senility. A well-fed alligator will grow rapidly if kept in an atmosphere of the right temperature, and become a real giant among alligators. On the other hand, a specimen of a foot or so will remain much about this length if fed just to maintain it in health. This does not happen with warm-blooded animals —however we treated two foals, we could never create such large discrepancies in size and weight as in the reptiles.

Here is a scene on an alligator farm at Los Angeles where the reptiles are cultivated for their hide. They are, of course, carnivorous and will eat any kind of meat, although

FEEDING TIME

their diet is mainly fish. The power of their jaws is enormous. Their method of devouring their prey is by securing a firm hold on it with the foot and then tearing the flesh.

TINY CROCODILES LEAVE THE EGG

Crocodiles are hatched from eggs, like birds. They are then about nine to ten inches long; complete miniatures of their parents and equipped by instinct with the habits of the mature reptile. The small creatures will snap at a finger with great ferocity.

Two groups of reptiles have returned to water and made it their home. They are the crocodiles and the turtles. The latter have become marine, and travel far from land, needing to return to it only at the breeding season. Crocodiles and alligators spend their time in the water or on the banks of tropical or sub-tropical rivers. But neither of these groups of reptiles has returned to the water to live as fish. They have developed lungs which are fitted only for breathing dry air, and not for obtaining the air dissolved in water which fish use. When a crocodile or turtle dives under water, it ceases to breathe, and holds its breath until it reaches the surface again. Cold-blooded animals can hold their breath for very long periods, especially those whose kind for thousands of generations has made a habit of so doing.

We therefore find that crocodiles and turtles will dive under water to escape from danger or to hunt for food, but when there is no need for them to be submerged they will float to the surface and rest. Remarkable adaptations have been developed for such a rôle. For ease in swimming, the crocodile's body is beautifully narrow and streamlined, with a very muscular, flattened tail as the main propulsive organ. The hind feet are webbed, and are used in manoeuvring when swimming slowly. During rapid movement under water the legs are pressed to the sides, and the body is

MONSTER OF A TROPIC RIVER

There is a sly look about this alligator, basking on the banks of a tropical river, which is not belied by the reptile's behaviour, for it is quick and cunning. The slit behind the eye is part of the hearing apparatus and permits the alligator to hear when almost submerged.

LYING IN WAIT

*An African crocodile lurks in a backwater near Murchison Falls on the Upper Nile.
In such a tangle of branches and mud, its brown scaly body becomes difficult to detect
from its surroundings, as it exactly simulates their colour and texture.*

driven forward by the side-to-side lashing of the tail. The powerful muscles at the root of the tail constitute the crocodile "steak", prized as an article of food among the natives of crocodile-infested districts. These animals are protected by a covering of scales, those on the back being reinforced by a number of bony processes. A reptile bears true scales quite unlike the false scales of a fish.

The true scales of a reptile are no more easily removed than human finger-nails. They are not all of the same size or shape, but where there is little or no movement, the scales are large, and where movement must not be too restricted, such as around the neck and legs, very much smaller. All these points may be seen in our illustrations. Creatures fitted for diving and swimming under water and floating on its surface when at rest must of necessity be just about the same weight as their own volume of water. By drawing air into the lungs, they float,

and easily sink when they expel it. This, of course, means that when they float they are all but submerged, a small portion of the upper part of the head and of the middle ridge of the back being the only parts above the water-line. There, as the creature floats motionless but alert, it has to breathe, see and hear. To this end the pair of nostrils is placed on a raised pad at the end of the nose. They are slit-like openings whose edges can be pressed together when the creature is about to submerge. We see the same shaped nostrils in a hippopotamus, and for the same reason.

The eyes of crocodiles are placed sufficiently high in the head to be completely clear of the water while the creature floats. The iris of the eye does not close, as in ourselves and in many other animals, so that the pupil becomes a smaller and smaller circle, closing in slit form, as we see in cats and some snakes and lizards. The third eyelid is well developed in crocodiles. If we try to tickle the eye of one of these reptiles we see this third eyelid rapidly drawn across the surface of the eye. In ourselves it is functionless, and has been reduced to a tiny blob in the inner corner.

The ear of a crocodile—that is the membrane which vibrates in response to the sound-waves in the air—is well below this floating water-level. To get over this difficulty, a small flap of skin, which arises on the head above the water level, has grown down to cover the ear cavity, pressing against the side of the head sufficiently to keep the water out of the ear. Where this flap is above the water-line it is held slightly away from the head, creating an easily closed slit-opening which allows the air with its sound-waves to reach the membraneous ear-drum. Careful inspection of our photograph of the head of the alligator will reveal this vertical slit-opening behind the eye (page 367).

Saurian's Terrible Jaws

Perhaps the most striking thing about these creatures is their jaws. Even in small specimens the teeth can be dangerous, but in large individuals the jaws are really terrible. The teeth are not fitted for chewing or biting pieces off the prey, but for seizing and holding it. A crocodile will lie for hours on the surface of the water as motionless as a log, and looking like a log, but as soon as a fish swims sufficiently near its head there is a quick sideways action of the neck and the jaws snap down. The sharp, conical teeth have the victim in a vice-like hold. If the fish is small enough it is manoeuvred into the right position by the jaws and the front feet, and is then swallowed whole.

If it is too big for that it must be torn up into comparatively small pieces. To do this the hind leg on that side comes forward, and the back of it—that is, the upper part of the foot—is pressed against the angle of the jaws as it slides forward. The nails of the first three toes on the hind foot are strong, conical and sharp, and as they move up to the writhing victim they deeply enter the flesh and secure a strong hold. Then by a powerful stroke of the hind foot the main part of the fish is torn from the portion held within the jaws. Often the rest of the victim is literally skewered on these sharp claws and is brought back for bite after bite until it is all torn up and swallowed. Land animals and swimming birds are usually dragged under water and drowned before being dealt with.

Boughs and branches of trees which break off and fall into the rivers are carried downstream and become held up in quiet backwaters. Here the crocodiles or alligators are almost indistinguishable among the floating driftwood, for their brown colour and scaly covering almost exactly simulate the colour and texture of the bark.

When Crocodile Attacks Man

Tales of large crocodiles attacking man are common. The writer knew of a native who was fording a river in Equatorial Africa when he was seized by one of these large brutes and dragged under. It dived with him to a submerged hole in the bank and thrust him into it, there leaving him, no doubt, for future reference. The negro thought he saw a faint suggestion of light and, struggling along the hole towards it, he finally came up out of the water and into the air from a hole some yards inland from the bank. Apart from fright and teeth marks, he was little the worse for his terrible experience. When these brutes pull down a powerful victim, there is a desperate struggle, and in such a fray the teeth of the crocodile may get torn out. But each tooth is hollow and covers another in place and ready for commission.

Strangely enough, these dangerous creatures can be tamed quite easily if taken young and constantly handled. Their intelligence seems to be about on a level with that of a domestic fowl. In captivity they know strangers from their owner and can associate the clanking of a tin with the arrival of food. Specimens of the Mississippi alligator under the observation of the writer would hold out their front legs to be tickled under the arms. But if not handled they become fiercer as they grow older. With several 50-inch specimens which had been reared from the egg, it was found that the only way to handle them was to grip them by the base of the tail. If the head or neck be seized, the lashing tail can give some painful blows and the hind legs can come forward, as we have described above, and the claws will then inflict deep and painful scratches. Gripping the base of the tail prevents attack from all angles.

Reptile Anatomy

If we look carefully at crocodiles or alligators we see that, almost joint for joint and bone for bone, they are built like ourselves or any other four-limbed animal. Their elbows and knees are all very obvious, but we notice that during rest they lie flat on their stomachs with their legs straddled out beside them. Even when they walk or run, the legs of these reptiles are never actually under them, but always at their sides, so that their bodies are only just clear of the ground. This sort of under-slung carriage of the body is seen in almost all the ancient types of four-footed animals. Horses, cattle, cats, dogs and the typical modern creatures have developed longer legs which carry the body above them. Such legs act as jumping poles, and are the badge of the galloping animal.

How Crocodiles Move

Many of the reptiles are exceedingly rapid movers, but they are never able to maintain their pace. A crocodile or an alligator can run fairly rapidly, but after perhaps a couple of dozen paces it has to pull up and rest. Lizards and snakes behave in the same way. Their movement is never sustained, but always a series of rapid spurts with a few seconds' rest between them. Reptiles therefore never travel far on land from what they regard as their sanctuary and head-quarters. In the case of the crocodile family they are so much at home in the water that they take to it immediately they are molested or frightened, and so they frequent low beaches beside the river, where they may be seen sometimes in dozens, sleepily stretched out on the burning sand.. They have few enemies in wild nature, as the other creatures do not care to interfere, and are therefore not at all difficult to approach. But where they have learnt to understand the native's spear and sportsman's shot they become extremely wary, and will plunge and dive at the slightest sign of danger.

We have said that the members of the crocodile family lay hard-shelled eggs. According to some observers, these are deposited in masses of lush water vegetation scratched together to form a heap. The fermentation of the mass produces heat, which assists the incubation of the eggs. It would be useless for the parents to sit on the eggs, as their bodies are no warmer than the surrounding air. The youngsters hatch out and leave the egg-shell in a very bird-like manner. They are engaging little fellows, about 9 to 10 inches long, and almost perfect miniatures of their parents. They are born with a number of ready-made tricks, a sort of inborn equipment which we sometimes call instinct, for they can swim and dive and bite and tear their prey at once, needing no instruction from their parents or previous experience.

Crocodiles and alligators are strange creatures, which obviously are remnants of a past age. In many of their former homes they are now extinct, for in the march of civilization man finds them an intolerable nuisance. Great carnivorous brutes sometimes reaching a length of 15 to 18 feet are unpleasant neighbours for man and his domestic animals.

Another group of reptiles has taken to the water in much the same way as have crocodiles. They are the Turtles and Water Tortoises. So remarkable are they that if we knew them only as fossil deposits we should regard them as some of the most marvellous creatures which have ever inhabited the globe. But as they are alive to-day, and in the case of the Grecian tortoise can be purchased for a few pence, we just take them for granted.

Everyone knows that a tortoise is protected by a shell into which head and legs can withdraw when danger threatens. It is common knowledge, too, that crabs and lobsters possess hard shells. Many people, therefore, regard them as animals that are fairly nearly related. But there is a very wide difference. Tortoises and turtles, being reptiles, belong to the group known as vertebrates, and possess a definite backbone. We shall see later

ALLIGATOR AND ITS PREY

The alligator in the above photograph is only a young one, but well able to fend for itself. It has cornered two bull-frogs and is shown devouring one of the defenceless pair, while the other remains frozen with fright until its own turn comes to be eaten

how part of the shell is evolved from this backbone. Crabs and lobsters are invertebrates, and possess not a vestige of internal skeleton, or even of bone. Their covering is lifeless and must be cast off bodily when they have outgrown it. But the shell of a tortoise grows with the animal in just the same way as our own bones grow from infancy to maturity.

The upper shell or carapace of tortoise or turtle is formed by extensions of the spines of the backbone and the linking up of these and certain bony processes which grow upon the ribs. Within the cavity formed by carapace and plastron, or lower shell, are contained all the usual organs found in a vertebrate animal, such as heart, lungs and digestive tract.

Tortoises and turtles are widely distributed over the hottest parts of the globe. Some are flesh-eaters, others are purely vegetarians. All are toothless, possessing very parrot-like beaks which are capable of inflicting nasty bites.

Tortoises, though not indigenous, are quite able in the case of some individuals to bear the Southern English climate if given dry and frost-proof shelter in the winter. The writer has two specimens of the Moorish tortoise, a common North African and Levantine species. One walked into his bivouac sixteen miles north of Jerusalem on an April morning in 1918 and was packed up and sent by parcel post to England. The other was handed to him in 1906 by a friend who

BABY SNAPPING TURTLES NEWLY HATCHED
Completely formed, with big heads and beaks, the snapping turtles crawl from their eggs. The snapping turtle is a giant river tortoise which when fully grown attains a length of three feet. It catches its prey with a sharp snap of the jaws.

FIT FOR A BANQUET

The green turtle, here seen, provides the famous soup. It is a marine animal, but visits land during the breeding season. This photograph was taken near the Great Barrier Reef.

wanted it to have a good home as he had possessed it for over twenty-five years. Both tortoises are still living and healthy, though in the comparatively cold climate of Britain they increase but little in size.

Many of the tortoises have taken to the water habit and have evolved the usual aquatic features, but all the true turtles are purely marine animals and are often seen far from land, which they visit only during the breeding season for the purpose of laying their eggs. These are deposited in holes scooped out well above the tide-marks in low sandy beaches. They are spherical and soft-shelled. After covering up the eggs and carefully flattening down the sand above them the parents hurry back to sea. On hatching the youngsters struggle to the surface and instinctively make for the water, which they will not leave again until they are old enough to breed.

The three best known turtles are the Loggerhead, the Green and the Hawksbill. The last is the source of real tortoise-shell and the green turtle is usually associated with civic banquets. All are beautifully adapted to their sea-going habits. They are practically tailless and therefore must swim by means of their legs. The hind pair has become flattened and heavily webbed. The fore limbs have been transformed into a pair of powerful paddles which they use with wonderful effect. The body between its upper and lower shells has become flattened and thin, enabling the turtle to swim through the water with a minimum of resistance, but preventing withdrawal of head and limbs within the shell.

FRUIT BATS OF THE OLD WORLD

Of the five hundred or more kinds of bats distributed throughout the world, the fruit bats, also known as flying-foxes, are the largest. Their nocturnal forays cause great damage.

CHAPTER TWENTY-ONE

BATS—THE FLYING MAMMALS

by HORACE DONISTHORPE, F.R.E.S., F.Z.S.

Bats and their relatives. How they are enabled to fly. Their "blindness" and sharpened sense of smell and hearing. Principal species. Bats that fly over the sea. Twelve kinds of British Bats. Bloodsucking Vampires of the Tropics. Superstition concerning Bats.

O F all the denizens of the air, the Bat is perhaps the most curious and interesting. Bats are mammalia and belong to the order *Cheiroptera* of Cuvier (which means wing-handed); the *Vespertilionidae* of Gray (from the Latin Vespertilia, a bat). The order which comes nearest to them is the Insectivora (Shrews, and the like); but bats belong to an order which is entirely isolated.

Doubtless bats are descended from a form of so-called flying animal such as the "Flying Lemur" of Borneo (an entirely herbivorous creature) and the flying squirrels. These animals possess a membrane stretching from the front to the hind legs, which when extended enables them to glide downwards through the air, from branch to branch of a tree.

The most interesting parts of the structure of a bat are, undoubtedly, the ample wings which, when at rest, it wraps round itself like a cloak. These are not composed of stiff feathers, as in birds, arranged in order upon the bones of the fore-arm, but of a large thin, delicate membrane stretched between the fore and hind limbs and between the latter and, when present, the tail. The bones of the hands and arms principally support this membrane, and act as the necessary levers of motion. The sections of membrane stretched between the limbs and bones of the hands may be compared to those of an open umbrella between the ribs. Some bats have no membrane between the hind legs, and the tail is absent.

The peculiarity of the structure of the hand of a bat is that the junction between the thumb and the rest of the fingers is cleft to the wrist, leaving the thumb quite free. The latter is short, consisting of three bones, and terminates in a short and powerful hook or claw. The bones of the fingers are extremely long and slender, terminating in narrow points, not supplied with nails or claws, except in a few cases where the first finger possesses a very small hook-like nail. In some genera the first finger only consists of one long fine bone. The fingers diverge from each other, and are enclosed in the membrane of the wing, but never-

375

RARE BARBASTELLE

This tiny British bat, which is no more than two inches long, is of solitary habits in flight and also in hibernation. It is an exception to the generally gregarious habits of the bats.

theless they are movable from the wrist, and are capable of closing together, and being folded down upon the fore-arm when the wings are closed and folded. The fingers are essential in keeping the wings spread to their full extent, in stretching the margins and helping to fold it up when desired.

The muscles of the body are extraordinarily developed to give play to the necessary movement of the large expanse of wing. Parts of the skeleton of the animal, therefore, on which the muscles are fixed, are considerably modified.

The senses of smell and hearing are, as might be supposed from the extraordinary development of the nose and ears, extremely acute in bats. They possess, however, to an extreme degree, an "extra sense"—perhaps the most wonderful thing of its kind in the world. As we have seen, their wings are composed of nearly naked membrane, and are of great amplitude, and these as well as the membranous tissues of the ears and nose, are supplied with a close, delicate network of fine nerves. These can detect in advance the slightest vibrations of the atmosphere, rendering the bat as aerial in feeling as in habits; and can also take the place of sight itself.

Aerial Sensitivity

This almost incredible endowment has been proved by numerous experiments. For instance, a blindfolded bat has been let loose in a room with a thousand obstacles in its way—threads stretched across the room in various ways and directions, etc.—and it has avoided all, neither flying foul of the slightest thing, nor striking against the walls, and threading its way through the interspaces of the threads with precision.

This "extra sense" enables bats to fly through the darkest night, through the thickest forests, when of course the eyes can be of little use, in pursuit of the insects they prey on, without striking against a single tree or branch.

One genus of bat (*Nycteris*) possesses the power of inflating its body to such an extent that when this faculty is exerted the animal looks, according to Geffroy, speaking of Geffroy's Nycteris bat from Senegal, like a little balloon fitted with wings, a head, and feet. The males, and rarely the females, of a number of species of bats possess glands and protrusile sacs, situated in various parts of the body, and these are probably odoriferous. In a large number of bats the fur of the male is lighter than in the female.

These animals possess two pectoral mammae, and the young are carried, hanging head downwards, from the neck of the mother. Their powers of endurance are great. For instance, bats have been seen wandering by day over the Atlantic Ocean; and two North American species regularly visit Bermuda at a distance of 600 miles from the mainland.

All bats favour dusk or darkness, resting by day suspended upside down in caves, hollow trees, thick bushes, church towers, old barns, deserted buildings, and the like. Numbers often congregate together in a common dormitory in caves. In Java, and other islands near there, an extraordinary sight may be witnessed when a tree is covered with a vast number of huge bats all clustered together, hanging along the branches. But in the dusk they are full of alertness, pursuing their insect prey, as they utter their short, sharp cry.

Bats will not alight on the ground if they can help it. When they do the wings are folded, and their movements are clumsy and shuffling. They use their claws or hooks to catch hold of any irregularities to drag themselves along.

A great number of different kinds are known, their distribution extending to

FALSE VAMPIRE

This specimen is not a blood-sucking vampire, as the absence of upper incisor teeth proves, but feeds upon smaller members of its kind. The photograph was taken in a district of Queensland, Australia.

NOCTULE OR GREAT BAT
This picture shows the vicious-looking teeth of the noctule. It flies at great height and speed, catching and eating in mid-air the insects which provide it with its food.

most parts of the world; except the very cold latitudes.

Wandering species have found new homes, where they have become modified in relation to their new positions, and this may account for the presence of endemic bats on oceanic islands. Two species occurring in New Zealand are not found anywhere else in the world. Nine species inhabit Bachian in the Malay Archipelago. In the tropics, however, they are most abundant and reach their largest size, some species measuring quite 5 feet across the wings. Here also occur bats which are not insectivorous—the Flying Foxes, so called because their heads are similar to that of a fox in appearance, live on fruit, as, for all its 5-foot wing-spread, does the Kalong of Java. With these fruit-eating bats the sense of sight is well developed. The fur of the male is of a bright hue. The natives of Bachian eat the great fruit-eating bats, and consider the flesh to be a great delicacy.

Damage Done by Bats

Some of the bats living in Brazil are also frugivorous and do considerable mischief by devouring the fruit of fig trees. It appears to be almost impossible to prevent them. Creeping like mice, they get beneath the netting or other covering used to protect the trees.

Some bats living in Ceylon and Assam catch and devour small birds and smaller bats; but the Vampire bat (so named no doubt from the medieval legends of vampires sucking human blood) which inhabits South America seeks out every kind of animal, including man, and sucks their blood.

Vampire bats are said to be able to run, when on the ground, nearly as fast as a rat. With regard to its attacks on animals, cattle are generally bitten in the ear, but always in the places where blood flows spontaneously. They sometimes bite the wattles and crests of fowls whilst asleep, and suck their blood. The fowls generally die of this, as gangrene is engendered in the wounds. Vampires also bite horses, asses, mules and horned cattle—usually on the shoulders, buttocks, or neck, as they are better able to get at those parts on account of the facilities afforded by the mane and tail.

Many authentic accounts are given concerning these bats sucking human blood. Inflicted on the naked foot, the bites are so slight that those bitten feel nothing until the bed is covered with blood which flows from the envenomed wound in great quantities. It can only be stopped with difficulty, and the peril is great unless a cure be effected by prescribed remedies.

We now come to the inhabitants of our own lands. Some fourteen species have been recorded for the British Isles, but twelve of these, at least, are truly indigenous to Britain: the Greater Horseshoe; the Lesser Horseshoe; the Pipistrelle or Common; the Barbastelle; the Noctule, or Great Bat; Serofine; the Long-Eared bat; Natterer's, also called, the Reddish-Grey bat; Daubenton's, or the Water bat; the Whiskered bat; Leisler's, or the Hairy-Armed bat; and Bechstein's bat.

Britain's Smallest Mammal

The food and habits of most of these are fairly well known, only a few of which can be noticed here. The Little Pipistrelle, for instance, is abundant everywhere. This is our smallest bat; indeed our smallest Mammal. It feeds during flight on small flies, especially gnats, and upon the smaller moths. It was through this species that the writer made his first acquaintance with bats in the early 'seventies. They used to fly round the tower of his father's country house in Leicestershire, round the stable yard, and along the avenues and paths of the extensive gardens. The village lads, when they saw a bat on the wing, used to call to it: "Bat, bat come under my hat and I'll give you a slice of bacon"— a saying of which the author has been unable to trace the origin. The women also declared, and they undoubtedly believed it, that bats delighted in getting entangled in a woman's hair!

Britain's largest bat, the noctule, feeds principally on beetles, cockchafers and the like, which it captures and devours during flight. It has also been observed feeding on winged ants and mayflies. In 1905, the writer witnessed the evolutions of this animal when feeding. He was staying at Shepherd's Well at the time and recorded the fact as follows: "In July last, when I was staying with Mr. E. A. Waterhouse, near Sandwich, we noted the evening flight of *Rhizotrogus solstitialis* (*i.e.* an evening cockchafer). Towards dusk, along about two miles of road, they were in countless thousands, flying over the top of a small fir wood, over a cornfield, and round the telegraph poles and wires; they also flew against and settled on us. On our way home we saw a single large bat, flying in the direction from whence we had come. The next night we went to see if the same thing occurred again, and found hundreds of these big bats chasing and catching the beetles in the air, though they often missed them. A hedgehog, too, was picking up those that fell to the ground. On the third night there was not a single beetle to be seen."

Receptacle for Food

When bats catch very large beetles they require to "pouch them" in, as described by J. A. Coward, "a receptacle or pouch formed by the interfemoral membrane when the tail is bent forwards".

The Whiskered bat will enter a room in pursuit of moths, and chase them when attracted to light. Leisler's bat feeds very voraciously, chiefly on flies, of which a number of species have been found in the contents of the stomach, together with the remains of moths and beetles.

STAG-BEETLE AND CRICKET

The male stag-beetle, largest of the British coleoptera, has powerful, horn-like jaws, though these are used to crush vegetable matter rather than attack other insects. The cricket in the foreground is undisturbed.

CHAPTER TWENTY-TWO

MARVELS OF THE INSECT KINGDOM

by HORACE DONISTHORPE, F.R.E.S., F.Z.S.

*A world of teeming millions and its main divisions. Beetles, Butter-
flies and Moths. The amazing life-cycle of the Butterfly. The social
insects—Ants, Bees and Wasps. Flying insects and their habits.
The marriage flight. Wonderful organization of an ant colony.*

THE insect kingdom is so vast that it would be impossible to explore all its ramifications in a lifetime. Curiously enough, the very commonness of insects makes many people overlook their fascination as objects of study, though to the diligent observer an ordinary garden with its insects may provide as much food for thought as an African jungle.

All insects are *arthropods*—they belong to the invertebrate creatures without a backbone—and possess a segmental body, a hard outer skeleton and jointed limbs. In the insects the body is divided into three parts—the head, bearing a pair of antennae; the thorax, to which six legs are attached (the related arthropods, the spiders, possess eight legs), and the abdomen. Wings, when present, are also attached to the thorax. The mouth parts vary in the different orders. Without giving a highly scientific classification, it is necessary to enumerate the different orders recognized to-day. They may be listed as follows: *thysanura* (bristle-tails), *collembola* (spring-tails),

protura, *orthoptera* (cockroaches, stick and leaf insects, preying insects, locusts, grasshoppers and crickets), *dermaptera* (earwigs), *plecoptera* (stone-flies), *tsoptera* (termites), *embioptera*, *psocoptera* (book-lice), *anoplura* (lice), *ephemeroplera* (may-flies), *odonata* (dragon-flies), *thysamoptera* (thrips), *hemiptera* (bugs), *neuroptera* (lacewing flies), *hecoptera* (scorpion flies), *trichoptera* (caddis-flies), *lepidoptera* (butterflies and moths), *coleoptera* (beetles), *strepsiptera* (stylops), *aphaniptera* (fleas), *diptera* (true-flies), and *hymenoptera* (ants, bees, and wasps, saw-flies, ichneumons and other parasitic Hymenoptera).

It is obvious that only a few of these can be dealt with here, and some of those only very briefly. Let us start with the beetle, of which at least 180,000 species are known, over 3500 of these being found in Britain alone. The name *coleoptera* is derived from the Greek *koleós*, a shield, and *pterón*, a wing (shield-wings), on account of the fact that in most beetles the fore-wings consist of two horny sheaths, called *elytra*, which

GOLIATH BEETLE

This strikingly marked beetle is found in West Africa and grows to the size of a man's fist. The grub, which feeds on rotten wood, spends the chrysalis stage in an underground cocoon. This is of remarkable construction, having a thick ridge round the outer surface.

LONGHORN BEETLE

As the name suggests beetles of the genus Longicorn are notable for the length of their antennae. The larvae live in timber, and construct long galleries by means of boring.

cover the delicate pair of membranous under-wings used in flight. Some beetles do not possess true wings and the *elytra* are immovable, being welded together down the middle. The outer skeleton of the body is composed of chitin, a brittle substance forming the horny part of the shell which encloses the fat body, internal organs, nervous system, etc. The principal mouth-parts consist of a pair of biting jaws, called mandibles, and a second pair of horizontally-moving jaws called *maxillae*. It would be out of place to give a full description of the structure of these insects here. Suffice it to say that all the parts—antennae, jaws, legs, etc.

—vary considerably in the different families, and according to the uses to which they are put.

Beetles vary enormously in size, some being exceedingly minute, others are very large; Goliath beetles, for example, being larger than a mouse. They live in every possible kind of habitat—sound and rotten timber; in and under the bark of trees; in fungi, vegetable refuse, moss; in and on all kinds of plants and roots; in grain and granaries, the nests of moles and other mammals; and in ants' and wasps' nests, etc. Many beetles are aquatic, passing their whole life in small lakes, ponds, pools and streams. One

CONFUSION IN THE ANT-HEAP

A rose-bug which has grown up in the ant-heap shows signs of wishing to leave its hosts and hence the excitement of the worker ants, which are nervous lest the bug should disturb the pupae they are guarding. Their excitement evinces itself in their open jaws.

species is actually a parasite on the beaver. Some are very destructive, causing much damage to furniture, wooden beams and roofs, furs, provisions and the like; others are useful as scavengers, living in dung, carrion, etc. Others destroy pests and devour noxious insects.

Metamorphosis is complete in the *coleoptera*: they deposit eggs in suitable places according to the habits of the species. The larvae, which hatch from the eggs, either possess legs and are active and often predaceous, or are fleshy, legless grubs living at the source of their food supply, and differ considerably in the time they take to become full-grown. They then change into a quiescent pupa, either in a cocoon, prepared or spun by the larva, or in cells in the ground, in wood, plants, or sometimes in galls. Eventually they emerge as an adult, or perfect insect.

We will now briefly mention a few of the more striking and better-known beetles. The larvae of the larger water-beetles belonging to the genus *dytiscus* are very predaceous, feeding on tadpoles, worms, insects and small fish. The adult beetle, which is a handsome insect and powerful swimmer, is also carnivorous. It can take to flight after leaving the water. The brightly-coloured yellow and black burying-beetles are very useful, for they bury the dead bodies of small mammals, etc. Pretty, spotted lady-birds, of which more than 2000 species are

UGLY CATERPILLAR OF A BEAUTIFUL MOTH
Strange in appearance is this spine-covered caterpillar about to enjoy a vegetable meal. It devours a variety of leaves including those of the hickory and persimmon trees. It is one of nature's wonders that this hideous creature eventually turns into a beautiful moth.

N

(W.L.)

THE BEAUTY OF AN INSECT'S WINGS

Butterflies and moths are deemed the most beautiful of insects in colour and markings,
and include an immense number of varieties. The name of the order—Lepidoptera—
refers to their covering of feather-like scales. Above is a tiger moth, laying eggs

A REMARKABLE INSTANCE OF CAMOUFLAGE

Nature abounds in camouflage but some of the most amazing examples are to be found in the insect kingdom. From the photograph above it can be appreciated how closely the seemingly haphazard markings of the lime hawk moth harmonize with the tree bark.

found, are also of considerable use to man, as both they and their larvae devour large quantities of plant-lice, which are often such a pest in gardens, hop-fields, etc. The much-dreaded Colorado potato-beetle belongs to a large family of plant-eaters. It is prettily striped yellow and black, and both the adult and its larvae destroy the foliage of potato plants. It has been introduced on various occasions into this country, but has been stamped out before it has had time to become a serious pest. The *longicorns* all possess longer or shorter antennae; in some species they are very long. In a handsome species called the Harlequin beetle, on account of the markings of the *elytra*, the front legs of well-developed male specimens are extraordinarily long. One metallic-green species, found in parts of England where willows grow, is called the Musk beetle, on account of its smell. In some of the weevils, in which the head forms a beak, bearing the mouth parts at the tip, this prolongation or beak is very long. This is the case with our Nut-weevil, especially in the female. She uses her rostrum to bore a hole into a quite young nut, in which she lays her eggs.

The Lamellicorns

African Goliath beetles belong to the large group of *lamellicorns* of which our well-known Stag-beetle and the sacred Scarabeus of the Egyptians are also members. The name *lamellicorn* is given to them because the joints of the clubs of their antennae are formed of plates or *laminae*. These large beetles fly round the tops of high trees, and to catch them they are often shot, sand being used instead of bullets to bring them down, as is the custom when shooting at humming-birds. The largest of the species,

goliathus druryi, comes from Sierra Leone.

The order *lepidoptera*, as we have seen, includes the butterflies and moths. The name is derived from *lepis* (a scale) and *pterón* (a wing), and these insects are so called because their wings are covered with scales.

Butterflies and Moths

Over 80,000 species have been described, of which 2000 occur in the British Isles. All the species undergo complete metamorphosis—egg, larvae (usually called caterpillar), a quiescent stage, the pupa or chrysalis, and the adult or perfect insect. The pupae are often enclosed in a cocoon. Caterpillars mostly feed in the open on the leaves of all kinds of plants and trees; some, however, live in the wood of trees, and the larvae of the harmful clothes-moths destroy fabrics, etc.

Very much could be written on caterpillars alone—their structure, development, colours, etc., etc.—but we must press on to the perfect insects. Butterflies usually possess clubbed antennae and fly in the day-time; moths have feathery antennae and fly at night. The colours and wing-patterns of most of the former at least are very beautiful, which may explain the fact that these insects have been studied more than most of the other orders. The adults feed chiefly on the juices of flowers, which they suck up through the proboscis.

Some of the most striking butterflies in the world are the *morphos* found in South America. They are large insects, and their wings are of a most brilliant metallic blue. These lovely wings are used in the manufacture of fancy jewellery.

The best known of our own species

BUTTERFLY EMERGES FROM THE CHRYSALIS

Of the eighty thousand known species of butterflies all pass through the stages of complete metamorphosis—that is, the egg, larva (usually called caterpillar), pupa or chrysalis, and finally adult insect. The swallow-tail butterfly here seen has emerged from the chrysalis.

IN A FOREST OF GRASS

*A cockchafer crawls over the tips of the grass-blades. The eggs of this beetle are laid in
the ground and the grubs feed on the roots of grass and other plants. They remain for
three years in this condition, after which the complete insect emerges.*

HOW A GRASSHOPPER LAYS
ITS EGGS

*The grasshopper deposits its eggs in
hollows bored into the stems of plants, or,
occasionally, in decaying wood. The short-
horned species encloses the mass of eggs in
a capsule of hardened secretion.*

are the Red Admiral, Peacock and the
Common Tortoiseshell.

All the species belonging to the
order *hymenoptera* possess four naked
membranous wings which are intersected
by a larger or smaller outwork of nerves.
This is one of the largest orders of insects,
over 60,000 species being known, but by
far the most interesting of these belong to
the social families, ants, bees and wasps.

Formicidae, or ants, form a natural
family which is now divided into eight
sub-families. Quite 10,000 species of
ants must have been described to date.
In the British Isles, however, only thirty-
six species and a few varieties are known.

They vary greatly in size, structure,
colour and habits; and are found in all
kinds of situations, nearly all over the
world. Some of the most ancient and
primitive forms occur in Australia.

The various habits of ants are very
wonderful. They keep flocks and herds,
in the shapes of plant-lice, and scale
insects, which they milk, keeping some
in shelters, and visiting others on the
food-plants. The eggs of some plant-lice
are collected and kept in the ants' nests
during the winter, and when they hatch
in the spring the ants carry them out and
place them on their proper food-plants!
Some spend the whole time free in the
nests; others are root-feeders resting on
roots growing in the nests. Ants cultivate
mushroom-gardens, using pieces they
have cut out of leaves on trees with which
to manure them.

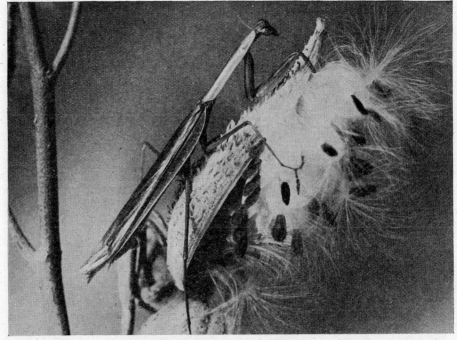

THE PRAYING MANTIS

Commonly known as the praying mantis, this voracious insect is found in the tropics and southern Europe. It is very aggressive, and its fore-legs, armed with spines to grasp its prey, are powerful weapons. Here it is seen waiting in a milkweed pod for its insect prey.

Some bring up worker ants to serve as living honey-pots to feed the rest of the colony. Numbers of other creatures live in ants' nests; some of these are fed and milked by the ants, and even placed on the ants' brood to allow them to feed on the same. Others are enemies in disguise, which prey on the ants.

The marriage flights of these, the most interesting insects in the world, differ considerably in different species. The males and females in some meet and pair in the air, flying together, others when paired fall to the ground. There are wingless males in some genera when, of course, pairing takes place in the nest between brothers and sisters. The colony-founding of ants differs considerably in different genera. The simplest form is when a female, after the marriage flight, removes her wings and founds a colony unaided. In other cases the female has to return to her own nest or to that of another colony of the same species. Others, again, force their way into the nest of another species of ants, the workers of which accept her and bring up her brood. In the coffee-fields in South America are small ants which cultivate root or scale insects. When the female goes for her marriage flight she carries in her jaws a female scale-insect. When she founds a new colony at the roots of a fresh coffee plant she places the scale insect on its roots. This is very injurious to the coffee plants, and it will at once be seen that as thousands of these females after their marriage flights are doing the same thing, these ants are very harmful to man.

We may now enlarge our survey of the insect world by considering them from the aspect of flight. Some insects spend the whole of their mature lives on the wing, saving when at rest. Such are butterflies, moths, dragon-flies, may-flies. Others, including certain beetles and earwigs, use their wings very seldom, to move to a fresh locality or to seek out the other sex. In the ants the winged forms are only developed for the purpose of the marriage flight. In various orders one sex only is winged—either the male or the female as the case may be. A good example is the Stylops, a small insect

parasitic on certain wasps, and early summer solitary bees. Cases are known of species being parasitic on an ant; and of a "frog-hopper" bug also.

The fore-wings of the male stylops are very peculiar, being large and twisted, and the hind-wings fold longitudinally. The female is a mere sack, being blind and worm-shaped, and never leaves the body of the host. Only a small part of it protrudes between the segments of the hind body of the latter. Stylops has been classed as a beetle, a view with which the writer does not agree.

Flight and its mechanism vary very much in the different orders of insects. A typical insect possesses four wings; in house-flies and other allied species they have been reduced to two, and in others

GREEN GRASSHOPPERS IN HIDING

The two insects seen in our photograph peering from the safety of a cluster of toadstools are green grasshoppers. This variety lives in inland country as opposed to the common grasshopper which is usually found in the region of the coast.

ANT HERDSMAN

The wonderful organization of an ant colony ensures a plentiful food supply: herds of various insects are tended, either in the ants' nest or on their own food-plant. In this picture an ant herdsman guards the aphis which secretes a substance called honey-dew.

they have altogether disappeared. In some cases, such as beetles, the fore-wings have become armoured wing-cases (*elytra*) for the protection of the membranous hind-wings.

Most of the orders of insects have been classified on the possession or absence of wings, and the formation or condition of the same. Some may be instanced: *aptera*, no wings; *orthoptera* (grasshoppers, locusts, crickets, cockroaches), straight wings; *coleoptera* (all beetles), sheath wings; *hymenoptera* (ants, bees and wasps, saw-flies, and a number of parasitic insects, mostly small), membranous wings; *lepidoptera* (butterflies and moths), four wings, mostly covered with scales; *diptera* (blow-flies, house-flies, hover-flies, gnats, etc.), two wings; *neuroptera* (may-flies, dragon-flies, etc.), nerve-winged insects, possessing four similar wings composed of numerous veins and scales.

Let us first consider the order of *hymenoptera* to which belong the social insects: bees, wasps and ants, with their wonderful communities which have reached a state of perfection unsurpassed by anything similar in the world. The wings of *hymenoptera* are four in number, being clear, membranous and furnished with a few branching veins, which are sometimes wanting in the smaller species. As in several other orders, the veining of the wings is a valuable help in determining the genera.

MARRIAGE FLIGHT

Various species of ants differ in the propagation of their kind. The wingless male ant pairs in the nest. Some meet in mid-air and fall to the ground, some pair whilst in flight. After the marriage flight a female casts her wings and, unaided, forms a new colony.

DIFFERENT FUNCTIONS OF AN ANTS' NEST

An ant colony provides an amazing example of high development of social life in the insect world. This drawing of the wood-ants' nest shows: A and B, Worker ants dragging twig and a dead fly. C, Quedius Brevis Beetle. D, Queen laying eggs. E, Larvae. F, Pupae. G, Winged female. H, Winged males. J, Winged males leaving nest.

One of the most wonderful instincts possessed by these creatures is their power of being able to find their way home. To test this power the celebrated French naturalist, Fabre, captured nine females of a species of wasp from the common territory of their nest. These he marked and took to a neighbouring town, nearly two miles from their burrows, and let them loose in the middle of a street. They immediately mounted vertically into the air and, rising above the roofs of the houses, instantly turned in flight in the direction where their nests were situated. Next day five of them were back again at their nests.

The present writer made an experiment which proved that bumble-bees, when seeking their nests, are guided by the recognition of local features. On August 30, 1930, he discovered a nest of bumble-bees in Windsor Forest. The entrance to the nest, a small hole in the ground, was situated close to a heavy, fallen bough. He moved the bough, and turned it over. The entrance to the nest was then about two feet behind the bough, instead of an inch in front.

Homing Instinct among Bees

Homing bees were unable to find their nest; they all flew over the entrance, hovering over and alighting just the other side of the bough where the entrance should have been. They kept hunting about, flying up and down, and always returning to the same spot, but never found the entrance to their nest until the bough was swung back to its former position. The writer also found

CARPENTER ANT

The interior of the home of the carpenter ant is here exposed to view. With their sharp jaws these ants carve tunnels and galleries in dead trees. Some of the chambers are used as dormitories, others as nurseries. Above, cocoons containing baby ants are carried away.

BUMBLE-BEE ON CLOVER

Known also as the humble-bee, this species is of vital importance to the life-cycle of flowers and fruits. They are the instruments of cross-fertilization, by carrying pollen.

that even the pulling up of some long grass near the entrance interfered with their power to find their way home. This experiment shows that the insects depend on sight alone in finding the nest, and it implies previous locality study, and exact memory of impressions received.

Queen's Courtship

In the case of the honey-bee, and indeed with all the *hymenoptera*, their very existence, food and courtship, depend on the power of flight. The queen selects a sunny day, leaves the hive, and flies off into the air in search of a mate. After a successful courtship she returns home, and soon commences to lay eggs. A queen may live for three years or more, but a worker bee often wears herself out with incessant flying in search of honey, and dies with frayed wings in three weeks or less. The male bees, called drones, are produced in some numbers to ensure that the queen may find a mate. He possesses large, powerful wings, and often has to fly for miles before he encounters his mate, and after mating he dies.

The old queen, usually before the young queen, or queens, hatch and emerge from their cells, leaves the hive and flies away to seek another abode, taking with her a large number of the older worker-bees. They fly surrounding her, and when she settles, all cluster upon her, hanging to each other with their claws, and form a huge mass of moving bees—a swarm. The marriage flight, or rather the courtship, in certain bees which are not truly social, is very different from that of the honey-bee. On July 10, 1930, at 11 a.m. summer time, the writer observed this in one of these bees. The species in question was found in considerable numbers on a level stretch of sand in Windsor Forest. The bees were flitting over the surface of the sand in every direction, some entering their burrows and coming out again in a few seconds, and all in a considerable state of excitement. Little clusters of bees could be seen here and there rolling over in the sand; on closer inspection they were found to consist of four bees. When a male had seized a female, two other males pounced upon them, and all four rolled over and over together in the sand until eventually two males broke away and flew off. This was observed with numerous different groups.

The life of the social wasps is not as completely organized as that of the bee. The colony does not last for twelve months; for towards the end of the year such larvae and pupae as are left are dragged from their cells by the workers, and thrown out of the nest to perish. Eventually all the workers die off also. Only a few young fertile queen wasps survive. These hibernate, and next year start a new colony of their own. The courtship of wasps does not take place on the wing.

The Wasps' Nest

Wasps fly for considerable distances in search of wood-pulp for the construction of their nests, food, etc. A worker wasp which visited the writer's study evidently came from a distance. When it left, it always flew straight out of the window across the length of the garden and over some trees in the distance. The writer made the following notes at the time: "Whilst writing at my study table on August 22, 1925 (at Putney), I noticed a worker wasp which had come in at the window, hovering over and flying down into a small jug which contained honey with which to feed my ants. Only a small quantity of honey was left at the bottom of the jug, and the wasp had to go right down to the bottom to get at it. On and off I found that the wasp kept coming back to the honey, so I determined to put down the times of its arrivals and departures.

"I found that it continued to come regularly from August 22 to September 9, after which date it was seen no more. It started coming as soon as my study window was opened in the morning— 7.30 a.m. being the earliest time I have noted, and 7.36 p.m. being the latest

departure before the window was shut. The times it spent at the honey varied considerably, but the time between its departure and its return was mostly about seven minutes. It was very nervous at first, and the least shake of the table, or shadow cast over the honey-pot, caused it to fly off; but eventually it got quite tame, and did not fly away even when I moved the honey-pot about. When it returned it was more deliberate than when it left, entering the window with a 'buzz' and circling over the honey-pot before dropping into it. In the morning it was generally waiting outside for the window to be opened, when it entered at

BATTLE AREA

Members of ant colonies each have a special rôle assigned to them. This thorough system provides for a means of defence against raiding parties of other species of ant, and a body- guard of warriors is maintained. In this photograph these warrior ants resist the attacks of red slave-making ants and a fierce encounter at close quarters is taking place.

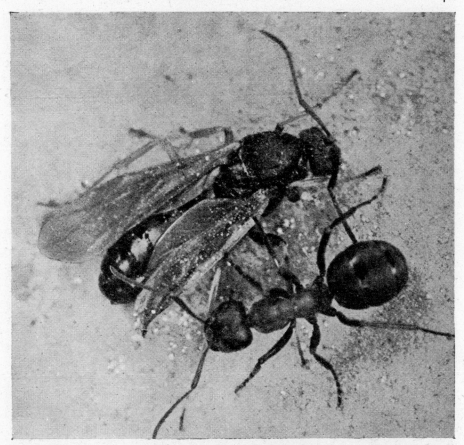

FEMALE ANT AND WORKER

*The female has just emerged from the pupa and a worker ant is stroking her wings into
shape. The wings will be retained only until the female lays her eggs.*

once; and on several occasions it continued to come during heavy rains. It was
found to make this evidently long journey
on the wing thirty-four times backwards
and forwards on an average in a day."

Wasps kill flies, blue-bottles and the
like, pouncing on to them when at rest.
They cut off the head, wings and legs,
and fly home with the body to the nest.
Here it is cut up and fed to the larvae.

The flying habits of some of the
parasitic *hymenoptera* called Braconids
vary greatly. A very interesting case is

that of a species first discovered by the
writer in the vicinity of Weybridge in
1906. It is parasitic on the wood ant,
and may be seen hovering over the nests
of the latter. These insects hover in the
air over the nests like birds of prey, every
now and then swooping down on the
ants. They hover steadily over an ant,
gradually getting nearer and nearer to it,
and when they get the opportunity,
strike at it to lay an egg between the
segments of the ant's hind body. The ant
often notices the presence of the Bracon,

BUMBLE BEE VISITING A LUPIN

*In this picture the humble-bee is seen in flight but about to open the petals of a lupin.
Though they give no honey these bees are very useful in the fertilization of flowers.*

NEW HOMES FOR OLD

The population of a hive varies from fifty thousand to as much as eighty thousand bees. When the hive becomes overcrowded the queen bee, and thousands of workers, leave to form a new colony. This is usually found before swarming by a scout sent out for the purpose,

and reaches up into the air to endeavour to drive it away, but it only removes itself out of reach. When the ant runs away the insect darts after it. The act of laying the egg is lightning quick; all one sees is a sudden dash, or strike at an ant, and next instant the parasite is in the air again. Only the female hovers over the nests.

The males of a genus of considerably smaller Bracons sport together in airy dances like gnats on warm, sunny afternoons. The writer once saw such a dance in Windsor Forest. The afternoon was still and sultry, and he noticed what he took to be a cloud of "midges" swaying gently up and down over his companion's head. Striking at them with a small fly-net, he found he had captured some small Braconids. The insects then transferred themselves to him, "dancing" over his head, in what was evidently a kind of love dance, or prelude to a marriage flight.

Another group of very small parasitica, which live on the eggs of other insects,

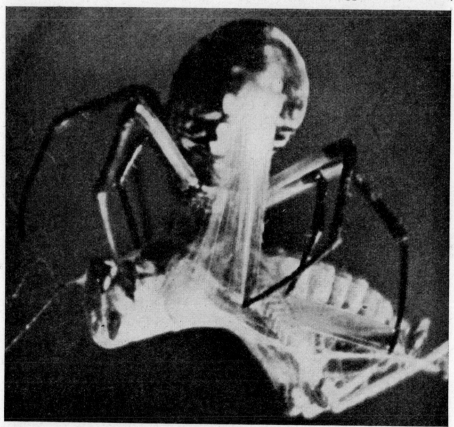

GARDEN SPIDER AND GRASSHOPPER

The garden spider has captured a grasshopper and is wrapping it round with its silken mesh. An immense number of microscopic globules are dotted on the spiral threads which divide the spider's web into a series of steps. These make the web adhesive. Spiders belong to the same sub-kingdom as insects but, with scorpions and mites, form a separate class.

DEADLIER THAN THE MALE

The female spider is practising her art of allurement by making advances to the male spider. He knows only too well that his final doom is to be devoured by the enchantress.

are called Mymarides. They possess four rather long, battledore-shaped, fringed wings, and are not very visible in flight.

The wings of Saw-flies are large, and when in repose lie horizontally on the back, overlapping each other. They are called saw-flies because the females possess an ovipositor in the form of a saw used for piercing holes in leaves, etc., in which the eggs are laid. Their larvae differ greatly from all others in the *hymenoptera*. They possess both the true and the false legs which are found in the larvae of the *lepidoptera*; indeed, they look very much like the caterpillars of butterflies and moths. These larvae do a great amount of damage, devouring the leaves of different trees, shrubs, plants, etc. A specimen of a certain saw-fly was beaten

off spruce by the writer in Windsor Forest. Fortunately no others have been found, as they might become a serious pest. It has been introduced from Europe into Canada, where it has caused immense damage in the spruce forests.

Male and female ants possess wings used only during the marriage flight. The males wander about and very many are devoured by birds.

The wings of ants are used in classification, but not to the same extent as in some other families in the *hymenoptera*. This is chiefly because the workers, which are most often seen, are always wingless, and the females are most frequently found after they have lost their wings. The males are wingless in some species, even in different sub-

INSECT PROVIDED WITH FORCEPS

*The earwig packs away its delicate but large wings by means of the forceps at the
tail (seen in the photograph) which are as serviceable as fingers. An unusual feature
of this insect is that the female broods over her young like a hen over her chicks.*

YELLOW SCORPIONS OF NORTHERN INDIA

The group pictured is of a baby a few months old, a one-season-old scorpion and a member of two seasons' growth. The sting, although most painful, seldom proves fatal.

families, and the females in others. When one speaks of a wingless female one refers to those born entirely without wings. Two of the species in which the males are wingless in this country may be mentioned. The most interesting case is that of an ant called *anergates* ("without a worker"), for in this species there are only males and females. This ant was first discovered in Britain by the writer and W. C. Crawley in the New Forest on July 23, 1912. Indeed, this is the only occasion on which it has been found in Britain. The female is fully winged, but the male is a most curious object; it walks with difficulty and looks like a cripple. These ants are adopted and brought up in the colony of a totally different species. The workers of the host species carry about these males, but pay little attention to the virgin females. Mating takes place between brothers and sisters, and after fecundation the female flies away to seek out a new nest of the host species, where the workers then kill off all their own much larger males and females. The abdominal segments of the alien queen expand enormously, the segments of the same being represented only by small black bars separated by broad spaces of white membrane, and she lays numerous eggs.

SURFACE OF A STRANGE AND CROWDED WORLD

An extraordinary wealth of life is to be found beneath the familiar still water of a pond, from which the frog has emerged, after passing through the aquatic, tadpole stage. This aquatic life includes the lowest forms, visible only beneath the microscope.

CHAPTER TWENTY-THREE

TINY CREATURES OF POND AND STREAM

by RAY PALMER, F.R.E.S., F.Z.S.

Living world beneath the microscope. The rudimentary organisms.
Borderline of vegetable and animal kingdom. Soft-bodied water
creatures. Aquatic insects and their prey. The life-history of the
Dragon-fly. Carnivorous Beetles. Water-born Flies. Water-Spider.

MOST people have little idea of the extraordinary wealth of life to be found in the water of a stagnant pond, or the wonderful beauty of some of the lowest types of animal life; yet even the commonest aquatic creatures shown in an aquarium always arouse exceptional interest, while the myriads of animalcules revealed by the microscope cause almost incredulous wonder to those who behold them for the first time. The naturalist takes some water from a muddy pond and puts a drop under his microscope. He finds a great multitude of minute organisms whose very existence is unsuspected by ordinary people. It is, indeed, like a peep into another universe.

On first examining these strange beings through a microscope the number and variety amaze us; some wriggle along waving long tails, some are covered with coats of vibrating bristles; some seem mere specks of jelly, others are of more complex structure, often having the most grotesque appearance imaginable.

The whole field of vision may be a mass of moving specks too small to see in any detail. There is a commotion at one side, a current in the water, and the tiny specks are all moving as though in a whirlpool. Suddenly the cause of this disturbance appears—a strange flattened creature with rounded ends and what look like bubbles clearly visible in its transparent body. A current of water seems to be rushing along its sides, and if the lighting is properly adjusted we can sometimes see that this current is caused by a fringe of short bristles vibrating rapidly and rhythmically when the creature is in motion. There are larger and more rigid bristles at either end, also a funnel-shaped mouth in the middle of the body into which flows a stream of water carrying particles of food.

This curious creature is *Paramoecium*, commonly called the Slipper animalcule, because its shape is something like a slipper or the sole of a boot. In ponds where there are decaying leaves this

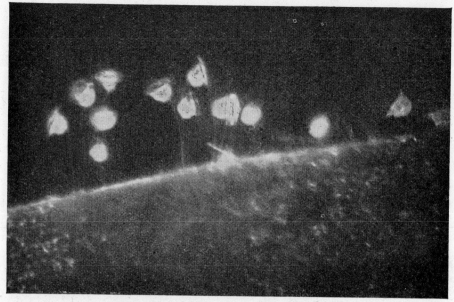

THE BEAUTIFUL BELL ANIMALCULE

This micro-organism, though resembling a plant, is animal, as is evident from its activity and mode of feeding. Each vorticella consists of a bell-shaped, flower-like head on a long stalk.

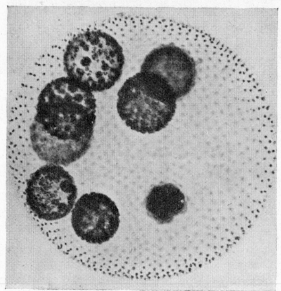

BORDER-LINE BETWEEN ANIMAL AND VEGETABLE

A tiny green speck in the water is the volvox or globe animalcule. It consists of green spots joined by threads.

animalcule is usually plentiful, particularly in autumn. One of the largest of the *Protozoa* (whose bodies consist of only a single cell), it is less than a hundredth of an inch long, and is invisible without the aid of a microscope.

The *Paramoecium* is an example of a group of animalcules called *Ciliates,* because their bodies are covered with short hairs called *cilia,* by the vibration of which they both swim and obtain their food supply from the current of water that is drawn towards them. In one sample of water these kinds of organisms may predominate to the exclusion of all else, as they breed with extraordinary rapidity by the simple process

FRESHWATER POLYP CATCHES WATER-FLEA

The hydra, or polyp, has entangled its prey in its tentacles which will bend over and absorb it. The water-flea is a minute transparent crustacean.

of division. Another sample may contain quite different creatures, especially if taken from the muddy bed of a shallow pond with plenty of light. In this case *Paramoecium* may be quite absent, and instead we may find flat, broad organisms, pointed at both ends, which swim with an undulatory motion, having a long filament at the head end. These creatures are usually bright green with a red spot looking like an eye at one end. The long, waving filament is like a whip-lash, and they are called Flagellates, from the Latin *flagellum*, a whip.

Another organism that lives on the mud at the bottom is the *Amoeba*, considered the most primitive form of animal life. It is little more than a minute speck of living jelly called *Protoplasm*. There is a denser spot in the middle called the nucleus, and there are usually one or more clear spaces called vacuoles; but the amoeba itself has no definite form and can be watched changing its shape as it moves about. It frequently stretches out long projections as temporary limbs, which are known as pseudopodia; then the rest of the body follows with a flowing motion and absorbs the limbs. The amoeba feeds by flowing round and taking within its body any smaller objects it encounters and later ejecting the indigestible remains through any part of its surface. It multiplies by the simple process of division. The nucleus divides in two, then each nucleus breaks completely away from the other, surrounded by half the original protoplasm.

The Globe Animalcule

At certain seasons pond-water is often full of little semi-transparent green specks, just visible to the naked eye. If examined through a hand lens in a jar of water these green specks will be seen moving about, so it is evident they are alive. Through the microscope we find that each of these objects consists of a perfectly round globe or sphere, made up

DIVING BEETLE ATTACKS

This carnivorous beetle does not hesitate to attack any member of the pond community. It has affixed itself to a large tadpole by the suction cups with which its front legs are provided and thus preventing its prey's escape, attacks it with its powerful jaws.

of little green spots joined by a network of colourless threads. Each green spot has two flagella, and it is by means of these that the sphere moves through the water with a rolling motion, and from this action it gets its name of *Volvox*, though it is often spoken of as the Globe animalcule. It is doubtful, however, if it is really of an animal nature; botanists claim it as a plant, while many zoologists still maintain that it is an animal. It is undoubtedly on the border-line of the animal and vegetable kingdoms, as are a number of other micro-organisms.

Free-swimming Animalcules

There are many other free-swimming animalcules, but some of the most beautiful and interesting are found attached to water plants and other objects. Get some weed out of any pond and examine it with a hand lens in a glass of water. Very likely tiny patches of greyish "mould" will be visible. Examination under the microscope will most likely show that we have a group of beautiful creatures known as Bell animalcules, or *Vorticellae*. Although resembling plants in appearance and mode of growth, they are certainly animals, as is evident from their active movement and mode of feeding. Each *Vorticella* consists of a bell-shaped, flower-like head on a long, flexible stalk. The head is perfectly transparent, and usually visible in outline only, unless seen against a dark background. Around its mouth is a fringe of cilia hairs, which vibrate so as to make a vortex in the water, and thus draw in particles of food. Then after a few moments each vorticella seems to tire; its head assumes a globular form and is drawn back, while the stem is twisted into the shape of a spiral.

A group of bell animalcules seen under a good microscope with proper lighting is one of the most beautiful objects imaginable; but there is little doubt that the Rotifers are the most interesting and remarkable of the pond's micro-inhabitants. These creatures are much more highly developed than the protozoa, but most of them are quite invisible without a microscope, the largest being only about a fiftieth of an inch long.

Rotifers are found in a great variety of forms—some elongated, others rounded or pitcher-shaped—but they all have a definite mouth with a pair of jaws, and distinct internal organs, including a gizzard. At the tail end is a "foot", with which the rotifer can clasp plants and other objects. At the head end are two or more wreaths of cilia, the rotary action of which constitutes the chief characteristic of these strange creatures and has given them their name of rotifers or "wheel-bearers". Many kinds of rotifers are free-swimming, but some of the most beautiful are fixed to a permanent abode for the greater part of their lives. Of these, the Tube-dwelling rotifers are the most remarkable, particularly *Melicerta ringens*, known as the Brickbuilder.

Method of Tube Construction

This quaint little creature surrounds itself with a tube formed of pellets of mud and debris collected out of the water. Examining pond-weed through the microscope we find a little brown tube, about one-twentieth of an inch long, attached to a leaf and no inhabitant visible. We notice that the tube is built up of little pellets arranged like bricks in a wall. If we keep quiet we shall presently see something begin to emerge from the tube. Two rounded pale-coloured objects

AQUATIC SNAIL

The ramshorn, illustrated above, is the largest of the aquatic snails. An interesting feature of this freshwater family is the possession of two means of respiration—gills which enable the snail to breathe under water, and lungs for obtaining air from the surface.

looking rather like a mouse's ears appear first, followed by a kind of neck. The head of the rotifer then opens out into a flower-like form, two larger lobes above and two smaller ones below, with something in the middle remarkably like a face. All at once there is a commotion in the water and small objects are seen rushing towards the expanded head, which waves about gently in all directions. The rotifer is feeding, and at the same time collecting indigestible matter for building purposes. After a few moments we see the head bend down to the edge of the tube; two little arms appear, and can be seen carefully depositing another brick on the wall and patting it into position.

Coming to somewhat larger creatures, we must mention the Hydra, which is a fresh-water representative of the sea anemones. A large hydra fully extended may reach a length of half to three-quarters of an inch, but many are much smaller. It consists of a hollow body which can be contracted into a globular form or extended long and thin, and surrounded at the head or mouth end by a number of tentacles. It is usually fixed at the base to some object, though hydras have the power of moving about. When in search of food it spreads out its tentacles and waits until a small creature such as a cyclops comes in contact with one of its tentacles. This immediately becomes entangled in sticky threads that are shot out from certain cells, together with a toxic secretion, then the tentacles all bend over and push the prey into the mouth. Later on the indigestible remains are ejected through the same opening. The reproduction of the hydra is remarkably plant-like, consisting mainly of a process of budding; young buds growing out of the side of the parent, developing tentacles and eventually breaking away. It can also produce large, seed-like eggs, which become detached and hatch into tiny hydras.

Blood-suckers

Among soft-bodied aquatic creatures are many kinds of worms, of which the best known are the leeches, which are blood-suckers. The medicinal leech, distinguished by orange bands on the back, was that used by doctors in the old days for withdrawing blood from persons suffering from feverish complaints. The Horse leech is common in many farm ponds, and fastens on to the nose or mouth of horses or cattle when they come to drink.

There are many kinds of Water snail, and the most completely aquatic is the River snail (*Paludina*), which can breathe water by means of gills like a fish. This large snail has a shell about 1¼ inches long, greenish-brown with spiral bands, and is unique in possessing a horny lid which closes the shell when the animal has withdrawn inside. The river snail is also remarkable for the fact that it is viviparous: the eggs hatch internally and the young are produced alive. This snail is found in canals and sluggish rivers. It is also frequently encountered in lakes and reservoirs.

Other types of fresh-water snails resemble land snails in their manner of breathing air by means of lungs. They can remain under water for a very long time, but periodically come up for air.

Mussels are near relatives of the snails, but are bivalves, having the body enclosed by a pair of flattish shells instead of one only. Fresh-water mussels, of which there are several kinds, exist in large numbers in the beds of slow rivers, canals and lakes. At the lower end they have a long "foot" with which they anchor themselves in the mud and move about, and at the upper end are an inlet and an outlet siphon; through these the animal sucks in and ejects water to obtain its food supply.

Water-Fleas

Some of the most abundant of the smaller inhabitants of stagnant ponds are minute Crustaceans known as water-fleas. The two principal types are called *Daphnia* and *Cyclops*. Daphnia is a little, oval-shaped creature with its body enclosed in a pair of transparent shells through which all its internal organs are plainly visible. It possesses two pairs of feathered antennae, by means of which it swims through the water with a jerky motion. It feeds on the microscopic animal and vegetable life of the pond and does much to purify the water, as well as providing abundant food supply for fish in the larger ponds and lakes. The *Cyclops*, though closely related to the last species, is quite different in form. It is pear-shaped, with antennae spreading out sideways from the head, and a single eye from which it gets its name. Until they hatch the female carries her eggs about in two large bundles at each side of the base of the tail, looking rather like tiny bunches of grapes.

DEATH OF A FROG

A giant water-bug is seen to have dragged the body of a frog to a corner in order to begin its feast, watched by a circle of dragon-fly nymphs waiting for what is left.

A larger crustacean is the Fresh-water Shrimp, which is very active, and about half an inch long, with a curved, brownish body and a large number of legs. It prefers running water, and is commonly found in streams where starwort and water-cress grow.

A larger member of this class is the Crayfish, which is really a little fresh-water lobster. It is found in many rivers or even quite small streams, and apart from its smaller size greatly resembles the marine lobster in form and habits.

Some very curious crustaceans are the Fish Lice (*Argulus*), which are blood-suckers on various kinds of fresh-water fish. They have very flat, disc-shaped bodies, with four pairs of swimming legs and a pair of suckers at the head-end. They stick on to a fish for a time, to feed, but periodically come off and swim about.

There is a large number of insects which are aquatic at some stage of their existence, and they are all of remarkable interest, but only a few representative species can be mentioned. The various adaptations and contrivances by which these insects are adapted for their mode of life make fascinating study. Insects are essentially aerial creatures, all of them needing to breathe atmospheric air in the adult stage. With the possible exception of certain ancient and primitive groups— such as the Stoneflies, Mayflies and Dragon-flies—we may assume that insects were evolved on land and not in water. Yet many insects have taken to the

water at a later stage in their evolution. In all cases these insects breathe air in the adult stage, and many of their larvae are unable to obtain oxygen from the water, but pay frequent visits to the surface.

Aquatic Bugs

Out of twenty-three natural orders into which insects are now classified, no less than ten orders contain aquatic representatives, while in four of these all the species are aquatic. The order *Hemiptera*, or Bugs, containing some 1300 British species, has a small group of about fifty species which are completely aquatic, and show great diversity in form and mode of life.

One of the best known of the aquatic bugs is the Water Boatman; and one has only to see this insect in its natural element to realize how suitably it is named. Its body is distinctly boat-like in shape, and the two back legs are formed into long "oars", which stretch out on either side of the body when the insect is at rest.

Another aquatic bug of very different form is the Water Scorpion. There are two kinds of water scorpions in Britain, though they are so different in appearance that at first sight they would appear quite unrelated. One is flat and broad—leaf-like, in fact—with no appreciable thickness; while the other is long and thin in every part, with a rounded, stick-like body. The Common water scorpion can mimic a dark brown dead leaf to perfection; while the rarer Long water scorpion is an aquatic stick-insect. In both insects the front legs are modified into pincers for seizing prey. Nothing comes amiss in the way of food; only the hardest types in insects, such as shiny, well-armoured beetles, escape. Most

other insects and larvae of all kinds, tadpoles and young newts are caught and sucked dry; indeed, anything will be tackled which is soft enough for the insect's beak to pierce.

Both these water scorpions seem to need very little air, and can remain submerged for long periods. The long tail in both species is really a breathing tube; thus when the insect needs air all it has to do is to walk backwards up an aquatic plant until its tail-tip touches the surface and air can be drawn in.

The water scorpions are recluses of the insect world; they need looking for or they are never seen; but some of the insects which frequent the surface of the water are very noticeable by the most casual observer. The best known of these are some very active long-legged insects, which glide swiftly about on the surface of the water with quick, jerky motions. These are called Pond Skaters, and there is a number of species which are difficult to distinguish.

Of more unobtrusive habits is the Water Measurer, a long, thin insect with hair-like legs. It also lives on the surface, but moves much more slowly, and is usually found in sheltered positions under the banks.

The Larval Stage

Water-Bugs, to which group all the foregoing insects belong, are aquatic throughout the whole of their life; now, however, we come to several groups of insects which live in the water during their immature or larval stages only. Dragon-flies show the most striking example of this type of life-history. The young dragon-fly—the larva or nymph—is an ugly creature crawling about in the mud of a pond bed, deriving air from the

WEIRD DRAMA OF POND LIFE

*A giant water-bug is seen swooping down at the top of the picture while just beneath a
smaller water-bug is eating a water-boatman. A water-scorpion, with queer, elongated
limbs, crawls in at the left. In the foreground another water-boatman looks on.*

water without going to the surface. It
has a special extensile pincer arrangement
under its head, with which it catches
soft-bodied aquatic creatures; unlike the
bugs, it has jaws with which it can chew
up and devour solid food. Tadpoles form
a favourite food of the larger kinds of
dragon-fly larvae.

Dragon-fly Nymph

In the later stages of the life of the
dragon-fly larva it has rudimentary
wings, and is usually called a "nymph".
As it approaches maturity the nymph
shows a liking for the surface of the

water, and the four large spiracles on its
thorax become open, so that it can
breathe air to a certain extent. One day
the great moment of its life arrives; it
climbs up a reed stem and leaves the water
for ever. The final transformation of a
large dragon-fly is a wonderful spectacle
to behold and a sight never forgotten.

The dragon-fly is well named, for it is
indeed a dragon of the air to all smaller
winged insects, which find it impossible
to escape such a powerful pursuer which
pounces upon them at terrific speed.

The aquatic life of a dragon-fly may
be as long as three years in some of the

The pupa of a caddis-fly has its limbs free, not encased in a hard shell like a moth pupa. The hind pair of legs are long and fringed with hairs, in a similar manner to the "oars" of the water boatman. When ready to assume the winged state, the caddis pupa forces its way out of its case, and uses its long legs to row itself to the surface. There it floats for a moment or two, and then the skin splits open and the winged caddis-fly emerges with remarkable rapidity. Caddis-flies live for only a short time, and are unable to take food in their mature state, as their mouth-parts are merely rudimentary.

Water-Beetles

Beetles form a very large order of insects containing thousands of species, but only a few are aquatic. The true water-beetles can be divided roughly into three distinct groups, which we may call the carnivorous water-beetles, the vegetarian water-beetles, and the whirligigs. The carnivorous beetles are the best known; they prey on other aquatic creatures which they catch below the surface. Their method of swimming is characteristic, and consists of an energetic rowing action of the back legs only, these being feathered with stiff bristles to form oars. The best known species is *Dytiscus marginatis*. All water-beetles obtain air from the surface, and in the present example the beetle has a hollow space under the wing-cases as an air reservoir in direct communication with the spiracles or breathing pores on the upper surface of the abdomen. At the tip of the body is an aperture protected by fine hairs that never become wetted, so that a bubble is always visible between them. Thus the hinder part of the body is much lighter than the rest, and so the

beetle always rises to the surface tail first. The unwetted bristles at once break the surface film, and thus allow the beetle to expel the vitiated air from its reservoir and take in a fresh supply.

Encased in horny armour, this beetle fears no enemies and boldly attacks any members of the pond community.

The larva of *Dytiscus* is quite as fierce and voracious as its parent. Unlike the adult, the larva cannot take solid food, but has sharp, pincer-like mandibles, by means of which it can suck the life-blood of its prey.

The largest British species is the great black water-beetle, which belongs to the vegetarian group. It is lethargic, and lives among dense growths of aquatic plants, on which it feeds. Having no occasion for vigorous motion in chasing prey, it swims rather feebly by working its fringed legs alternately, and uses both the middle and hind pairs. The female deposits her eggs in a curious silken cocoon attached to a plant stem. Unlike its parents, the larva is carnivorous, but of sluggish habits and feeds mostly on snails.

Whirligigs, which constitute the third group, are very much smaller, and are familiar objects on any pond or ditch during the summer. They are carnivorous, feeding mainly on insects that alight or fall on to the surface of the water.

Two-winged Flies

Many kinds of insects are spoken of as flies, usually qualified by a prefix—such as dragon-flies, may-flies, caddis-flies, etc.—but the term "flies" by itself is only properly applied to members of the order *Diptera*, or Two-winged Flies. As indicated by their name, these insects have only one pair of functional

The fis

and hin

wings;

and are

seen m

"Daddy

projecti

liquid s

only a p

Flies

both sp

other ty

are aqu:

very few

The

quito fa

in stagn:

tubs. T

creature

and tho

bristles.

tail end

the surf:

the wate

ONE OF NATURE'S MARVELS—A DRAGON-FLY IS BORN

The larva of the dragon-fly may spend years in the water; but there comes a time when it leaves for ever. It climbs the stem of a reed and the transformation into the adult insect occurs as seen above. The empty nymph skins are seen at the foot of the picture.

LOVE SERENADE OF A TOAD

A male American toad puffs out his throat to make the resonant sound which attracts his mate. Mouth and nostrils are closed and air is driven into the balloon-like organ shown.

and so escape downwards into the water. It is only the female gnats and mosquitoes that are blood-suckers, males feeding on vegetable juices and nectar from flowers.

There are small flies known as Midges which have aquatic larvae, some of which are sufficiently well known to have been given distinctive English names.

One type is the Phantom larva of the midge *Corethra*. This larva is so transparent as to be practically invisible in the water as long as it remains motionless. The only visible parts are its small black eyes and a pair of air-sacs near each end of the body.

The Rat-tailed Maggot is the larva of a large, bee-like insect called the Drone-fly, which is commonly seen on garden flowers at the end of the summer. The maggot lives in foul ponds where there is much decaying matter, in the water that collects in the hollows of

beech trees, and even in the drainings from cattle-yards and manure-heaps. In such situations it must obtain its air supply from the surface while feeding amongst the filth below, and to do this it uses what is in effect a diver's air-tube. The tail is several times as long as the creature's body, and is telescopic, so that it can reach the surface to suck in air.

Spiders and Mites

With these few examples we must leave the aquatic insects, and turn our attention to the Spiders and Mites, which form a large class of Invertebrates with a few aquatic representatives.

Only one species of spider really lives *in* the water, though there is a number which frequent margins of ponds and streams, and even run on the surface. Spiders differ from insects mainly in having eight legs instead of six, the body divided into only two parts instead of three, and in the absence of antennae.

The Large Water Spider is similar in form to many land-dwelling species, and is about half an inch long. The abdomen has a downy covering which does not get wet, so that when the spider dives it takes down a bubble of air surrounding the hind portion of its body, and it is only this which makes its life below water possible. The water spider spins silk, and thus makes a remarkable underwater nest. This is like an inverted thimble anchored to the weeds, and the spider fills it with air by carrying down bubbles. Inside this silken thimble the spider rests and keeps a look out for passing prey, being able to breathe air meanwhile and to replenish the supply from the surface when necessary. The eggs are laid in a special chamber at the top of the nest, and then the female keeps guard below until the young are hatched. The young spiders generally use at first natural cavities such as empty snail shells for hiding in, filling these with air.

The remarkable development of frog and toad from the egg to the tadpole, and finally to the four-legged, air-breathing amphibian is seen on pages 424–5.

This brief account gives merely a rapid survey of some of the outstanding examples of lowly aquatic creatures, whose number is legion.

NEWTS EMERGING FROM A POND

A common dweller in ponds and ditches is the tailed amphibian, the newt. Newts are ravenous feeders on worms and insects and are very tenacious of life, reproducing lost or injured limbs. They pass through a tadpole stage like frogs and toads.

POISONOUS TENTACLES OF THE SEA-ANEMONE

This photograph was taken underwater by a scientific expedition at Bermuda. It is in such tropic waters that the sea-anemone, of world-wide distribution, attains its greatest size and most vivid colouring. The tentacles are armed with innumerable stinging cells.

CHAPTER TWENTY-FOUR

LIVING FOSSILS OF THE SEA

by F. MARTIN DUNCAN, F.R.M.S., F.Z.S.

Tiny builders of the chalk cliffs. Nature of the sponge. How Sea-anemones capture their prey. Reef-building corals. Worms of the sea. Structure of Starfish and Sea Urchin. The Molluscs. Octopus, Cuttlefish. Nature's jet propulsion. Bivalves. Crustaceans.

FORMS of Invertebrate life exist in all parts of the sea—in the shallow tidal inshore waters, the open surface waters of the ocean, and in the cold, dark depths of the ocean abysses—decreasing, so far as is known, in the deeper waters where daylight fails to penetrate.

They include representatives of the most ancient forms of life, so little changed in habit or aspect, that they might well be termed "living fossils", closely resembling the ancestral forms which have been preserved in the oldest of the fossil-bearing rocks.

Only a very brief outline of some of the more striking examples is possible, for a detailed account of one group alone would fill the pages of more than one large volume. Therefore we have selected as examples from the Protozoa, or simplest one-celled forms of life, the Foraminifera, which, though mere microscopic specks of living matter, yet are capable of forming protective coverings composed of carbonate of lime extracted from the surrounding sea, or of sand-grains and sponge spicules. The name Foraminifera has reference to the numerous minute openings in the protective shell, or test as it is termed, through which slender protoplasmic threads are pushed out from the body mass. It starts as a single chamber and may persist as such, though in most species the chambers increase in number and assume the most varied and beautiful shapes; some like miniature nautilus shells, others flask-shaped, or tiny spheres, or slightly tapering cylinders.

Of those forms that secrete a test of carbonate of lime, the species called *Globigerina* is of particular interest, for not only are the chalk cliffs and downs of England largely composed of their fossil remains, but these organisms swarm in the surface waters of the Atlantic to-day. The test is composed of a series of globular chambers, the walls of which are perforated by numerous pores, while in many, though not all floating specimens, the outer surface is beset with delicate radiating spines which help to buoy up the little organism in the surface

429

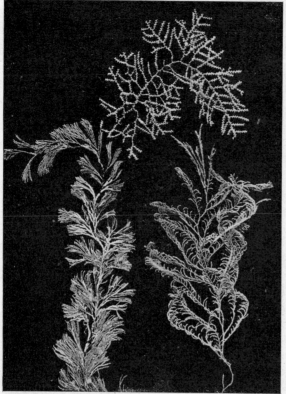

FEATHERY COLONY OF HYDROZOA

Often cast up on the shore are slender branching sprays, golden-brown in colour, like those shown above. Colonies are built up, by a process of budding.

the Earth's history, to rise as solid earth—a new Atlantis—above the surface of the waves.

Another interesting family of these unicellular creatures are the Radiolaria, so called from the radiate character of their minute skeletons. They are most abundant in tropical seas, where at depths of 2000 or 3000 fathoms great beds of Radiolarian ooze spread out for thousands of miles; while the fossil skeletons of their ancestors are found in the ancient Cambrian rocks and the strata of each succeeding geological epoch. In most species the skeleton is composed of silica obtained in the first instance in solution from the surrounding water, and built up by the tiny organism into the most beautiful designs, often in the form of globular, conical, star- or disc-shaped tests adorned with long, slender, radiating spines.

The exact nature of Sponges was a sore puzzle to naturalists from the days of Aristotle and Pliny, who considered them as being a form of life half animal, half plant, down to the early years of the nineteenth century, when the observations of the Scotch naturalist, Dr. Robert Grant, first established their true animal character.

If you will look at your bath sponge carefully, you will see that the whole mass of it is perforated by innumerable small holes, together with slightly more prominent, larger holes scattered about at intervals over the surface. The smaller holes are the openings leading into the

waters, and to form a support for the strands of protoplasm issuing from the pores and forming a living network for the capture and absorption of food. On the death of the Foram the tiny test sinks slowly towards the floor of the sea, loosing in its downward passage the more soluble radial spines. So, just as in the seas of past geological epochs, to-day at depths of 1000 or 2000 fathoms, on the floor of the Atlantic, great beds of light-coloured, oozy mud, known as Globigerina ooze, are forming; destined, perhaps at some distant date in a future epoch of

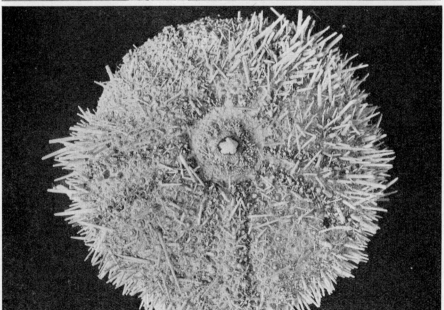

HEDGEHOG-SKINNED CREATURES OF THE SEA

The upper illustration shows a starfish with radiating limbs covered with an immense number of tiny tentacles which enable it to move. Below is the sea-urchin, protected by a spiny shell, each spine being movable at the creature's will. The sea-urchin is edible.

VARIED FORMS OF

At left, above, is the common sea-mat, frequently washed ashore after a gale. It forms a colony of tentacled animals called polyzoa. At right are shells of the paper nautilus.

interior, and known as the inhalant canals, through which the sea water bearing minute organisms is drawn and passed on along the radial or flagellate canals, ultimately to be discharged from the large openings of the exhalant canals. By the constant rhythmic movement of thousands of minute lashers, the water is circulated throughout the sponge, and food particles brought into contact with certain cells and assimilated by them.

The three main divisions into which the sponges are grouped are founded on the character and composition of the skeletal structure; those belonging to the division known as the *Calcarea* being characterized by a skeleton composed of calcareous material, while the second group, the *Hexactinellida,* all possess six-rayed spicules; finally, the third group the *Demospongia,* comprise a vast assembly of forms in which the skeleton may be composed of siliceous spicules of various shapes. These spicules of silica or carbonate of lime, which are such a characteristic feature of sponge structure, take very varied patterns, often resembling needles, anchors, crosses and stars.

The Glass-rope sponge and the Venus Flower-basket sponge are striking examples, the so-called rope of the former being composed of immensely long spicules, while in the latter the spicules are built up into a lattice-work skeleton.

The *Calcarea* mostly inhabit shallow water, and their spicules composed of carbonate of lime are three- or four-rayed, or needle-shaped. To the *Demospongia* belong the most widely distributed and dominant forms of the present day, including the large Neptune's Cup sponge, the fine-textured, cup-shaped Turkey sponge and the Bath sponge.

Rudimentary Bodies

The feathery branching Sea-firs, the true Jelly-fish, the Anemones and Corals, and the Comb-bearer Jelly-fishes, though so diverse in size and external appearance, all belong to that great division of invertebrate life known as the *Coelenterata,* whose members are distinguished by possessing but a single body cavity, or coelenteron, with but a single opening at one end, serving for all the purposes of digestion and the circulation of fluids.

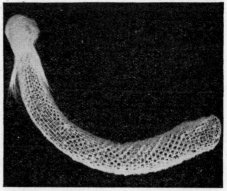

LOWLY MARINE ORGANISMS

At left, above, are the microscopic specks of living matter called foraminifera which form a protective shell from lime in the sea. At right is the Venus flower-basket sponge.

Entangled in the masses of seaweed thrown up on shore after a gale, one may frequently find slender branching, pale golden-brown objects, slightly horny in texture, whose graceful stems have a serrated edge which on closer inspection will be found to consist of a number of tiny semi-transparent cells.

Process of Budding

These very graceful, horny-textured sprays are built up by a process of budding into colonies of living animals composed of a multitude of individuals living an associated life, and at certain seasons of the year producing numerous specialized individuals charged with the vital business of the perpetuation of the species. They are reared in transparent urn-shaped receptacles, from which they ultimately make their escape as tiny medusae or jelly-fish in which the sexual organs are developed, and whose off-spring will in their turn become the asexual founders of new colonies. The *Scyphozoa*, to which belong the large jelly-fishes of our summer seas, also pass through this curious alternation of generations as it is called, in the course of their complete life-history, though in a modified form.

The gaily tinted Sea-anemones have a wide geographical distribution, being present in the colder seas as well as in sub-tropical and tropical regions, where they attain their greatest size and most vivid colouring. Many beautiful species are to be found in the rock pools and caves round the coasts of Britain. They are all extraordinarily voracious creatures, and capture and paralyze their prey by means of special stinging-thread cells, or nematocysts, with which their numerous tentacles surrounding the mouth are furnished. The anemone attaches itself to the rocks by its rather sucker-like base, and although normally leading a sedentary life, it is capable of slow gliding movements, or, should a change of situation prove desirable, float-ing away. Some anemones associate themselves with hermit-crabs, leading a curious existence anchored to a whelk shell inhabited by the crab. The anemone secures the advantage of transportation during the crab's wanderings in search

HOW THE ANEMONE IS REPRODUCED

The plumose anemone shown above (a British species) has developed a second individual by the process of budding.

of food, while the hermit-crab, when at rest, is partially hidden from view by the fully expanded anemone.

The anemones link up with the corals through the genus *Edwardsia*, small, slender anemones, usually living buried in the sand with only their tentacles expanded above the surface. They appear to represent a primitive and ancient stock, and are probably living representatives of the ancestors of the Stony corals or Madreporaria. In fact these stony corals might be termed anemones that have taken to secreting a dense limy skeleton. It is from the calcareous parts of their prey, plus the salts of lime in solution in the sea, that the hard, stony skeletons of the corals are built up.

Reef-building corals can only flourish in warm tropical seas where the temperature never falls below 68° F., and may rise to 86° F., and where the water is not only highly aerated by the constant movement of the waves, but is pure and free from sediment, and also contains an abundance of living organisms.

Where Corals Flourish

Such conditions are found in the neighbourhood of islands surrounded by deep water—conditions existing in the warmer waters of the Pacific, Indian, and Atlantic Oceans, the Red and the Caribbean Seas. Although the reef-building corals cannot exist at any great depth beneath the surface waters, on account of the rapid fall of temperature, about 20 fathoms being the maximum depth for luxuriant growth, many solitary cup-corals flourish in colder waters and at greater depths, some indeed being essentially inhabitants of the deep seas.

There are three typical forms of coral reefs: the shore-reefs, which fringe the shores of islands and continents; the encircling or barrier reefs, which, rising from deep water at a greater distance from land than the shore-reef, encircle an island or stretch along the coast. Thus the Great Barrier Reef stretches along the north-east coast of Australia for a length of nearly 1200 miles. Finally there is the atoll or lagoon reef. As one approaches an atoll island from the sea, it usually presents the appearance of a low, more or less circular belt of land dotted with a few feathery-crowned palm trees, and fringed by a belt of white breakers that for ever thunder against the reef, while within the ring of the reef the quiet waters of the lagoon shine like a burnished mirror.

The Worms of the sea are most diverse in form, size and habit. Some lead relatively sedentary lives, others wander over the floor of the sea, while many construct tubular dwellings of varied shape and material. The segmented worms, or *Annelida*, which constitute a very important group, all possess bodies divided externally into segments or rings upon which more or less numerous bristles are present, either mounted on projections called parapoda or false-feet down the sides of the body, or resting in depressions in the skin. The so-called many-bristled worms, or *Polychaeta*, comprise a great assemblage of marine segmented worms that are inhabitants of the sandy shores, rock pools and open sea. They are complex creatures possessing, in addition to the numerous bristles, tentacles and external breathing organs,

or branchiae, and pass through a series of changes of form before becoming adult.

Perhaps the most unwormlike of these Polychaetes is the so-called Sea Mouse, which may sometimes be seen on wide sandy shores at low tide. Its stout body is oval in shape and may measure 8 or 10 inches in length, its back being covered with a dense felting of hair, greyish-brown in colour. But the most striking feature is the armature of compound hairs and prickly bristles all down the sides of the body and mounted on the numerous parapoda.

The *Nereidae* are a family of marine worms notable for their long, slender, segmented bodies, flat heads and large, horizontally moving jaws; in fact, they

BREAKFAST OF A LIVING SEA-FLOWER

The open anemone is about to seize and devour a small fish. This has come in contact with the nettle capsules which shoot out poisonous threads, paralysing and enveloping the prey. In spite of their innocent, flower-like appearance, anemones are extraordinarily voracious creatures. Their substance is gelatinous and fleshy.

remind us very much of centipedes in general appearance. Two species, popularly known as Cat-worms, are familiar to all sea anglers, who often use them and the nearly related Lug-worm for bait; while a third species, known as the Creeper, also used for line-fishing on some coasts, is the giant of the family, reaching a length of 18 inches or more.

Strange Marine Worms

One of the strangest looking of the tube builders is the so-called Bull's-head or Vari-footed worm. Both popular names well describe its general appearance, for the head and front part of the body make up what appears to be a caricature of a bull's head, while the false-feet are of varied shapes and sizes. Although leading a sedentary life, this curious worm becomes brilliantly phosphorescent at night. Many tube-building worms show a marked preference for certain materials for the construction of their homes; thus the Fan Sabella, whose feathery branchial plumes are a deep red or brown banded with lighter tints, makes its tubular home chiefly of mud, resembling, when finished, a piece of narrow-bored rubber tubing sticking up out of the sand. The little Sand Mason worm, on the other hand, builds a slightly conical-shaped tube composed of carefully selected sand grains of a given size imbedded in a cementing mucus secreted by the builder. The Shell-binder builds a far more elaborate structure resembling a miniature tree trunk and stunted branches, covered entirely with fragments of shells, tiny pebbles and sand grains. Lastly, the Serpulids secrete carbonate of lime from their special secreting glands, and form their tubes entirely of this substance.

The deeply interesting Lamp-shells, or *Brachiopoda*, to give them their scientific name, although at first glance presenting some outward resemblance to bivalve molluscs, are quite distinct from them both in structure and life-history, the only feature in common being the bivalve shell. Their popular name is derived from their resemblance in shape to ancient Greek and Roman lamps, over 6000 fossil species having been recorded from the different ancient sedimentary rocks, while barely 150 living species exist at the present time in shallow water. The majority live attached to rocks, usually by a short, horny stalk. The dorsal, or brachial valve, in the higher genera has attached to its inner surface a pair of curious calcareous bars on loops, from which these animals have derived their scientific name of Brachiopoda (arm-footed, from the Greek *brachion*, arm; *pous*, foot). These curious "arms" when first described were supposed to resemble in structure and origin the "foot" of the Mollusca.

Spiny-skinned Creatures

The Starfishes, Sea-urchins and their relations make up a great and wonderful group of marine invertebrate animals called the *Echinodermata* (from the Greek *echinos*, hedgehog; *derma*, *skin*), or spiny-skinned animals. They possess a complicated internal anatomy and have an almost world-wide distribution. The group includes, in addition to the true starfishes and sea-urchins, the fragile, slender armed Brittle- and Sand-stars, the Feather-stars and so-called Sea-lilies, and the Sea-cucumbers or Holothurians. The principal organs of the body are arranged and repeated almost like the spokes of a wheel round a

GIANT CLAM BARED BY THE TIDES

In the tropic seas of Australia are to be found colonies of giant clams which may measure about four feet in diameter and weigh several hundred pounds. They are a constant source of danger to pearl divers, on whose limbs the valves of the clam close like a vice.

FISH OF FLAME AND FLOWERS OF STONE

central axis. Their development forms one of the most interesting and remarkable life histories in the animal kingdom.

We might take the common Five-fingered starfish, found on most shores in the rock pools at low tide, as a typical example of the first division, the *Asteroidea*, to which all the true starfishes belong. It has a star-shaped body consisting of a central body-disc from which grow out five symmetrically arranged, gradually tapering rays or arms. On turning the starfish over on to its back, we can then see in the centre of the body the five-rayed aperture that communicates directly with the mouth. From this aperture radiate five narrow grooves, each traversing the entire length of a ray, filled with a great number of tubular bodies terminating in sucker-like ends. These are the tube-feet by means of which the animal creeps along over the rocks, and, on occasion, grasps its prey. At the end of each ray there is a small bright red "eye-spot" sensitive to light, and near it what looks like a small tube-foot minus its terminal sucker, which functions as an olfactory organ for guiding the starfish to its food. The mouth opens through a short passage into a capacious stomach, portions of which project into each ray, and this large digestive bag is capable of being partially everted through the mouth and folded over any object desired for food, so that the process of digestion can actually start outside the body. Starfish also have remarkable

CUTTLEFISH RESTING

The tentacles of the creature are extended as it lurks among the rocks. Cuttlefish are found in many parts of the world, and are frequently seen off the coasts of Britain.

powers of replacing lost limbs, a new one growing out from the base of the severed member, though rarely attaining to the size of the original limb.

The Sand and Brittle Starfishes are all creatures with small disc-shaped bodies, and long slender rays that very easily break up, and may be regarded rather as appendages than actual portions of the body, as in the Asteroidea. Many of these slender-armed brittle starfish are delicately tinted in hues of rose-red, pale yellow, mauve and brown. Perhaps the two most curious species are the Shetland Argus and the Gorgon's-head, whose arms are repeatedly forked, so that a regular series of interlacing branches is formed. Both argus and gorgon's-head are dwellers in fairly deep water off shore.

The Sea-urchins are all more or less globular or oval-shaped animals, with a skeleton forming a complete cuirass of plates of hard carbonate of lime except for the space around the mouth, and covered with a forest of spines. These spines are attached to round knobs, or bosses, by cylindrical sheaths of muscular tissue, by which they can be moved in all directions. By the combined movements of the spines and tube-feet, the sea-urchin is able to walk over the floor of the sea and to climb over the rocks. The mouth, which is placed on the under surface, is provided with a complicated dental structure arranged into a five-sided conical skeleton, not unlike an old-fashioned horn lantern, and called Aristotle's lantern, in memory of the famous philosopher to whom we owe the first accurate description of a sea-urchin. The fossil remains of their ancestors are abundant in the sedimentary rocks formed in the seas of Mesozoic and Palaeozoic times.

The so-called Sea-cucumbers which compose the fourth division of this great group are easily recognised by their more or less cylindrical, elongated body, rather like a warty cucumber or gherkin in shape. They have no complete stony test, like the sea-urchins, their sausage-shaped bodies being enclosed in a tough, leathery skin in which are embedded countless small spicules, often of very great beauty of colour and shape. A fringe of tentacles surrounds the mouth, and serves to pass the sand and mud, containing particles of organic matter on which the Holothurian feeds, into the mouth. Down the entire length of the body, tube-feet arranged in zones afford a means of transit; though in some species like Synapta, which lead a sedentary life buried in the sand, they are entirely absent. Certain large species which abound in tropic seas are used as food. Partly sun-dried, partly smoked, they are known as Trepang, or Bêche de Mer, and find a ready sale in the markets of the Far East, particularly in China.

Finally we come to the lovely so-called Sea-lilies, cup-shaped, flower-like animals with feather-like, branching arms, attached to the ground by a jointed

BATTLE BETWEEN CUTTLEFISH AND LOBSTER
One of a series of photographs taken underwater as part of an instructional film, this picture shows a contest between cuttlefish and lobster—in which the lobster has taken the initiative. The common cuttlefish is generally not more than about eighteen inches in length

stalk; and their near relations, the Feather starfishes. Now chiefly restricted to tropical seas, they are the last living representatives of a class that must have swarmed in the seas of past geological epochs, judging by the abundance of their fossil remains. They differ from all other members of the Echinodermata in that, instead of crawling about by the aid of tube-feet, mouth downwards, they remain more or less permanently fixed in one spot and mouth upwards; either growing on a long, slender, stony stalk, or, as in the Feather Stars, anchored by little clawed hooks, or "cirri", to seaweeds and stones. The Rosy Feather Starfish is not uncommon off the south-west coasts of Britain at depths of 10 fathoms.

Rosy Feather Starfish

It possesses a small, disc-shaped body, from which arise the long, slender arms clad with short fine branchlets or pinnules, that give them their feather-like appearance. The upper surface of each arm has a groove corresponding to that of the Common Starfish, but lined with filaments or cilia instead of tube-feet. It is by the movement of these cilia that particles of food are swept into the mouth, which is also situated on the upper surface of the body. Attached to the under surface of the body are the small, slender anchoring hooks. In its larval stage the rosy feather starfish very closely resembles a miniature sea-lily. The young first escape from the egg as free-swimming larvae, which soon settle down and become fixed to a base by a slender stalk that gradually lengthens, and the little creature looks like a microscopic tulip with closed petals. Gradually the graceful rays grow out, and eventually the little feather starfish parts from

the supporting stem and swims away by undulating movements of its slender arms.

Of all the forms of invertebrate life inhabiting the sea, the molluscs are probably the most familiar. More than 50,000 species are known, of which more than half inhabit the sea. Many are almost microscopic in size, while others are veritable giants. The octopods and cuttlefishes are active creatures, capable of swift movement, armed with formidable weapons both for capture of prey and for defence, while their sight and senses are almost as highly developed as in some vertebrates. Other molluscs creep slowly about on the floor of the sea, or lead an entirely sedentary existence, fixed throughout the greater part of their lives to one spot, depending for their food to be brought within reach by the ebb and flow of the tides.

Structure of the Mollusc

All possess a soft, unjointed body which is largely surrounded by the fleshy, flexible skin of the mantle, provided with special glands that play a very important part in the secretion of the shell, chiefly composed of carbonate of lime, and in the formation of the pigments which give the varied colours to the shell. Reproduction in all cases takes place by means of eggs, which, in some species, are produced in prodigious quantities, the common oyster, for example, being credited with producing more than 3,000,000; but only a very small proportion ever reach maturity, the majority being eagerly devoured by other denizens of the sea. In the more highly developed molluscs the sexes are separate, but in some of the lower forms they are united in the same individual; or the same individual may, at different

TERROR OF THE DEEP

The octopus, photographed on the sea-bottom under powerful lights, raises itself on its eight legs like a giant tarantula. The body of the common octopus is the size of a football.

stages of its life, possess only male or female organs, as is the case, for example, in the so-called Slipper Limpet.

The molluscs are divided into five main groups or classes—(1) the *Cephalopoda* (literally head-footed), comprising the Octopus, Cuttle-fish, Squids, Paper and Pearly Nautiluses; (2) the *Gastropoda* (literally stomach-footed), by far the largest class of molluscs, including the whelks, winkles, cowries, cones and volutes, harp-shells, limpets, etc., etc.; (3) the *Scaphopoda* (literally boat-footed) comprise a small but distinct group that differs from all the other molluscs in several ways. Their shells are tubular in shape, slightly curved and open at both ends; while one end is slightly smaller, so that in shape and outline the shell somewhat resembles a miniature elephant's tusk. They live buried under the sand in fairly deep water. The fourth class, the *Lamellibranchia*, so called because their gills are usually in the shape of broad plates (from the Latin *lamella*, plate), are also sometimes called Bivalves because the body is enclosed in a shell formed of two pieces (valves) hinged together on one side, so that it opens like a box. All lead a more or less sedentary life, some temporarily or permanently attached to the rocks or similar solid objects; while others burrow in submerged timbers, soft rocks, and in the sand and mud. They have no definite head, neither do they possess the ribbon-shaped tongue or radula found in the Cephalopods and Gastropods. Of the

*The corals, which may be described as anemones possessing solid skeletons of lime, take on
most varied and intricate shapes. Among them swim tropical fish gaily striped and*

SUBMARINE GARDEN

patterned. Their colour harmonizes or contrasts with that of the coral and, as in this coral pool, the whole scene with its shifting lights and colours is full of mystery and living beauty.

445

RETREAT OF THE HERMIT CRAB

The hermit crab inhabits the shell of a mollusc. This forms a refuge in which its unprotected tail can find a secure covering.

efficient organization, strength, ferocity and large size; in fact the Giant Squid is the largest of all invertebrate animals, fully grown specimens measuring over 50 feet in total length. Perhaps the most striking and distinctive feature in the external anatomy of these remarkable animals is their long, extremely active, sucker - clad arms. These arms, eight or ten in number, and encircling the mouth, are not jointed, neither have they any supporting bony skeleton, but they are strong and appallingly efficient. They are beset with numerous suckers, cup-like organs which firmly grasp any prey that come within their reach; and in the Squids and Cuttlefish two of the arms are specially adapted for reaching out beyond the others, and have specially modified suckers at their ends, for seizing and holding their prey. The mouth is furnished with a pair of strong, horny jaws with which they can crunch their prey, while the toothed tongue, or radula, rasps the food into smaller fragments. Another characteristic organ is the ink-bag, which secretes an inky fluid that can be discharged at will into

fifth class, the *Amphineura* (literally double-nerve, in reference to the nerve system of these molluscs), the most familiar examples are the Chitons or Coat-of-mail molluscs, which have the distinctive feature of a shell divided up into eight plates.

The Cephalopoda are the most highly organized of all the molluscs. They stand out from all other invertebrate animals not only on account of their strange appearance, but by their highly

the sea so as to form a cloud, and serves as a means of concealment and escape from foes. It is from the contents of the Squid's ink-bag that artists' sepia paint is manufactured. There are two large eyes, placed one on each side of the head. The Cephalopods can crawl about head downwards by means of their arms, but they are swift and expert swimmers, either progressing slowly by rhythmic movements of their arms, or propelling themselves rapidly through the water by the aid of a special organ called the funnel. This is in the form of a muscular tube, opening into the mantle cavity at one end, and to the exterior at the other. Water is drawn into the mantle cavity through the wide mantle aperture, which is then closed by special muscles, and the water thus retained under strong pressure is then forcibly driven out through the partially retracted orifice of the funnel, the ejection of this jet of water driving the animal along backwards with rapid darting movements. Although moving backwards, the animal can see quite well the direction in which it is going, and uses its arms to steer its course. Thus millions of years before man appeared on earth—for these Cephalopods are of very ancient origin—Nature had evolved and perfected the principle of jet propulsion.

Ten-armed Mollusc

The squids and cuttlefishes are distinguished by possessing ten arms. The

ARMOURED KNIGHTS OF THE WATER WORLD

Freshwater relations of the lobster, crayfish are similar in appearance and display a like degree of ferocity. This photograph shows how two crayfish engage in battle, making effective use of their claws. The combatant on the left has lost a leg—though this can be grown again.

MITTEN CRAB CATCHES A FISH

*The crab has grasped a small fish between the largely developed claws which give it its name.
Like all the marine crustacea, crabs possess segmented limbs which are covered with a hard,
limy armour. This, in a sort of moulting process, is discarded and replaced at intervals.*

body is elongated and "stream-lined".
While the cuttlefishes are mostly found
in shallow waters off the shore, the squids
are a large and diverse group, containing
many strange forms, including the Giant
squids, which live in the Atlantic and
attain an over-all length of fully 50 feet.
These giant squids form part of the food
of the toothed whales, whose bodies often
bear numerous scars scored by the
powerful suckers of the squids.

The members of the order *Octopoda*
are provided with eight sucker-clad arms,
the prehensile tentacles of the Decapods
being absent. They are active, powerful
creatures, for the most part living on or
near the floor of the sea. The Common
octopus of northern waters sometimes
spans 12 feet across from tip to tip of
opposite arms, while the Giant octopus
of the Pacific attains a span of 30 feet.
The Paper Nautilus is one of the most
remarkable of the tribe. Unlike most of
the octopods, the female has an external
shell of great beauty and delicacy formed
from glandular secretions from the skin
of two specialized arms of the little
argonaut which tightly clasp it. It is the
lovely cradle in which the mother
deposits her eggs and carries them until
the young are ready to take on a free-
swimming existence. The male argonaut
is quite small, and does not secrete a shell.

The Pearly Nautilus is the sole living
representative of a once large and
thriving group of Cephalopods called
Ammonites, which flourished in the seas
of Palaeozoic times. It is found in the

seas around New Caledonia, the Fiji and Philippine Islands, where it lives in relatively shallow water. The natives capture it for food, and at one time its large and handsome shell was of some commercial value. The shell is distinguished by the fact that it is subdivided into a number of compartments by a series of transverse walls or septa, the animal living in the last formed and largest chamber.

Types of Bivalve

It would be difficult to imagine a greater contrast, both in form and habit, than that which exists between the active, highly organized Cephalopods and the Lamellibranchs enclosed in their box-like shells and, for the most part, leading sedentary lives. Yet these bivalve molluscs often display great beauty of form and colour in their shells and attain to considerable size. The giant Clams of tropical seas sometimes measure over 3 feet in diameter and weigh a good 500 lb. Some show remarkable adaptations of structure in response to their environment, while many species are of considerable economic importance. A striking example of adaptation is that of the so-called Ship-worm, with a rasping shell reduced to two small valves that cover only a small portion at one end of its long, naked, wormlike body. In the old days of the wooden ships it was a scourge to mariners, boring into the ship's timbers below water-line; while towards the end of the eighteenth century, Holland suffered serious inundations through the damage done to the piles and other timber-work of the dykes by the ship-worms.

Among those species of lamellibranchs that bore into submerged rocks, the external surface of the shell is beset with rows of sharp spines which present a file-like appearance, as in the Piddock, while in those that burrow into the sand there is a remarkable development of the foot, as in the Razor-shells and the Cockles, enabling them to dig down and disappear beneath the surface with great rapidity. In the Scallops, Oysters and Mussels we have examples of species which supply valuable food; while the so-called Pearl oyster is the source from which the finest pearls are obtained, and its brilliant nacreous shell is employed in the manufacture of pearl-buttons, knife-handles and a great many other articles of commercial value.

Foot of the Gastropod

In structure and habits the marine gastropods show a decided advance from the lamellibranchs, among the chief outward distinguishing features being the broad, flat, muscular foot which occupies the entire under-surface of the body, and the possession of a spiral univalve shell. The remarkable development of the foot enables the Gastropod to creep or glide over the rocks, the seaweeds and floor of the sea, while it also serves as a means of secure attachment to the rocks or any object that affords a convenient foothold. The gastropod possesses a distinct head which is furnished with two eyes, and there is usually one pair or more of contractile tentacles; while the mouth is furnished with a toothed, ribbon-like tongue for rasping and breaking up food. Almost every conceivable modification of the spiral occurs, from types like the Ear-shell or Ormer, in which the spiral is reduced to a few apical whorls, the body whorl being inordinately large, to the long, slender spiral of the Screw-shells,

P

(W.L.)

with fifteen or twenty whorls, gradually decreasing in size from base to apex. In many species the spiral shells are very beautiful both in form, surface texture and colour; and for this reason gastropods have always been very popular with shell collectors, who, in mid-Victorian days, when shell collecting was as popular a hobby as stamp collecting is to-day, were ready to pay very high prices for a single uniquely marked and coloured specimen. Among some of the most lovely are the cowries, cones, olives, volutes and harp-shells. While many marine gastropods are vegetarian in habit, browsing upon the seaweeds, others are definitely carnivorous. Some act as natural scavengers in devouring dead fishes and other sea creatures; while others seek living prey, boring neat round holes by means of their rasp-like tongues in the shells of their unfortunate relations, the lamellibranchs, and sucking them out of house and home. Certain species of whelks are very serious pests on the oyster grounds, where they devour large numbers of young oysters. The large species of cones that live in tropical seas can be very dangerous if handled incautiously, for the barbed teeth of their radula have a basal poison gland and are capable of inflicting serious, sometimes fatal wounds. Although the Common Limpet clings with amazing tenacity to its position on the rocks when the tide is out, it becomes an active creature when submerged, creeping along the rocks to browse upon the coating of fine green weeds that cover them, particularly at night, and displaying a remarkable homing instinct.

The marine crustacea comprise a vast assemblage of animals most diverse in habit, size and shape, yet all possessing in common certain well-marked features.

Thus the body and limbs are more or less distinctly divided into segments covered with a hard, limy armour or tough skin, which is completely moulted from time to time as the animal increases in size; while many species pass through a most remarkable series of changes in form before the adult stage is reached.

Some Curious Life-histories

Indeed, so dissimilar are young forms from the adult, that in many instances the relationship was unrecognized, the young larva, when first discovered, being described as distinct species. There is one type of larva, however, known as the nauplius, which occurs in the life-history of many widely different species. It has an oval, unsegmented body with three pairs of limbs surrounding the mouth, and a single simple eye in the middle of the head. The Common Shore Crab, for example, passes through quite a remarkable metamorphosis, ere reaching the adult form. Mother crab at certain seasons of the year carries on the underside of her body a vast number of eggs. From these escape queer little creatures with helmet-like heads and shrimp-like bodies. Very shortly after they cast their skin, or moult, and have a long, tapering spine on the back, rather like a dunce's cap, and a second on the front of the head reminiscent of a carnival false nose, while the body is long and slender. In this stage the little creature swims in jerks through the sea and after successive moults certain changes can be observed to have taken place. Gradually the dunce's cap disappears, and the long frontal spine decreases in size, the body broadens, the future claws and walking legs appear, the eyes become mounted on stalks and the slender shrimp tail decreases rapidly in length. In the final stage, the little creature settles down on the floor of the sea, moults once more, after which it tucks up its now greatly abbreviated triangular tail beneath its body, and acquires the adult form. Thence forward no further change of shape will occur, though the crab will continue to cast its shelly armour from time to time. All the true crabs and all the lobsters, pass through a very similar change before reaching the adult form. In some of the shrimps and prawns a still more complex series of transformations takes place, including a nauplius stage; while the familiar acorn barnacles that cover the rocks and groynes have all first passed through an active free-swimming stage.

From the pools on the shore and the surface waters of the open sea, down to the deepest abysses of the great oceans, crustacean life abounds; ranging in size from the microscopic so-called water-fleas to the great crabs and lobsters. Some lead a more or less sedentary life, like the curious masked crabs that spend much of their time buried in the sand; others, like shrimps and prawns, are extremely active, and others, again, lead a partial or entirely parasitic life, assuming strange shapes, and passing through complicated life-histories. But perhaps the most important species of all are the minute forms, particularly those belonging to the sub-class *Copepoda*, which live at or near the surface of the sea, often in such countless multitudes as to discolour the water for many miles.

THE LOBSTER'S FORMIDABLE CLAW

In shape and appearance the lobster differs from the crab. The rear half of the body is made up of six segments and it has a fan-shaped tail. The unequal size of the claws is often due to fresh growth after one or other of the claws has been injured or lost.

THE SALMON'S LEAP

Returning from the sea to its river breeding-ground, a salmon rises in the air to leap a weir. A jump of ten to fifteen feet is not unusual.

CHAPTER TWENTY-FIVE

FISH, THEIR NATURE AND HABITS

by LEO WALMSLEY

Anatomy of the fish: weapons and tactics of sea war: camouflage: problems of food and reproduction: different methods of hatching young: the eel's astonishing double voyage: some mysterious char- acteristics of fish: unexplored territory of the sea: Dr. Beebe and his bathysphere: amazing fish life discovered in the ocean deeps.

WHY is a flat-fish flat? Why does a worm-pipe fish produce twenty eggs in a season and a cod several million? Why do pike and bream die in sea-water, and hake and mackerel in fresh, while the salmon and flounder are at home in both? Why is the cutlass fish thin and flat like a sword, and the tunny shaped like a torpedo? Why is the mackerel coloured like a tropical sunset, and the ling as sombre as a winter fog? Here are a few of the questions and problems that intrigue the naturalist and make the study of fish one of the most fascinating branches of zoology.

Fish have a bony spinal column and a nerve cord running through it to a brain. They breathe the air dissolved in the water through gills: they are covered with fairly small scales, and have paired and unpaired fins and a tail. The tail is the organ of propulsion, and consists of one almost solid mass of muscle termi- nating in a fin with equal lobes whose edge may be straight, concave, or convex

when viewed sideways. The unpaired fins (dorsal and ventral) on the back and belly, act as keels to keep it on its course. With the paired fins (pectoral and pelvic) it maintains its fore and aft trim, but the pectorals are used for quick turning. Thus a stroke of the starboard pectoral with the port held in, brings about a turn to the left.

Food and preservation of the species as well as of the individual are the chief determining causes of the varying nature and habits of all living things.

A flat-fish is flat because at some remote period in the everlasting struggle for living-room, certain species of "non- flat" fish found a better food supply and better security by living on the bottom of a fairly shallow sea where there was mud, sand or shingle. In turn these fish were preyed upon by other and larger fish. But some of them had already formed the habit of lying close to the mud or sand while feeding. Their backs, too, became coloured and marked very

453

ABOUT TO CHARGE

This underwater photograph shows a shark rolling over as it attacks, its formidable jaws gaping. The shark's mouth and throat are lined with sawlike teeth, its appetite is exceptional among voracious fish.

much like the mud and sand. These would be less likely to be seen and slaughtered by their enemies. They would survive to reproduce their own kind, which by the laws of heredity would tend to have the same habit. A round fish would be more easily noticed than a flat fish in the bottom of shallow water because of the shadow it would cast. This obviously does not apply where the bottom is of a rocky nature where there are more shadows. And so gradually was evolved a fish that had little depth. The flat-fish which evolved in sandy and shingly bottoms did so in a peculiar way, for the body was not compressed from back to belly, but from side to side, and it was one "side" that became the fish's belly, with the eye that belonged to that side moved round to make a pair with the one on top, only a rather irregular pair. A flat-fish therefore actually lies on its side. Its mouth opens sideways, instead of up and down!

We know that the flat-fish, dabs, plaice, soles, flounders, turbot, to mention

A NATURAL TORPEDO

The "sword" of the swordfish is an extension of the snout and may reach a length of three feet. Strong and sharp, it provides the fish with a dangerous weapon with which it has been known to stab a whale and to pierce deep into stout ship's timber.

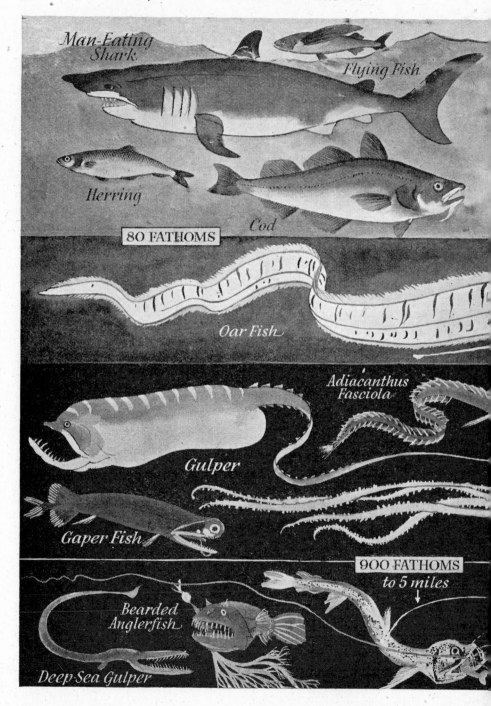

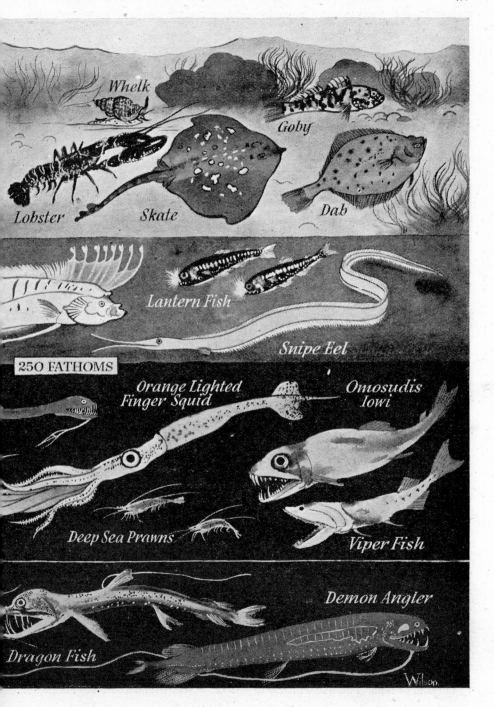

Whelk

Goby

Lobster Skate Dab

Lantern Fish

Snipe Eel

250 FATHOMS

Orange Lighted Finger Squid

Omosudis Iowi

Deep Sea Prawns

Viper Fish

Demon Angler

Dragon Fish

Wilson

FISH OF NORTHERN WATERS

A species of cod is seen in this underwater photograph taken off Heligoland. Codfish frequent the ocean in vast numbers, the main fishing-grounds being the Dogger Bank and the waters in the neighbourhood of Iceland and Newfoundland.

some of the best-known kinds, had ancestors which were not flat and that they had eyes like ordinary fish. The growth of any animal from the egg to maturity gives us a condensed picture of the evolution of the species itself from the most primitive to its present form. The baby fish that hatch from flat-fish eggs are not flat. Indeed, you could hardly distinguish them from those of cod or ling. They are hatched with a yolk sac attached to their bellies, which nourishes them during the first few days of their free existence, which, by the way, are the most perilous for them. But quickly their shape and colour change. The side which is to become the back takes on the colour and mottling of the sand or mud. The side which is to

be the belly grows light. The bones of the skull shift and bend to accommodate the "belly" eye and the sideways-moving jaws, and we have a recognizable baby flounder or sole.

Food, of course, is the primary essential of all existence: first in the form of non-living substances, then in the form of plants and flesh. Microscopic marine plants form the direct food of marine organisms. On the whole, however, it is the small animals (not necessarily fish) that feed on the plants. And it is on the small animals that the bigger ones feed, and so *ad infinitum*. There is a perfect illustration of this in what happens every summer along the coasts of the British Isles, and especially on the shallow reef-bound coast of Yorkshire.

Usually about July huge shoals of herring fry move in from the deep water where they were hatched, to feed on the minute plant and animal life that abound in shallow water in warm weather. These shoals are immense, often covering an area of a quarter of a square mile, and many feet in depth. The little sprats are packed in them almost as tightly as sardines in a tin. They are attacked incessantly by gulls, diving birds and by billet, codling, pollack, whiting, mackerel, gurnard, which simply swim among them with their mouths wide open, bite and swallow and open again. Gradually the sprats are driven close into the beach, where flounders, eels and various rock-fish join in the massacre. But later on when the gorged marauders return to deeper water to digest their banquet, they are themselves assailed by shoals of dogfish and larger sharks; and, well away from the coast, by giant tunny.

Underwater Geography

The sea itself is not just an immense uniform depth of salt water filling up the hollows of the earth between the continental coast-lines. Its surface is comparatively level, but below, its con-tours are as irregular and varied as dry land. There are mountains and plains, cliffs and valleys. The "ground" may consist of sand, or mud, shingle, boulders, or solid rock. The vast majority of fish spend at least some part of their lives in the shallow waters, for here is the most plentiful supply of food, microscopic plants, worms, molluscs, shrimps, crabs, the eggs and young of other fish. A keen competition starts as to which fish shall have the food. Remember too that the animals which *are* the food, the molluscs, the shrimps and crabs, have to do their

best to avoid being consumed. If it is to survive as a species, the species must develop some means of defence. In fact there is very little in modern human warfare that has not its counterpart in the war that goes on everlastingly among the animals of the sea. The weapons and tactics of the small weak animals are mainly defensive. Worms burrow deep in sand or mud or hide in rock crevices, or cover their bodies with particles of sand, or build limestone tubes for themselves, with a door and a sharp spine over the doorway. Anemones anchor themselves in rock fissures and contract into them when danger threatens. Squids discharge ink, the counterpart of a smoke-screen. Crabs have armoured and spined shells, but they are adepts at digging "fox-holes" for themselves when the enemy approaches. Molluscs, like the oyster and clam, rely on thick armour. In hunting, the hunter himself may be hunted, and the most successful species (proved so by their survival) are those that have been able to combine efficiency in their methods of assault and protection.

Attack and Defence

Speed, both for attack and defence, is brought to perfection in the mackerel, salmon, shark, dolphin, flying-fish and the barracuda of tropical waters: pro-tective colouring and marking is used for attack and defence by almost all fish: armour, for defence, is shown in the spines of the gurnard, the sea-viper and the sea-porcupine of the tropics; special teeth for seizing fast-moving prey are those of the pike and the cutlass fish; or for crushing thick-shelled molluscs, those of the repulsive-looking British "wolf-fish", specially large and sensitive eyes aid all fish that hunt by pursuit.

The mackerel is streamlined like a torpedo, and it has an immensely powerful tail. Because it is one of the most luscious and nutritious of all fish "foods" and is pursued by all the big hunters, its main defence is speed in escape. But it does a great deal of its own hunting near the surface of the sea, and its back is therefore barred with dark blue bands on green, so that to a diving bird like a gannet it is hard to distinguish from the rippling sea. Its belly, however, is iridescent silver, shading into green, so that to a fish attacking from underneath this blends with the light of day shining through the rippled surface and makes it equally difficult to see.

How is it, then, that all fish are not coloured and marked in the same way as a mackerel? Obviously because their habits are not the same. Quite a large number of fish have little need for defensive coloration, and it is likely they have acquired it merely as a general inheritance.

The ling, as a typical example, is a slow-moving, bottom-feeding fish which does very little chasing. It browses among the rocks and patches of shingle on molluscs and crabs and the spawn of other fish, easy-going, and too big to fear any other fish except a really big shark. Like the conger, it likes to be among rocks, and a favourite haunt is the hull of a sunken ship. Its dingy colour is certainly protective, but for no important purpose.

Loveliest of Fish

The brightest and loveliest of all fish are those of the South Seas, and are called coral fish. They are shaped like perch, and are mottled and barred with every colour of the rainbow. Looking at a faithful colour photograph or painting of one of them on white or neutral paper, you would say that nothing could be more conspicuous. But to see these fish (or rather *not* to see them without looking very hard) their background must be their natural haunt, the brightly coloured clumps of living coral fringed and decked with bright and varied-coloured weeds, into which, if they keep still (which is the condition of all successful camouflage), they blend as perfectly as a half-buried flounder on a patch of mud or a green caterpillar on a cabbage.

Marine Camouflage

Perhaps the inventors of military camouflage took some of their inspiration from fish. There is one fish very common on the rocky coasts of Great Britain about half-way to low-water mark, called the father-lasher. If you happen to turn over a biggish flat stone in a clear rock pool, you will often see something dash away towards the pool edge. Out of the tail of your eye (which is very sensitive in perceiving movement) you may mark the place where it seemed to stop, but on looking at that place, unless you are practised, you will probably decide that the tail of your eye deceived you, or that the fish has vanished through solid rock. But touch the place with your finger. It *looked* like rock, stained as the rock in most pools is, with a weed that resembles lichen. Instantly the rock moves and darts away again, and if this time you are more alert and catch the fish, you will see that it has two or three irregular light-greyish bands running diagonally across its body and continuing over its pectoral fins. The effect of those bands is to destroy the continuity of outline by which, if it had been all the same colour, you would have easily recognized

THE SAIL-FIN FISH OF THE AMAZON

The sail-fin fish has the general characteristics of the tropical spiny-finned species—being brilliant in colour, with laterally compressed body and fins of relatively very great size.

the shape of the fish. Guns and army lorries and buildings are painted exactly the same way.

Food, then, is the first thing we have to consider in trying to understand the nature and habits of fish. It is this that governs their short and distant, daily and seasonal migrations. The next question is reproduction. The sea is vast, more vast in actual area than the dry land of the globe, and remember that, considered as living-space, it is three-dimensional. Many species of fish live, as it were, in strata of the water, spending their entire lives within certain limits, and never venturing very far up or down. One might think, then, that the living-space had no limits at all.

In point of fact there actually seems to be a natural law of population control,

and one of its principles is that no single species of animal or fish, no matter how efficiently it is armed for defence or offence, shall multiply to such an extent that it upsets the general balance of population.

The balance is maintained, and the law seems to be that, the more eggs a fish produces, the greater the rate of infantile mortality from the moment, and even before the moment, of hatching, for the eggs of such fish are deposited usually in the most haphazard way, and it is not uncommon for the parents themselves to take a hand, or rather a mouth, in their destruction, and of the fry too. The herring deposits its eggs on the bottom, but the cod and most others of the prolific layers simply lay eggs and milt in the sea, but they shoal for this purpose,

BARRACUDA PREPARES TO SWALLOW A GURNARD

The barracuda of the tropics, which attains a length of eight or ten feet, is as ferocious as the shark and in similar fashion dashes among shoals of smaller fish, devouring them as it goes. The above close-up gives a dramatic idea of the process.

and very few eggs remain unfertilized. The hatched fry drift about in the tidal current and are the food of many bigger fish. Some, however, have learnt to seek protection in a novel way. They get inside the long swaying curtain of stinging filaments of the huge jellyfish which abound in summer seas, and swim there quite happily as the jellyfish is carried along by the tide. On the face of it, this over-production of eggs looks like bad economy. But it's sound enough when you work it out. Few of the eggs or fry are wasted, even to the species that produces them. They are eaten by smaller fish, which later on may be eaten by the surviving individuals of the same brood.

With fish that produce only a small number of eggs, like the dog- and pipe-fish, stickleback and wrasse, things are very different. The dogfish, for example, lays only one egg at a time. This is produced in a horny capsule, square in shape, with long, coiling tendrils at each corner. The capsule is laid among fronds of weeds or anything else sure to give anchorage against the tidal current, and the tendrils are engaged on it in very much the same way as the climbing tendrils of the garden pea. The egg hatches in due course, and it is complete with the usual yolk-sac, on which it feeds until there is none left. Then the youngster wriggles about until it finds a valve at one end of the sac, and out it goes on the big adventure of life. Skate produce their young in much the same way, and it is interesting to note that the skate embryo is exactly like an embryo dog-fish or shark, and that, like the flat-fish, it does not become flat until a later stage of its development. True sharks, however, are like some snakes —viviparous. The eggs develop inside the parent's body (but not attached to it, like the embryo of a mammal), and are produced alive, and well able to take care of themselves from that moment. The sea-horse, one of the most fantastic of all fish, might almost be regarded as viviparous, but with one important difference. The male has two pieces of loose skin on his belly, which, folded, make a sort of pouch, not unlike that of a kangaroo. Into this the female lays her eggs. The flaps are closed, and in time out comes a crop of miniature sea-horses, which father sea-horse looks after for several days in the most devoted manner, while his mate is quite apathetic to the whole business.

But the female of a near relative of the sea-horse, the worm pipe-fish, has a more conscientious idea of her parental duties. This fascinating creature may be found in weedy pools close to low-water mark on most European coasts. It is the female you notice first if you disturb the pool. You will see her jerking along the bottom in a most conspicuous way. She wishes to distract attention from her mate, just as a plover feigning a broken wing will run along the ground trying to distract your attention away from its nest. The female worm pipe-fish is bigger than the male, and is quite conspicuously patterned. He is shaped and coloured almost exactly like a stem of the dark brown weed in which, if you look long enough, you will find him. Indeed, he is as perfect an example of direct

CODFISH EATING MACKEREL

Another aspect of the fierce life of the ocean in which unremitting war goes on is seen in this picture. Most fishes are carnivorous. The teeth of fish all point backwards for seizing, but not for tearing, the prey, which is swallowed whole.

ODD DENIZEN OF THE SEA

The so-called angel-fish is not so angelic as its name suggests: in fact, as may be seen from our photograph, it is ugly and repellent in appearance. It is related to the shark.

mimicry camouflage as you will find in nature. He knows it too, and even when touched does not give any sign of movement or life. But, if separated from the weed and placed in clear water, you will see that he is all right, and note that cemented to his belly are about a score of eggs. These were deposited there by the female, and fertilized by him, and his job is to remain unnoticed until they are safely hatched.

The female fresh-water stickleback has a more cynical view of her duties; but, then, perhaps she has good reason. For one thing, she is only one of a harem. But, then, it is the male who makes the home. He fashions this out of strands of weed carefully woven and cemented together. It is a real nest, not unlike that of a wren's, with a hole about an inch in diameter. When all is ready he sallies forth to the feeding-grounds of the stream where the local community of sticklebacks are congregated and selects his first mate. His choice may coincide with that of another male, and there may be a fight, and even if he wins, he may find her coy and reluctant and be obliged to drive and prod her into the nest to lay her eggs. When she has done this he drives her out, deposits his own milt, then goes out and fights for another wife. The operation is repeated (not without some damage to the nest, which he is obliged to repair) until he is satisfied that he has done his tribal duty in the way of quantity, and he now mounts guard against all comers until the fry are hatched. He then opens the nest at the top, and, like a mother bird, will rescue any of the "fledglings" which get out before he is fully satisfied that they can face life in the stream on their own.

The evolutionary processes by which a "flat-fish" became flat are fairly easy to comprehend, but how the stickleback acquired this complicated and seemingly intelligent method of assuring the continuance of its species is less clear. Even more "intelligent" is the method of a small member of the carp family, for this deposits its eggs inside the shell of a living fresh-water mussel, the female developing a special tube for this purpose and seizing the chance when the mussel's double shells are gaping. The eggs hatch inside the shell, receiving a hundred per cent prenatal security. The mussel does not object. Indeed it co-operates, for when the fry are ready for the free life it envelops them with swarms of its own almost microscopic young. Some of these attach themselves to the skin of the departing lodgers, who discharge their obligation to the mussel by distributing *her* young far more efficiently than if they had just floated out of the gaping shells.

Life-history of the Eel

How was this co-operation evolved when neither fish nor mussel, so far as we can tell, possesses a mind with powers of reasoning? Does the method of experiment and trial by error explain it? Then how explain how the fresh-water eel began making its nuptial odyssey from the rivers of Europe across the Atlantic to the depths of the Gulf of Mexico. The discovery of the life-

QUEER FISH

The sea-hedgehog is seen in the upper illustration, its goggle eyes looking out in different directions. The wels, shown below, is another queer fish, one of the freshwater species of the large family of catfish.

history of the eel by a Danish marine zoologist, Dr. Johannes Schmidt, is a classic of scientific research. It started when Dr. Schmidt, while dredging for zoological specimens near the Faroe Islands at a depth of 3,000 feet, captured a single specimen of a larval eel. Specimens had previously been captured, but the creature had looked so unlike the eel itself that it had been supposed to belong to a different species. Dr. Schmidt began his painstaking dredging soon after this, but it was not until sixteen years had elapsed that he was able to prove beyond all doubt that every European common eel does make this astonishing double voyage.

Eel's Journey

No boy who has lived near to an English brook or shallow river will have missed seeing, when wading and turning over stones, numbers of small, active, wiry fish about four inches in length, with almost translucent bodies and sharp snouts. It would be a wonder, too, if he had not found under larger stones, or actually caught on a hook, a recognizable eel without, however, realizing that the small fish were a young edition of it. Elvers they are called, and at certain times of the year if you watch a stream where it enters the sea you may see thousands of them actually entering the fresh water from the salt. If there are no humans to watch them, then depend on it something else will, for they are almost as attractive to gulls as the summer sprats. This is the final stage of the eastward voyage which began three years previously across the Atlantic. But then they were not elvers. They were flat, ribbon-shaped, but with a very tiny head, whereas the elver's body is round. According to Dr. Schmidt, they do not

travel very far in the first year of their babyhood, and remain at a great depth, and it is not until they have grown and become stronger that they ascend nearer to the surface and begin their eastward voyage, which does not bring them to mid-Atlantic until their second year. They are still larvæ, and about 2 inches in length. At the end of their third year they are 3 inches long; and they have reached European waters before they begin to change into elvers, and while doing this they have to stop feeding, for their larval teeth are shed and they grow an entirely new "set".

It is not long before the elver takes on the general characteristics of its forgotten parents, but by this time, as in the case of the cod and herring, the original brood has been ruthlessly pruned. In no rivers or lakes do you ever find shoals of eels. From now on they are real fresh-water dwellers, and they live in whatever stream or river they have found for a period of about seven years, but there is no way of proving that this particular stream was the one their parents lived in, as happens with the salmon. One day comes the irresistible urge to fulfil their own true destiny.

Bound for the Gulf of Mexico

They start down river and swim to the sea, and there they turn eventually west into the Atlantic. How long their voyage takes still remains one of the unfilled blanks in the story, but there can be no doubt at all that the adult eels do eventually reach their own birthplace after this arduous and lengthy journey, that the female's eggs are discharged and then fertilized by the male, and that both parents, their life task ended, die.

If you can believe that swallows which

FISH THAT BUILDS A HOUSE

The little stickleback, so common in our streams and ponds, is one of the few fishes to make a nest for the protection of its eggs. The male, in the picture above, is collecting building material, and below, a female has just disappeared inside the nest to lay.

nest in the British Isles spend their winters in South Africa and next spring return to the same nest; that the American golden plover nests in Alaska and winters in the Argentine, and the Pacific golden plover nests on the coasts of Siberia and Alaska and during its outward and return migrational flight travels to Japan, North Australia, the South Sea Islands, and Hawaii (these migrations have been proved by ringing), it is easy enough to believe that the eel can do its double journey in a lifetime. But we are no nearer explaining *why* it should do it, when it might equally well deposit its eggs in the rivers where the adults spend most of their lives, or at least in the nearest deep sea.

Mysteries of Fish Habits

There are many other mysteries about the characteristics and habits of fish. There is a very peculiar fish called the remora. On the top of its rather flattish head is an elliptical sucking-disc with a muscular rim and several secondary muscular flaps. With this the remora attaches itself to the belly of any big fish, but for choice a shark, just abaft the mouth, and heading the same way. It gets free transport and, what is more important, the pickings of any meal the big fish may be taking. The faster the big fish travels the tighter the sucking-disc holds, but to disconnect itself all the remora has to do is swim ahead until its own speed is slightly greater than the "carrier", when the sucker automatically comes loose. Sucking-discs are found in other fish too. That extraordinary fish, the sea lamprey (the one mentioned in our history books as being responsible for the death of an English king who ate too many of them at one go), has a

sucking-disc instead of a mouth, and attaches itself to other fish with the object of getting direct sustenance from its host's body, almost like a leech. There are small rock-fish, very common on the coasts of Britain, which have ventral suckers, these being used for "glueing" the fish to the rock, and here again the device seems justified, although there seems no important reason why these fish should have one and not, say, a father lasher or a blenny or a butterfish.

Problems of Evolution

The most powerful-looking of all sucking-discs, however, is that of the Lumpsucker or Sea-hen. This in more ways than one is a very peculiar creature. It looks like one of those queer armoured land animals that lived in the time of the dinosaurs. It is squat with a relatively small, almost cupid mouth. It has a thick skin covered with tubercles, and is brightly coloured, especially in the summer breeding-season. The disc is ventrally placed, circular in shape, and about $2\frac{1}{2}$ inches in diameter. The eggs are laid by the female usually on the roof and walls of a declivity in the rock just at low-water spring tides, and, like the pipe-fish and wrasse, it is the husband who has to mount guard over them; and you would guess that this is what his disc is for. He certainly does anchor himself to the rock with his disc. But the slightest touch with your hand dislodges him, and one cannot help feeling that in his case the thing is not a success; that the lumpsucker would have done much better if he had drawn a better set of fins out of the evolutionary lucky dip, or a more streamlined hull. Still another problem in evolution is the case of the hammer-headed shark, and how and

FAMILY LIFE OF THE BLUE ACARA

When the eggs of this gaily marked tropical fish have been laid, the male fans them to keep a stream of fresh water in movement and prevent sediment from settling. When the brood hatches, both fish, as shown in the lower picture, remain to defend their young.

why it evolved a head shaped like a flattened double-headed hammer, with an eye stuck on each extremity!

The excitement of watching fish is just as great as that of angling. It has been the author's good fortune to sail in tropical seas and watch schools of dolphins gambolling or superbly speeding in front of a ship's bows, and shoals of flying-fish shooting out of the glittering sea and gliding with outstretched pectorals into the wind, soaring sometimes 20 feet into the air before crash-landing. Days can be spent on the coral reefs of Mombasa and Zanzibar watching, spellbound, the sheer beauty of the coral fish moving among the fronds of weed and the coral stems, lovelier than any butterflies. The author has fished in the turgid, glacier-fed rivers that flow from the slopes of Mount Kilimanjaro, in competition with crocodiles and hippos, and the experience was no less exciting because the water was too dirty to see the fish that were in it until they were caught. Mostly they were a species of barbel, coloured like the mud, and not particularly interesting, but it was here that the author had his one and only experience of an electric fish. It was only small, something like a smelt, but when he tried to get it off the hook he received a smart electric shock; and that is another of the mysteries of fish life— the precise nature of the chemical "outfit" that produces the shock. The electric torpedo ray is supposed to stun its quarry by electrocution, and there are many species of tropical salt- and fresh-water fish which have this power.

Salt and Fresh Water Fish

Some fish die in fresh water, others in salt, while some are equally happy in either. But all fish are marine in their origin, and those which became fresh-water must have adapted themselves gradually by living in the brackish water of estuaries.

Most fish possess inside their abdominal cavities an organ called the swimming-bladder, but it is very difficult to give a precise description of the purpose this fulfils, what gas it contains, how the gas gets there, and whether the pressure in it is controlled voluntarily or automatically, or whether it is controlled at all. Another mystery is the behaviour of a certain species of fresh-water fish known as the brown trout, which one day will bite greedily at almost anything on a hook, and another day, under precisely similar conditions of weather and time, will bite at nothing.

Our Scanty Knowledge of the Sea

But perhaps fish would lose something of their fascination if one knew everything about them. The sea, or rather the depths of the sea, after all, is the one sphere that man has not yet explored, and is likely to remain so for many years to come. Except for the shallows, the knowledge we have of it is infinitesimal. Trawling, dredging, sounding, give us some idea of the physical nature of its bottom and of the fish and other animals that live there, but trawling is confined to narrowly circumscribed grounds, and its object is commercial, and not scientific. Purely scientific trawling and dredging are immensely costly, and at best can only give us microscopic samples. Submarines are blind, and can dive only to comparatively shallow depths. In articulated metal suits with self-contained aeration apparatus, divers have made very deep descents for salvage purposes, but it is a hazardous business, and only gold like

NATURE'S STRANGE DIVERSITY

There are at least ten thousand species of fish and in no form of life is there a more extraordinary variety of shape and colour. The white telescope veil-fish, with its protruding eyes and diaphanous fins, is one of the many phantom-like creatures of the sea.

THE STRUGGLE IN THE DEPTHS

The discovery of fish no one had ever set eyes on before, at the depth of half a mile, was like that of a new world. In the intense darkness demon-like shapes, lit up by their own multi-coloured phosphorescence, fiercely pursue their luminous prey.

that of the sunk liner *Egypt* justifies the expense. In their deepest descents these divers have given us very little new knowledge of the under-water world, for their vision was restricted by the darkness and clouds of mud stirred up by the powerful tides. Only to a few favoured human beings has been granted the profoundly exciting experience of seeing into the real depths of the ocean. The man who has told the story of this experience is the courageous and brilliant American marine zoologist, Dr. William Beebe, who with a companion made the record ocean descent of 3028 feet, more than half a mile. The physical record, however, was nothing to the amazing record of the fish life that was seen on this and less deep descents.

Descent by Bathysphere

The descent was made possible by a device named the bathysphere. Together with Capt. H. J. Butler, this had been designed by Mr. Otis Barton, who was Dr. Beebe's companion in this perilous record-breaking achievement, as well as on many other descents. It was a steel globe, furnished with an entrance hatch and three circular windows composed of special quartz lenses 3 inches thick, and designed to withstand a pressure of nearly 1 ton to the square inch. An air-regeneration apparatus was provided. There was a searchlight and telephone connection with the ship from which the apparatus was lowered and, as on previous occasions, the expedition was supported and sponsored by the National Geographical Society of America. This, of course, was in the clear and relatively steady waters of the Atlantic, near to the Bermudas.

It is not easy to write with restraint about Dr. Beebe's description of what he and his companion saw on this and other descents. Everyone can appreciate the scientists' wild excitement at seeing, through the windows of the bathysphere, fish such as no one had ever set eyes on before. And what fish! Some, of course, had been caught in special deep-sea nets years before, and had been described and classified and named by other marine zoologists, notably the Prince of Monaco. But there were many that had eluded nets. The view from the bathysphere was very restricted and gave only a fractional view of the life that existed in the area passed through in the descent and ascent. Was it fairy land or was it demon land? Judging from the paintings made by Else Bostelmann from Dr. Beebe's telephoned verbal notes and checked later from the remembered observations of both members of the "crew", there were both fairies and demons. Below a depth of 1,000 feet there was no light of day in the water itself. This was sepulchral black. But there were two illuminations. One given by the searchlight, a beam penetrating the ink like limelight on a stage, the other provided (when the searchlight was out) by the fish themselves, for nearly all of them carried phosphorescent lanterns, white, green, blue, red, and yellow!

Dragons of the Deep

Had one read Dr. Beebe's books and not known his scientific standing, one might have thought that his bathysphere had never been outside a Hollywood studio and that he had employed an Oriental artist to illustrate it, for here are creatures more hideous than ever scared the sinners in a Chinese temple. Dragon fish with enormous fangs and great bulging eyes

ANY TIME'S FEEDING-TIME

*A sea mammal, the porpoise is a great de-
stroyer of fish, and the shoals which are
found both in the Atlantic and the Pacific
consume vast quantities of herrings, pil-
chards and even salmon and other large fish.*

and barbed tails, glowing with ghoulish
lights: fish ghouls, grinning like cats
with luminous teeth, fish that are all eyes
and fangs, and sabre-fish that look like
sabres that have drawn blood. Here is a
fish which Dr. Beebe has called the
Black Swallower, which engulfs another
fish three times its size, and you see the
big fish actually inside the swallower's
transparent stomach. But there were
fairies too. Shoals of vermilion Arrow
worms, the Five Constellation Butterfly
fish, brilliantly illuminated as a pulsating
aurora borealis, with phosphorescent
light organs, and the Scarlet shrimp,
which, being attacked by one of the
ghouls, shot out a cloud of luminous
fluid to blind it. Most of the fish seen
were fairly small, but some were
monsters, and at the record depth of half
a mile, still a long way from the bottom,
Dr. Beebe had the impression that they
would be larger still lower down.
Perhaps the fabulous sea-serpent was
lurking there!

The struggle for existence is as fierce
under the canopy of a calm tropical sea
as in our own waters, but in the depths
the main source of food is the plant and
animal matter which sinks down from
above. What Dr. Beebe saw in the
total of his descents can represent only
the tiniest fraction of the life that exists
in that marine underworld of the
Bahamas. Who knows how many more
forms of life will be found at the extreme
depths, when some super form of
travelling bathysphere has been invented?

COME UP FOR AIR

When the sea begins to freeze in the Antarctic winter the seal makes a breathing-hole through the ice. The picture shows it during one of its frequent visits to the surface.

CHAPTER TWENTY-SIX

MAMMALS OF THE SEA

by F. MARTIN DUNCAN, F.R.M.S., F.R.P.S., F.Z.S.

The depleted tribe of sea mammals; Sea-cows; Whales and Dolphins: valuable substances provided by the Whale: its food: Sea-lions, Walruses and Seals: breeding-grounds or "rookeries": warfare among Sea-lions: the remarkable Elephant-seal.

THREE groups of mammals in no way related to one another inhabit the sea. These are the Sea-cows (*Sirenia*), the Whales and Dolphins (*Cetacea*), and the Sea-lions, Walruses, and Seals (*Pinnipedia*). It is a sorry reflection upon our vaunted twentieth-century civilization that, thanks to modern mechanical methods of whole-sale slaughter, most of these harmless, useful, and deeply interesting animals will soon cease to exist.

While the sea-cows and the whale tribe lead an entirely aquatic life, the sea-lions and their kin yearly spend an appreciable time on land, as they have to come on shore during the breeding-season; while all show remarkable modifications of form and structure to fit them for their mode of life.

The sea-cows comprise three families —namely, the Manatees, the Dugongs, and the now extinct Steller's Sea-cow. On account of their superficial resemblance in shape and habit to the whales and dolphins, the sea-cows are frequently, but quite erroneously, spoken of as being related to the whale tribe, whereas in all points of anatomy they differ entirely,

and, judging from their habits, have probably descended from a swamp-dwelling ancestor. The surviving members are restricted to tropical seas, where they spend all their lives in the water, though never straying very far, but frequenting bays, lagoons, and the wide estuaries of large rivers. The well-proportioned head of the sea-cow is joined to the cylindrical, tapering body by a short neck, and the tail is flattened and expanded horizontally to form the broad tail-fin. The fore-limbs are paddle-shaped, with the fingers enveloped in a flat skin-sheath. There are no hind limbs in any of the existing species. The wrinkled skin of the body in some species is quite naked, or may be scantily clothed with bristles. While the mana-tees are confined to the coasts of North and South America and the West Coast waters of Africa, the dugongs inhabit the Red Sea and Indian Ocean, and are found as far East as Australia and the Philippine Islands. The now extinct Steller's sea-cow—the last one was seen alive in 1854—frequented Behring Strait and Copper Island in the North Pacific, and was the largest of the

BRINGING A WHALE ALONGSIDE

*Largest of the sea mammals, the whale has long been the object of an important fishing
industry and provides a number of valuable substances—whalebone, oil and ambergris.
Under modern methods very little of the whale is wasted, the meat itself being canned.*

Sirenia, attaining a length of 20 to 25 feet. All are vegetarian in habit, feeding upon seaweeds and other aquatic plants growing in the shallow waters off shore and in the tidal estuaries. The dugong seems to have been responsible for some of the old "mermaid" stories of the early voyagers. The female, while floating on her back, holds the suckling to her breast with one of her flippers in a suggestively human manner—though surely a more unlovely mermaid it would be difficult to conceive.

Specialized Mammals

The whales and dolphins are highly specialized mammals, their fish-like form affording a striking example of adaptation to environment and habit of life. No other group of mammals is so distinct in character, or so markedly cut off from the rest, nor have the fossil-bearing strata so far yielded sufficient evidence as to their exact ancestry. The supposition of their having a land origin is purely hypothetical and founded chiefly on the presence in some species when young of a few bristle-hairs near or on the lips, and of certain small bones, now useless vestiges of the hip-girdle and hind leg, deeply buried in the flesh of the sperm whale.

In many of the whales the head is of great size in comparison to the rest of the body, to which, externally, it appears as if joined without any neck; while the more or less cylindrical body tapers away to the tail, which ends in a large, forked, horizontal expansion, called the "fluke". The front limbs are in the form of flat flippers showing no division into hand, fore-arm, or arm; while hind limbs are entirely absent. The eyes are small in proportion to the massive head, and there are no external ears, their position being indicated only by a small hole situated just behind the eye. The body is naked, and under the smooth, hairless skin there is a thick and deep layer of fatty tissue, called the "blubber", the function of which is to conserve the heat of the body; and it is from this tissue that the valuable oil is extracted. The nostrils, which in some species have a single, in others a double opening, are located near the top of the head. The windpipe and lungs are quite cut off from the mouth, so that the animal can swim under water with its mouth wide open, and feed without fear of drowning. A whale can hold its breath for a much longer period than any other mammal, being capable of remaining completely submerged for an hour at a time without any apparent inconvenience. When a whale rises to the surface of the sea, it discharges the air from its lungs with considerable force, and as this exhaust from the lungs is saturated with watery vapour at a high temperature, contact with the cold external air at once causes it to condense into visible vapour. This constitutes the familiar "blowing" or "spouting" of the whale, thus revealing its whereabouts.

Living Prey of the Cetacea

All the Cetacea prey upon living marine animals, many feeding upon fish, small floating crustaceans, and other invertebrate forms of life, the largest members of the tribe, including the great Sperm whale, hunting and devouring various species of giant cuttlefish. The Killer-whale or Grampus alone hunts and devours other warm-blooded animals, preying upon seals and sea-lions, porpoises, and even the great Whalebone

The Commander or Kamandorski islands, near the coast of Kamchatka, form one of the
national animal sanctuaries of the U.S.S.R. Here is found a vast number of seals, sea-

THE BEHRING SEA

otters, polar bears, blue foxes and other wild creatures. The photograph above shows a large colony of seals on one of the islands, no longer slaughtered in enormous numbers.

Q

whales. There is great variation in size, some of the smaller dolphins scarcely exceeding 4 feet in length, while the largest whales may measure 95 feet or more in length and exceed in bulk any animal of past ages. They are mostly timid, inoffensive creatures, graceful and wonderfully active in their movements, even the great whales displaying remarkable agility. They display solicitude towards one another when injured or in difficulties, and the females show the greatest devotion for their offspring.

The existing cetacea may be divided into two sub-groups—namely, the whale-bone-whales (including the "Right-whales" of the industry), in which the functional teeth are wanting, the upper jaws being furnished with sheets of "baleen" or whalebone; while the second group contains the toothed whales, in which teeth are always present, and to which belong the great sperm whale or cachalot, the killer-whales, the dolphins, and the curious narwhal. One of the most important of the right-whales is the Greenland bowhead, or Arctic whale, a massive creature which attains a length of 65 feet, and whose great head exceeds one-third the total length.

The Greenland Whale

This animal, once abundant in Arctic waters, has now become so reduced in numbers that the ancient and once profitable fishery for it in Greenland and Spitzbergen seas has practically ceased. The upper jaw of this whale is greatly arched, to accommodate the sheets of baleen which, in some individuals, reached a length of 14 feet, and was greatly valued for its quality and elasticity. The black right-whales are distinguished by their relatively smaller heads and shorter baleen, and have a greater geographical distribution, being found in the North and South Atlantic and the North and South Pacific. The Northern Atlantic right-whale is a typical example, and is a massive creature reaching 54 to 56 feet in length. The great head is about one-fourth of the entire length of the animal, the lower jaw being more highly arched than in the bowhead, and consequently the baleen much shorter. This whale from the tenth to the sixteenth centuries was persistently hunted by Basque fishermen, but after the discovery of Spitzbergen in 1596, they turned their attention to the more valuable bowhead.

A Dilatable Pouch

The Rorquals or Finner-whales are easily distinguished from the true right-whales by their short and narrow flippers, long, slender body, deep parallel grooves in the skin of the neck, and the presence of a fin on the back. The neck furrows, which present such a striking appearance, form a capacious pouch capable of holding a large quantity of water containing small surface-swimming marine animals, including fishes, crustaceans, and molluscs. When the pouch is contracted, the water is driven out through the sieve-like fringes of the baleen, and the captured creatures retained are swallowed. Four species are known to have visited at one time or another the seas around the British Isles, including Sibbald's rorqual, which is the largest of all known mammals, and attains a length of 100 feet; all four are believed to have an almost cosmopolitan range. The Humpback whale is widely distributed over the Atlantic, Pacific, and Southern Oceans. It is nearly related to the

SEA-LION ON THE LOOK-OUT OFF THE COAST OF MEXICO

The sea-lion is a large hairy seal, now rare owing to the constant destruction wrought by hunters. Though its walk is slow and awkward it mounts a steep slope with ease.

rorquals, but distinguished by the compact shape of the body and the greater length of the flippers. It possesses a dilatable pouch, as in the rorquals, and a full-grown male is 45 to 50 feet in length. Both right and rorquals are hunted for their whalebone and the valuable oil extracted from their blubber; indeed, under modern methods very little of a whale is wasted, the best of the meat being frozen or canned, chiefly for sale in the Far East, while the rest of the flesh, blood, etc., are converted into meal and fertilizers.

Of the toothed whales, only the Cachalot or sperm whale rivals the larger of the whalebone whales in size, full-grown specimens reaching 70 to 80 feet in length. It is one of the most wonderful of the many remarkable animals that dwell in the sea. Its great head, which occupies one-third of the entire length of the animal, is rectangular in shape and contains an immense cavity filled with oil known as spermaceti. This natural tank is called the "case" by the whalers, and when cut open, the oil is simply baled out with a bucket; ten or fifteen barrels being an average yield. The spermaceti formerly

DOMESTIC LIFE OF THE SEAL

These two photographs taken in the Antarctic show Weddell's seals lying in the snow.
Above, the calf shows interest; below, the mother lies dozing, while suckling her young.

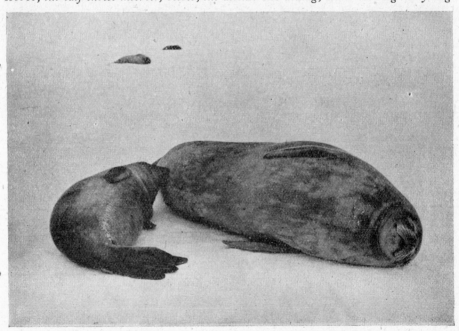

ENCOUNTER OF BULL SEALS

Two Weddell's seals, loudly roaring, prepare to fight at the mating season. Seals fight desperately and with stubborn persistence among themselves, and they often inflict very serious wounds with their strong teeth. The victorious animal rules a number of females.

entered into the composition of wax candles, but today is more valuable as a lubricant for delicate machinery. Another natural excretion of the sperm whale is the valuable substance known as ambergris, which forms in the intestines when the animal is in bad health. It is found floating at the surface of the sea in large masses, and when fresh has a most unpleasant odour. Occasionally whales are found with their intestines completely clogged with ambergris. £4 to £6 an ounce has been paid for it by the manufacturers of expensive perfumes and cosmetics.

The sperm whale feeds largely on giant species of cuttlefish, 20 feet or more in length, and the long scars on the whale's head, made by the formidable clawed or serrated edged suckers of these giant squids, testify to the terrific battles that must take place. Courageous and formidable when wounded, the sperm whale will turn upon its pursuers, and in the old days, before the invention of the harpoon-gun, many a luckless ship's boat was smashed by blows from the whale's tail, or crushed to matchwood between the animal's powerful jaws. This whale frequents most warm seas, extending its range northward to the Shetlands and Iceland, and southwards to the vicinity of the Antarctic.

The Bottlenose whale is a somewhat smaller animal, a full-grown male measuring about 30 feet in length. Gregarious in habit and usually travelling in small parties consisting of five or ten individuals, the bottlenose whales are well known for the great solicitude they display towards a wounded companion, rarely deserting him until he is dead. A full-grown bottlenose yields about two tons of oil from its blubber, and two hundredweight of spermaceti.

The White whale or Beluga is one of the most important of the toothed whales, as furnishing a very large proportion of the porpoise-hide and porpoise-oil of commerce. It frequents the colder waters of the North Atlantic and North Pacific.

The Grampus or killer-whale has been aptly termed the wolf of the sea, for it hunts in packs of twenty or more individuals, attacking and devouring the rorquals, humpbacks, porpoises, and the sea-lions, walruses, and seals; only the great toothed sperm whale appearing to be capable of successfully combating a herd of killers. Their rapacity is almost unbelievable, the remains of no fewer than thirteen porpoises and fourteen seals having been recorded as taken from the stomach of a killer-whale measuring 21 feet in length.

Dolphin and Porpoise

The dolphins and porpoises represent the smaller toothed cetacea. They associate in herds or schools, displaying considerable grace and agility in their movements; their food consisting chiefly of fish and small squids. Four species inhabit fresh water—namely, the Gangetic dolphin, which lives in the rivers Ganges, Indus, and Brahmaputra; the Yangtze dolphin frequents that famous Chinese river; while the two other species, confined to South America, are the La Plata dolphin and the Inia, which inhabit the River Amazon. While the dolphins have distinct beak-like jaws well furnished with teeth, the porpoises are blunt-nosed, though their

relatively short jaws also carry a good supply of teeth. Lastly we have the curious narwhal, distinguished by the peculiarity of its dentition. One of these teeth, in the male, develops into a long, spirally twisted tusk, that may attain to over 9 feet in length. The narwhal was the sea-unicorn of the ancient writers, and occasionally comes as far south as the Yorkshire and Lincolnshire coasts.

Fin-footed Carnivora

Sea-lions, walruses, and seals comprise the Pinnipedia, or Fin-footed carnivora, which have probably descended from land-dwelling ancestors. They all haul out on to land or pack-ice for the purpose of rest and breeding, so are not as absolutely aquatic in habit as the cetacea and sirenia. Their limbs are modified for their aquatic life, the feet having become transformed into "flippers", and the tail reduced to a stump. The majority of the seals, with the exception of the huge Elephant seals, do not appear to resort to specified breeding-grounds, and leave the sea only for relatively short periods, frequently giving birth to their offspring on the ice-pack.

The sea-lions represent something very like a connecting-link between the true land-dwelling carnivores and the more typical pinnipedia. Almost without exception, however, the whole group subsists upon fishes, molluscs, and the larger crustacea, of which enormous quantities are consumed. The sea-lions are distinguished from all other pinnipedia by the presence of small external ears, and from the true seals by the fact that the hind feet, when the animals are on land, turn forwards, *not* backwards, as in the seals. Moreover, the sea-lions are polygamous, while most, though not

SEA-ELEPHANTS RESENT AN INTRUDER

Sea-elephants, or elephant-seals, are the largest of their kind. They possess great bodily strength, but in spite of their threatening appearance are not dangerous to sealers in quest of oil and hide. One animal alone supplies over two hundred gallons of oil.

SEA-ELEPHANTS ENJOY A SIESTA

Guadaloupe, 135 miles off the coast of Lower California, is the home of a number of sea-elephants. Twenty feet or more in length, they lie on or burrow into the beach.

all, of the true seals are supposed to be monogamous. Both the sea-lions and the seals are widely distributed over the temperate and colder seas of the Northern and Southern Hemispheres.

In the early part of the nineteenth century the species of sea-lions commonly designated Fur or Hair seals lived in countless numbers in many parts of the world, but these vast herds have been reduced to such an extent that their pursuit has ceased to be a profitable industry. Even the once-famous seal "rookeries" of the Prybilov Islands in Behring Sea, though under restrictions as to the annual slaughter, are no longer densely crowded by the northern fur-seal. The piratical open-sea hunting of the animals by the Japanese has circum-

vented the breeding-ground restrictions and threatened the early extinction of that species.

The largest and older male sea-lions are always the first to arrive each season at the recognized breeding-grounds, or "rookeries" as they are inappropriately called by the seal-hunters. They at once select stations on the beaches, and from thence onwards a continual warfare is waged by the males, each striving to maintain his particular piece of ground, and, as the females arrive, to cajole or grab as many as he can, and to defend his harem against all claimants. The harem of the most active and powerful males usually consists of ten to fifteen females, the weaker males having to content themselves with a smaller number of wives. At the beginning of the season the pregnant females appear in small numbers, which increase daily, until the great mass arrive. Each male, while retaining his ground as best he may, strives to coax or to seize by the scruff of the neck any female that comes within reach; and a general warfare among the whole male population of the rookery ensues, the unfortunate females being very roughly handled in the general scrum. When things have more or less settled down, the females give birth to their offspring, each usually producing a single young one. The youngsters gorge themselves heartily on the rich creamy milk provided by their mothers, and

their growth at first is fairly rapid. That the adult males towards the end of the season become exhausted, is not very surprising. For two months, or more, these pugnacious males, which arrived at the breeding-grounds fat and strong from their winter haunts, have held their stations on the beaches against all comers, practically without tasting food or water, and almost without sleep, during the entire period.

Other members of the sea-lion family are the Southern sea-lion from the Falkland Islands and Patagonia; Steller's sea-lion from the North Pacific, which is the largest of all, specimens sometimes measuring nearly 12 feet in length; the

YOUNG SEA-LION

This close-up of a sea-lion shows the external ear and the peculiar nature of the feet. The hind flippers turn forwards, and when the animal is raised on its fore-limbs it can walk, although not in a very agile fashion, by pushing with the hind extremities.

South African sea-lion; the Australian sea-lion, and the Californian sea-lion, which is the species most often seen in Zoological Gardens.

The Walruses, of which there are two species, the Pacific and the Atlantic, may be regarded as intermediate forms between the sea-lions and the true seals. They have no external ears, and turn their feet forwards when on land, though to a lesser degree than in the sea-lions. Their upper canine teeth are in the form of long, massive tusks, which occasionally may reach a length of 3 feet. The rest of their teeth are admirably adapted for crushing the shells of the bivalve molluscs on which the walruses largely subsist. Full-grown males range between 9 and 12 feet in length, and are said to weigh from 2,250 to 3,000 lb. They are usually seen in large family parties, or small herds, in the vicinity of the Arctic shores, but seldom in the open sea. The breeding-season lasts from April to June, according to the latitude, and during this period, for about a fortnight, the adults remain on shore. Usually a single young one is produced at birth, never more than a pair, and it is stated that the young are suckled for upwards of two years, which suggests that the females breed but once in three years.

Characteristics of Seals

The true seals are distinguished from the sea-lions and walruses by the characters of their hind limbs, which are permanently directed backwards, so that they form a rudder-like organ. There is no trace of an external ear, the neck is much shorter, and the front limbs are always much smaller than the hind ones. They frequent the temperate and colder seas of both the Northern and Southern Hemisphere, the majority being characterized by their social habits and devotion to their young; some species assembling in large herds during the breeding-season, while others are gregarious throughout the year. All spend a large part of their time basking in the sun on sandy beaches or ice-floes. The young seals take very reluctantly to the sea, having to be taught the art of swimming by their parents, which seems to point to these animals having originally descended from land-dwelling ancestors.

Species of Northern Seas

The species frequenting northern seas are the Bearded seal, the Greenland seal, the North Atlantic Ringed seal, the Common seal, and the Grey seal. Both the common and the grey seals are British species; the grey being the larger animal, averaging about 8 feet in length, while the common seal rarely exceeds 4 to 5 feet. Those species frequenting the Antarctic include the Leopard seal, a large and handsome animal reaching, in the males, some 12 feet in length; the Crab-eating seal, frequenting the Antarctic pack-ice; Weddell's seal, and Ross's seal, a relatively rare species whose food appears to consist chiefly of cuttlefish and seaweeds. It has the curious habit, when on land, of puffing out its chest and throat in a manner reminiscent of a gigantic pouter pigeon.

The extraordinary Elephant seals are the largest of all the pinnipedia, adult males attaining a length of 20 to 22 feet, and a girth of as much as 15 or 16 feet. They have derived their popular name from a curious appendage on the nose of the male that looks like a short trunk, which can be dilated at the will of its owner. The females, however, resemble

WALRUS ON THE COAST OF LABRADOR

The enormous canine teeth, or tusks, of the walrus are its main distinctive feature. They are used for raking molluscs out of the mud, alternatively for climbing on ice-floes. The walrus is of commercial value, too: the oil, teeth, and skin being in great demand.

ordinary seals in the form of their head. The Northern elephant seal differs from the Southern in the longer and more slender trunk of the males. On Kerguelen Island the southern elephant seals arrive for breeding in August, and leave the following February or March. In the records of the voyages of Cook, Péron, and Anson we read of the existence of enormous herds of these remarkable seals, but during the last fifty or sixty years they have been completely exterminated from many of their old haunts, and the few remaining herds are fast disappearing. Indeed, all these wonderful marine mammals are doomed to early extinction unless universal measures can be enforced to stop their slaughter.

WHEN REPTILES RULED THE WORLD

Some 200 million years before the advent of man armoured monsters such as this Helmet-cheeked lizard, shown in a realistic reconstruction, had fully conquered the land.

CHAPTER TWENTY-SEVEN

THE MARCH OF EVOLUTION

by E. G. BOULENGER, F.Z.S.

Development of living creatures: their place in the pattern of
Evolution. The "First Animal". Monsters of the Reptile Age. A
turning-point in Earth's History. Discoveries of Charles Darwin.
The Linnaean method of classification. "Speeding Up" Evolution.

In the preceding pages we have seen the extent of the animal life which shares the world with Man, who himself represents the last link in a long chain of evolutionary processes.

Man is a reasoning animal, and by his mental capacity has, after many centuries, progressed some of the way towards solving the problem of his own origins and those of the other creatures that are found on land, in water or in the air. "How did we get here in the first place?" is a question which has been pondered through the ages. Attempts to provide an adequate answer have produced myth, legend and folk-lore: in more recent times scientists have laboured with amazing ingenuity to provide a solution based on observable facts and clear evidence.

We no longer regard the many strange creatures of which we have read, with amazed incomprehension, for their place in evolution is known and recorded.

With this in mind, let us, in the closing pages of our book, form a general view of the growth and development of animal life down to the present day.

The first animals, like an egg in its earliest stages, consisted of one cell only, devoted to the single purpose of maintaining its existence by the absorption of nourishment, chiefly organic matter. The Amoeba, common alike in water and soil, is the accepted type of a *protozoan*— i.e. a "first animal". It is a mere blob of living jelly (protoplasm) with a nucleus or centre of life. It progresses by throwing out extensions of itself, "false feet". It feeds by surrounding and absorbing any nutriment it can find and multiplies by "fission"—slowly breaking in half, each half developing a separate nucleus and presently going its own way to lead an independent existence.

This wonderful power of the living cell to gain bulk by absorbing matter outside itself, and to reproduce its kind by division, leads from one complexity to another, culminating over a period of thousands of millions of years in the higher vertebrates. The formation of a hard outer cuticle, and, later, of an internal skeleton, we have seen fore-

493

MAN'S EARLY ENEMY

Early man had to contest the rights of his domain with mammoth and mastodon, here reconstructed. The heavily tusked mastodon was not so large, however, as the largest of modern elephants. The diorama shown above pictures a herd during the Ice Age.

shadowed in the minute creatures known as *foraminifera* and *radiolaria*.

The latter make complex and beautiful shells of silex, hard matter, often deposited in such numbers as to form extensive rock layers. Our familiar chalk cliffs are largely composed of the carbonate of lime shells, once the minute homes of countless *foraminifera*. From such beginnings came about the infinity of minute forms collectively termed *animalculae*, a vast assemblage embracing such creatures as the Sporozoa. These latter organisms are so small that their crude eggs, or spores, may be carried like the spores of fungi, or plant pollen, by the wind.

Cellular division, plus the faculty to reinforce or enclose soft tissues with a horny or carbonate of lime skeleton, in time gave rise to the huge tree-like sponges, or the still larger coral formations —conglomerations of animal homes so extensive and solid as to comprise whole islands, and to be used by man for building material.

Land without Animal Life

For fully a half of geologic time—time as recorded by rock deposits and estimated by some at about three thousand million years—such animals must have represented the highest expressions of life throughout the world. There was, so far as we know, no animal life at all upon the land, but the sea, covering the major part of the globe, teemed with creatures incapable of sight or hearing.

Much vain argument, often at cross purposes, has in the past resulted from failure to understand the meaning of the word evolution. When Darwin first familiarized the world with this term the thoughtless at once proclaimed that the great teacher said we descended directly from monkeys. But evolution is derived from a Latin word which simply means to unroll, and therefore aptly describes the stupendous procession of ever-changing plant and animal forms which has appeared upon this planet.

A century or two ago, scientific workers scattered throughout Europe arrived at a means by which it was possible to estimate approximately how long a period was required for the deposition of any particular rock strata. If, for example, the time needed to form a layer of chalk an inch thick could be ascertained, the age of a chalk cliff 300 feet high or thick became a simple matter of mathematics, and the fossils contained in it could be more or less dated. By this means the ages of fossils throughout the world have been estimated, and a tolerably coherent picture of animal progress has been formed.

Glancing at the broad outlines of this

MODERN DESCENDANTS OF THE MAMMOTH

These elephants, photographed at Angkor (the mysterious ruined city of French Indo-China whose towers are seen in the background), resemble closely enough their forebears of thousands of years ago, but it has proved possible to enlist them in man's service.

MONSTER IN MINIATURE

All that this Moloch lizard lacks to rival the nightmare creatures of the past is size, for it can be held in the palm of the hand. It is quite harmless, but one of the evidences of the ceaseless movements of evolution.

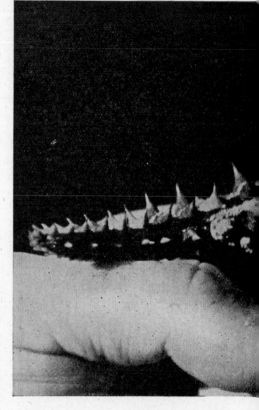

immense labour, it becomes obvious that animal life has in the first instance been largely dictated by plant life, and this in its turn has been produced by world-wide changes of climate and dispositions of earth and water. From the Cambrian period, the earliest yielding any fossil records, to the formation of the coal-forests, fully 1000 million years later, animal life was almost wholly aquatic, the sea covering much more of the earth than it does to-day. That most of the creatures at this time were of species now surviving only in the tropics points to generally warm and humid conditions.

With the uprising of the land, and the formation of the coal forests, the largest forms of animal life were represented by fishes, huge newts and salamanders, these latter dwelling among giant horse-tail reeds and tree ferns, to-day inseparable from the steamy tropics.

The coming of the air-breathing salamanders may be regarded as one of the greatest turning-points in earth's history. The giant amphibians marked the vertebrates' full conquest of the land, and it is now undisputed that these in time gave rise to the first reptiles, with well-developed lungs, hard skins and laying shell eggs. This last feature offered enormous advantages in favour of the embryo's survival in a world full of enemies.

Diversity of Reptiles

Once having set foot on the now steadily rising continents, the reptiles launched out in a hundred directions, adapting themselves to all kinds of conditions, and as a result presented great diversity of form. The earlier reptiles, like the pioneers in each great group of animals, shared a marked uniformity, but this gave place to the development of rich variety as foundation stocks explored and developed their environments.

The so-called "Age of Reptiles" covered about 150 million years, and ended some 200 million years before the dawn of Man. At its peak, the Age of Reptiles saw such monsters as the Brontosaur and Diplodocus, giant herbivores each about 80 feet long; the 15-foot high Dinosaur, the flying Pterodactyls, and marine turtles larger than any

known to-day. It is noteworthy that as the flesh-eaters appeared upon the scene and increased in size, so the herbivorous kinds developed ever more massive and bizarre armature for their protection.

From rock deposits of the Age of Reptiles have been recovered many remarkable skeleton remains, showing the existence at this time of small, insect-eating mammals, and also certain reptiles which were apparently in a transitional stage of development.

Development of Mammals

Their skeletons, particularly skulls and teeth, show unmistakable mammalian features. No doubt their blood was also undergoing a change from reptilian temperature—which changes in sympathy with outside conditions—to the stabilized temperature of the blood common to birds and beasts. Scales, in their turn, changed to fur or feathers—both vital factors in maintaining a temperature independent of what air or water may offer.

So it comes about that the close of the Age of Reptiles marks not only the advent of the first beasts, but also of the earliest birds. It is here well to remark that the various lines of avian development were well founded, whilst the beasts were largely in the making. Birds, much as we know them, existed long before the main branches of the mammalian family tree were formed.

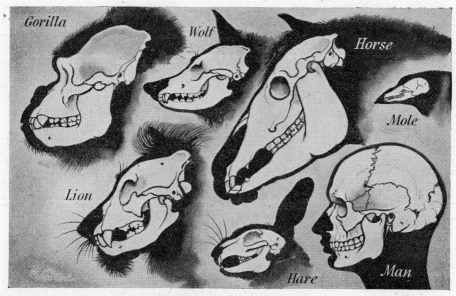

ANIMALS COMPARED WITH MAN—1

The comparative diagram given above is self-explanatory in detail but shows the steady tendency for higher forms to evolve from lower. The superior capacity of the human skull is evident when it is compared with the nearest likeness—that of the gorilla.

The birds, having gained command of the air, seemed to come to a dead end.

Many theories have been propounded to explain the dramatic and sudden extinction of the mighty dinosaurs that in their hey-day seemed built to outlast time itself. Disease and the uprising of the big self-helpful mammals are two suggestions, but climate, it seems, must have been the ruling factor in their downfall. Immense, but gradual, uprisings of land, and the consequent drainage of luscious swamps, synchronized with marked cooling of climate. With the cutting off of the giant vegetarians' food supplies, the starvation of the flesh-eaters which preyed on them followed automatically.

Speedy Progress of the Mammals

With the removal of the giant reptiles, mammalian development saw an astonishing speeding up—indeed, there has been a progressive acceleration of evolutionary "tempo". Between the appearance of the first small mammals and ourselves, there has passed a mere hundred odd million years. On the vast clock of geologic time, human history shows as a matter of hours.

From the Eocene, or "Dawn Age" onwards, earth's story has been marked by alternating epochs of heat and cold, and corresponding uprisings and subsidences of the land. All these are clearly marked in fossil deposits. Mastodon and hippopotamus bones from the Thames Valley, for example, clearly reflect a tropic period, just as mammoth bones as convincingly record periods of ice and snow. It is estimated that at least four ice ages have come, and passed, during the last million years, and as the late